Triplane to Typhoon

AIRCRAFT PRODUCED BY FACTORIES IN LANCASHIRE AND THE NORTH WEST OF ENGLAND FROM 1910

"They will rise on wings like eagles..."

Triplane to Typhoon

AIRCRAFT PRODUCED BY FACTORIES IN LANCASHIRE AND THE NORTH WEST OF ENGLAND FROM 1910

James H Longworth

BAE SYSTEMS

Lancashire County
Developments Limited

First published in 2005 by Lancashire County Developments Ltd., Robert House, Starkie Street, Preston, Lancashire, UK PR1 3LU, on behalf of Lancashire County Council.

British Library
Cataloguing in Publication data

ISBN 1 8 999 07 971

Typeface used: Gill Sans

Typeset and designed by
Lancashire County Council
Environment Directorate
Inhouse Design

Printed and bound by:
Galloways Printers Ltd.,
First Avenue,
Poynton Industrial Estate,
Poynton, Cheshire
SK12 1YJ.
Tel: 01625 870000

Reprinted 2006

DEDICATION

This book is respectfully dedicated to the memory of those who have given their lives in the development of the aircraft industry of Lancashire and the North West of England – and in appreciation of all those workers, past and present, whose combined efforts spanning nearly a century have made it the world class industry that it is today.

Frontispiece:
Eurofighter
Typhoon over
Lancashire's
Fylde Coast.

Contents

Foreword		i
Lancashire County Developments Ltd.		ii
Author's Acknowledgements		iii
Author's Introduction		vi
Chapter 1	Gravity Defied	1
Chapter 2	Controlled Flight	3
	The First Aviators	3
	Alliott Verdon Roe	3
	The Blackpool 'Flying Week' 1909	5
	A.V. Roe & Company, Manchester and Brooklands (1)	9
	The Blackpool 'Flying Carnival' 1910	11
	A.V. Roe & Company, Manchester and Brooklands (2)	14
	Vickers Sons & Maxim Ltd., Barrow-in-Furness	17
	Oscar T. Gnosspelius, Captain Edward W. Wakefield and The Lakes Flying Company, Windermere	20
Chapter 3	The First World War 1914-18	23
	Vickers Ltd., Barrow-in-Furness	23
	A.V. Roe & Company Ltd., Manchester and Hamble	28
	Vulcan Motor & Engineering Company (1906) Ltd., Crossens, Southport	32
	National Aircraft Factory (NAF) No. 2, Heaton Chapel, Stockport	33
	National Aircraft Factory (NAF) No. 3, Aintree, Liverpool	35
	The Oldham Aircraft Factory	36
	Dick, Kerr & Company Ltd., Preston and Lytham	37
Chapter 4	The Inter-War Years 1919-39	43
	Dick, Kerr & Company Ltd./English Electric Company Ltd., Preston and Lytham	44
	A.V. Roe & Company Ltd., Manchester, Hamble and Woodford	50
	Barton Aerodrome, F. Hills & Sons Ltd.	65
	Fairey Aviation Company Ltd., Heaton Chapel, Barton and Ringway	66
	Hooton Park Aerodrome, Comper Aircraft Ltd.	67
	Speke Airport, Liverpool	68
	Moss Brothers Aircraft Ltd. (Mosscraft), Chorley	69
	Squires Gate and Stanley Park Aerodromes, Blackpool	69
Chapter 5	The Second World War 1939-45	71
	Expansion and the Shadow Factories	71
	Fairey Aviation Company Ltd., Heaton Chapel, Errwood Park and Ringway	74

	A.V. Roe & Company Ltd., Newton Heath, Chadderton, Woodford, Ringway and Yeadon	78
	Metropolitan-Vickers Ltd. (Metrovicks), Trafford Park	78
	The English Electric Co. Ltd., Preston and Samlesbury	93
	Vickers-Armstrongs Ltd., Chester and Blackpool	100
	F. Hills & Sons Ltd., Ringway and Barton	107
	Rootes Securities Ltd., Speke	108
	Lockheed Overseas Corporation - British Reassembly Division – No. 1 Aircraft Assembly Unit, Speke	110
	Martin Hearn Ltd. – No. 7 Aircraft Assembly Unit, Hooton Park	110
	Martin Hearn Ltd. – No. 1 Packed Aircraft Transit Pool, Hesketh Park	111
	USAAF Base Air Depot (BAD) 1, RAF Burtonwood	111
	USAAF Base Air Depot (BAD) 2, RAF Warton	113
	Short Bros. Ltd., Windermere	113
Chapter 6	Post-War – 1945 to the Present Day	121
	Ushering in the Jet Age and Intercontinental Civil Aviation	121
	Fairey Aviation Company Ltd., Heaton Chapel and Ringway	122
	Hawker Aircraft (Blackpool) Ltd., Squires Gate	127
	The de Havilland Aircraft Company Ltd., Hawarden Aerodrome, Broughton, near Chester	130
	Hawker Siddeley Aviation, British Aerospace, BAE Systems and Airbus UK Ltd. – Airbus operations from 1970, Broughton (Hawarden), near Chester	140
	A.V. Roe & Company Ltd. (Hawker Siddeley Group), Avro-Whitworth Division of Hawker Siddeley Aviation, British Aerospace (Commercial Aircraft) Ltd., British Aerospace Regional Aircraft, Avro International Aerospace, BAE Systems, Chadderton and Woodford	150
	The English Electric Co. Ltd., English Electric Aviation Ltd., British Aircraft Corporation Ltd., British Aerospace, BAE Systems, Preston, Samlesbury and Warton	199
Chapter 7	Postscript	285
Appendix 1	Aircraft produced by factories in Lancashire and the North West of England from 1910	289
Appendix 2	With Map Timelines – The principal aircraft produced by factories in Lancashire and the North West of England from 1910	323
Appendix 3	What became of ...? – Brief histories of British airframe and aero-engine companies from 1945	325
Appendix 4	Overview of the restructuring of the British Aircraft Industry	331
Appendix 5	Abbreviations	333
Bibliography		335
Index		338

Foreword

By **County Councillor Terry E. Burns**,
Chairman of Lancashire County Council, 2006-2007;
Lancashire County Council's delegate to the
Northwest Aerospace Alliance (NWAA);
Member of the Board of Directors of Lancashire County Developments Ltd.
(LCDL), Lancashire County Council's Economic Development Agency;
Regional Officer, and Regional Political Officer, for AMICUS the Union, the UK's
largest union for manufacturing, technical and skilled persons.

The history of the aircraft industry goes back nearly a century in Lancashire and the North West, covering almost every type of aircraft from Triplane to Typhoon. I am proud to have worked for many years in this great industry, mostly at Lucas Aerospace in Burnley, on projects including Rolls-Royce engines as well as missile systems. Part of my role today, both as a Lancashire County Councillor and an AMICUS Union Official, is to encourage young people to think about careers through apprenticeships, particularly in engineering, science and technology.

Over the years Lancashire County Council, a founder member of the Northwest Aerospace Alliance, has strongly supported the aerospace industry which provides up to 30,000 jobs locally and over 50,000 in the region. The County Council is active in lobbying the interests of the industry and promoting Lancashire at major international air shows and I believe this book will make an important contribution to these activities.

It provides a detailed and accurate record of around 150 types of aircraft built in the area, the majority of which were also designed here. Altogether, the men and women of Lancashire and the North West have built some 50,000 aircraft in the region since 1910. Military and civilian, large and small, these aircraft serve as a lasting testimony to the dedication and craftsmanship of a workforce at the forefront of aerospace design, innovation and development.

I feel privileged to be a friend and colleague of the author, Jim Longworth. His knowledge, enthusiasm and attention to detail are evident in this account, which is illustrated with more than 250 excellent photographs. I would also like to thank Lancashire County Developments Ltd. for supporting the publication and to acknowledge the help of BAE Systems, including the provision of photographs and archive material.

Triplane to Typhoon is a fascinating and inspiring story and I am proud to be associated with its publication. I hope it will be read by people who like myself have worked in the industry, those who plan to make aeronautical and related engineering their career and those who simply have an interest in aeroplanes and their engines, Lancashire and its region.

County Councillor Terry E. Burns

i

Lancashire County Developments Ltd

Lancashire County Council has a proud history of economic development. This is currently delivered by our company, Lancashire County Developments Ltd. We are committed to promoting Lancashire and directly influencing economic growth in the Red Rose county.

There are 39,000 businesses in the Lancashire area and manufacturing remains the main provider of the area's wealth, accounting for a fifth of the 640,000 workforce and a quarter of local Gross Domestic Product. The aerospace industry, as a key part of advanced manufacturing, has a proud history and we believe an exciting future.

Specific Lancashire County Developments Ltd initiatives include:

• providing managed workspace for new and growing businesses at White Cross, Lancaster and the Lancashire Business Park at Leyland;

• generating growth in new and existing businesses with advice on grants, business support and economic intelligence;

• supporting an entrepreneurial culture by providing financial support and access to loans and venture capital, including assistance to small and medium enterprises via the Lancashire Rosebud Scheme;

• attracting inward investment and new employment to Lancashire through business events, missions, exhibitions and literature.

We are delighted therefore to support and publish Triplane to Typhoon as part of our promotion of the aerospace industry in Lancashire.

If you want to know more about us, telephone (+44) 01772 551888 or visit our website at www.lancashire.gov.uk

County Councillor Niki Penney,
Chair of Lancashire County Developments Ltd

Author's Acknowledgements

I would like to express my sincere thanks and appreciation to the following individuals and organisations who have directly and indirectly provided help, support and information which has proved invaluable in the preparation and publication of this book.

I am indebted to members and officers of Lancashire County Council for their sustained interest, encouragement and direct support. The County Council published my previous book *Classic and Modern Aero-Engines associated with Lancashire and the North West of England* in 1999.

It was largely as a result of a conversation with County Councillors Terry Burns and John Cavanagh at the Farnborough Air Show 2002 that I was encouraged to proceed with a much wider project dealing comprehensively with aircraft production.

Terry Burns, Vice-Chairman of Lancashire County Council and also Regional Officer of the engineering union *Amicus,* has consistently supported the need for a detailed account of the aircraft produced by the industry in Lancashire and the North West. This book is the result. My thanks also go to Lancashire County Council's Environment Director, Graham Harding and his team of officers including Peter Kivell, Head of the Economic Intelligence Team, the author of definitive sectoral studies of the Lancashire and North West aerospace industry of today which show beyond doubt how vital the industry is to the economy (www.lancashireprofile.com).

In particular I wish to thank Ann Weaver of the Economic Intelligence Team who has been my principal point of contact with the County Council and whose support has been invaluable. In a private capacity Ann is also a member of the Society of Indexers and in her own time has compiled the index to this volume. I would also like to thank Laura Helm, Head of Text Processing in the Environment Directorate and her team comprising Adele Smith, Jean Carter, Barbara Naylor, Nicky Hulme, Ann Dixon and Anne Rush who have resolutely refused to be beaten by my handwriting and have turned manuscript (and I have to admit many author's amendments) round with speed, efficiency and great good humour. I also express my appreciation to Steve Jordan, Head of LCC Environment Directorate Inhouse Design and in particular to Andrea Watson, Senior Graphic Designer, who generated all the artwork. Additionally my thanks go to David Jenks for producing the map within Appendix 2 and, for print liaison, to Viv Bull of Printdirect, County Hall.

From the aerospace industry, first and foremost I wish to acknowledge with my grateful thanks the generous financial contribution made by BAE Systems plc towards the production costs of this book. Specifically my thanks go to Gary Lydiate, Head of Communications; Andy Bunce, Head of Customer Communications; Jon Bonnick, Communications Manager and Jonathan Lee, Promotions Manager, at Warton. The company has also been unstinting in the provision of photographs and information. Among present and former BAE Systems' personnel I would like to record special thanks to Gordon Bartley, now of the aerospace consultancy IMAGINAIR, whose extensive knowledge of the company, its aircraft, aviation generally and matters photographical, I have been privileged to be able to 'tap into' for many years. Within BAE Systems and its predecessor companies I have been assisted by Malcolm Adams, Head of Public Affairs, Terry Taylor and Gary Barber at Woodford; John Mangan at Greengate, Middleton; David Charlton and Media Services at Filton, Bristol; Tony Salter-Ellis, Mike Smith, Alan Colyer and colleagues at BAE Systems Marine / VSEL, Barrow-in-Furness.

The BAE Systems North West Heritage Group at Warton are custodians of much of the company's photographic and information archive and in particular I would like to thank Ian Lawrenson, Brian Tomlinson, Bob Fairclough, Brian Sargeant, Graham Green, Rick Hardman, Ken Hillman, Malcolm Richards, Geoff Ainsworth, Bob Jones, Keith Spong and numerous others who on many occasions have willingly provided information, photographs and patiently answered my layman's questions. I have been privileged to be included at their meetings and on visits to aircraft heritage sites throughout the UK and, together with the Preston Branch of the Royal Aeronautical Society (Alan Matthews, Brian Sargeant, Guy Hindley, Craig Eckersley) and at the Avro Lancashire Club (Trevor Moncrief, Stephen Halsted), invariably made welcome. I have benefited from being able to attend the lecture programmes of these and other professional societies, as a result gaining useful detailed and contextual insight from some first class speakers including Squadron Leader Drew Steel, RAF (Warton), Dennis Morley (BAE Systems Warton) and John Turner, Director of Flight Operations (BAE Systems Warton).

I would particularly like to take the opportunity to place on record my appreciation for assistance provided by the late Dougie Godfrey of the Avro Heritage Centre and '603' Club at BAE Systems Woodford.

The North West is fortunate in having a number of established researchers, writers and speakers on aircraft heritage and general aviation. During the early stages of my project a number of published articles and occasional papers deposited with local libraries and museums by authorities including Barry Abraham, John Bagley, Phil Butler, David George, Harry Holmes, George Jenks, Richard Riding, Alan Scholefield, David Smith and others proved valuable sources of reference.

I also thank the following Government Departments, official bodies, museums, reference libraries and companies:

Ministry of Defence (Nicola Hunt, David Belson and Ash Amliwala for supply and permission to use photographs);
Royal Air Force Air Historical Branch;
RAF Scampton, Lincolnshire (Rachel Huxford);
Royal Air Force Museum, Hendon (Andrew Renwick) and Cosford;
Museum of Science and Industry in Manchester (Nick Forder);
Merseyside Maritime Museum, Liverpool;
Brooklands Museum, Weybridge (Mike Goodall);
Abbot Hall Art Gallery/Museum of Lakeland Life, Kendal;
Reference Libraries, Local Studies and Archive Offices at Barrow-in-Furness, Blackburn, Blackpool, Bolton, Chorley, Kendal, Liverpool, Manchester, Preston, Southport, Stockport;
Ian Lowe Photographic Services, Woodford (Ian Lowe);
Coulton-Lewis Communications, Chester (Michael Lewis – Editor and Publisher of Rapide magazine);
Ian Allan Publishing, Surrey (Peter Waller);
Dorway Public Relations, Luton (David Dorman);
Bombardier, Belfast (Alan McKnight).

Many individuals have provided information, photographs, loan of reference material, introductions, continuing support and encouragement, notably John Heaven (Bristol); Allan King (Windermere); Squadron Leader J.B. Airey RAFVR(T) (Ret'd) (Preston); Harold Ingham (Poulton-le-Fylde); Tony Ingham (Longridge); Mike Waters (Blackburn); Jim Hindle (Padiham); Eric Harrison (Cheadle); Chris Eggleston (Lammack); Michael Berry (Windermere); Peter Connon (Carlisle); Harry Yeadon (Lytham); Ron Greatrix (Garstang) and the late John Rochester (Romsey).

Numerous websites consulted include, in the North West, that of the Hooton Park Trust at www.hootonparktrust.co.uk

I have been fortunate in gaining access to and being allowed to use some first class photographs. The majority came from BAE Systems for whom a number were taken by that exponent of fast jet air-to-air photography, Geoffrey Lee; with others from BAE North West Heritage Group or via Gordon Bartley; Eurofighter GmbH; Rolls-Royce; Airbus Industrie; Airbus UK; Bombardier; the Ministry of Defence; Ian Lowe Photographic Services; the *Blackpool Gazette*; the Museum of Science and Industry in Manchester; the Brooklands Museum and *Aeroplane Monthly* (Nick Stroud, Mike Hooks). All reasonable efforts have been made to comply with copyright requirements.

Penultimately my thanks go to my publishers, Lancashire County Developments Ltd. (LCDL – the economic arm of Lancashire County Council), LCDL's Chairman, County Councillor Niki Penney, its Board of Directors including the Leader of Lancashire County Council, County Councillor Hazel Harding and Managing Director Steve Dean, who took the decision to resource the publication in pursuance of the County Council's continuing promotion of the Lancashire aerospace industry and the communities that depend upon it for their livelihoods. I should also like to thank Colette Taylor and Simon Emery of LCDL for managing the publication project and bringing it to fruition.

Last, but certainly not least, my thanks go to my wife Kath and daughters Helen and Sarah for their interest and encouragement throughout, particularly on those occasions when the magnitude of the task threatened to overwhelm even my own resolve to bring it to a conclusion.

Whilst I express my appreciation to all the above, what follows is essentially my own personal perspective on what appear to me to be the key elements in the huge canvas that is the history of aircraft production in the region. Accordingly I take full responsibility for any inaccuracies or omissions.

Author's Introduction

The centenary of man's first powered flight made by the Wright brothers in the United States on 17 December 1903 was the focus for worldwide celebrations and assessments of 100 years of progress by the aircraft industry, nowadays universally termed 'aerospace'.

The purpose of this book is to provide a comprehensive overview of the aircraft produced by factories in Lancashire and the North West of England since 1910, with as much relevant detail as is consistent with the confines of a single volume. It follows the publication by Lancashire County Council in 1999 of my previous book *Classic and Modern Aero-Engines associated with Lancashire and the North West of England* which was prompted by the 60th anniversary of the region's links with Sir Frank Whittle of jet engine fame.

North West England, comprising the counties of Lancashire, Cheshire and Cumbria (formerly Cumberland and Westmorland) together with the conurbations of Greater Manchester and Liverpool/Merseyside, is today the source of nearly a third of the UK's aerospace industry turnover. It is one of the world's top three centres of aerospace production ranking with Seattle in the USA and Toulouse in France. The industry represents a vast regional capacity of 'primes' such as BAE Systems, Rolls-Royce and – a mere stone's throw across the border in North Wales – Airbus, Original Equipment Manufacturers (OEMs) and a supply chain network of more than 1,000

small, medium and large subcontractors and suppliers. All branches of the industry are represented including design, airframe manufacture, aero-engines, avionics, in-flight and ground support equipment, aircraft final assembly and flight testing. They are supported by advanced technology 'high tech' engineering industries engaged in tooling, treatments, materials, technical analysis and testing, information technology, technical documentation and ancillary support services and are linked also to a wider defence sector encompassing ordnance, missiles and naval shipbuilding. The combined annual turnover of the North West aerospace sector amounts to £6 billion, providing on the most conservative of estimates 60,000 jobs in the region.

For most of the 'Century of Flight', indeed since the Blackpool 'Flying Week' of 1909, the North West has been at the forefront of developments in the industry and in aviation generally. A.V. Roe founded the world's first company established exclusively for the series manufacture of aeroplanes in 1910 in Manchester. Since then the growth of the industry in the region during the twentieth century, given powerful impetus by two world wars and a 'cold' war, saw it progressively replace declining traditional industries to become both the bedrock and driver of the regional economy. How this happened is a complex, interwoven story of individual and corporate pioneering and entrepreneurial effort, chance and opportunity, the devising and harnessing of new designs and technologies, political and social history in times of war and peace. Not least it is one of a talented and flexible workforce of men and women imbued with skills handed down from two centuries of manufacturing tradition.

Industrial heritage is no longer confined to aspects of the region's traditional coal, cotton, heavy engineering and transport base. North West aerospace is now of such maturity to have acquired its own extensive heritage of manufacturing operations which to date have produced over 150 different types of aircraft representing a total output approaching 50,000. The need for a 'record of achievement' detailing the aircraft involved and the locations of their production has been the motivating force behind this book. It is summarised in Appendix 1 which details production broadly in chronological order, subject to certain adjustments to conform with the sequence that aircraft types are dealt with in the narrative. These figures do not include the great number of aircraft of many types delivered from the USA under the Lend-Lease Act during WW2, to be assembled at various locations in the North West and elsewhere. Such were their numbers that even an account devoted primarily to indigenous production could hardly ignore them completely. Accordingly I have made some reference, albeit relatively briefly, to this additional element at the locations involved.

By definition therefore this is a history of the aircraft produced by factories in the North West rather than one of general aviation in the region – save for reference to certain wider developments in civil and military aviation that directly influenced the number and types of aircraft made.

Whilst unashamedly biased towards the aircraft themselves, it was inevitable that my narrative should also address the circumstances of their production with reference to some of the eminent personalities who designed, built and flew them. I am acutely aware that given the scale of this huge industry there are many, many more individuals than those I have been able to mention who would merit inclusion in a detailed account of such a great enterprise. Limitations of space and my overriding priority to achieve a comprehensive overview have been the imperative behind striking a balance between principle and detail. The same applies to technical content, always a potential hazard for an industry 'outsider', yet one which I hope I have portrayed adequately in relation to my overall remit. I would refer anyone requiring further detail to the Bibliography of some of the many existing publications which have come to my attention. Many are complete volumes devoted to individual aircraft in depth, others definitive histories of specific manufacturers.

My remit as defined has also precluded specific mention of all but a few of the myriad of subcontractors and smaller suppliers to the aerospace industry to which I have referred above. How these have clustered in response to the needs of the industry, some as a result of decades of diversification out of the region's traditional engineering base, including textile engineering, others during wartime or more recently from inward investment, is another story – alas not for this volume. Full details of the capacity of today's industry and its intricate supply chain network are however available from the Northwest Aerospace Alliance (www.aerospace.co.uk). The Economic Intelligence Team of Lancashire County Council also maintains extensive information on the economic impact of aerospace on the area at the present time (www.lancashireprofile.com).

The narrative that follows is very much my own personal perspective on the development of the industry in the region. Consequently, notwithstanding the considerable assistance which has readily been made available to me, any errors or omissions are of my own making. Certainly any content which might be construed as comment or opinion, unless specifically attributed, should be considered mine and mine alone, not necessarily reflecting any official policy or viewpoint of organisations such as Lancashire County Council, its economic development company Lancashire County Developments Ltd., or BAE Systems plc.

The aerospace industry worldwide faces acute challenges in the future. Hopefully, the following account of the magnificent achievements in aircraft production in Lancashire and the North West of England during its first century will add to the confidence with which the industry in the region approaches its second – and at the same time demonstrate to its potential customers a track record of achievement second to none.

JAMES H. LONGWORTH
PRESTON, LANCASHIRE, 2005

Chapter 1
Gravity Defied

To cast off the yoke of gravity and soar freely through the earth's atmosphere was one of man's earliest ambitions. Over the centuries it inspired many bizarre and mostly fatal attempts at heavier-than-air, wing-borne gliding flight by dauntless 'tower jumping' clerics and sundry eccentrics.

It was not until October 1783 that François Pilâtre de Rozier gained his place in history as the world's first aeronaut when, using lighter-than-air inflation but remaining tethered to the ground by ropes, he successfully overcame gravity by ascending in a Montgolfier hot air balloon. The following month, de Rozier and the Marquis d'Arlandes made the first manned free-flight aerial journey, drifting indeterminately but with appropriate *sang-froid* to and fro over the rooftops of Paris. A year later, James Sadler became the first English aeronaut when he departed the ground in a Montgolfier-type balloon at Oxford.

Lancashire's first experience of manned aerial voyage came on 12 May 1785 when 5,000 people witnessed Sadler rise into the heavens above Manchester, 'the largest and most flourishing village in England', in an 'inflammable air' hydrogen balloon filled by the action of a vat of sulphuric acid on iron filings. To the present day, Balloon Street in Central Manchester commemorates his flight which terminated in a landing near Radcliffe. Further exploits of intrepid late eighteenth and early nineteenth century balloonists drew vast crowds in Lancashire as elsewhere. Vincenzo Lunardi, accorded

the status of 'The First Aerial Traveller in Britain' following a flight from London to Hertfordshire in 1784, made an ascent from Liverpool in July 1785, landing at Simonswood. Sadler made return visits to Manchester in 1786 and 1812, crossing the Pennines into Yorkshire on both occasions.

Others followed as cheaper and more plentiful coal or 'town' gas became the preferred means of inflation. A Mr. Livingston caused a sensation at the Preston Guild of 1822 when, his balloon filled by courtesy of the Preston Gas Company, he 'rose majestically into the air to a considerable height' before a crowd of 10,000 people. Having ascended almost perpendicularly from land between Fishergate and Friargate, where the present day St. George's Centre stands, he returned to earth with considerably less dignity, suffering injuries when he was expelled from the basket in a heavy and protracted landing near Whalley. His unmanned balloon swept off to the east, its remains later being found near Selby.

James Sadler's son, William Wyndham Sadler, made ascents from Salford, Rochdale and Liverpool before his death in 1824 when, at the end of a flight from Bolton, he was flung out in a severe landing among trees, buildings and chimneys near Oswaldtwistle.

Father and son aeronauts Charles and Charles George Green made numerous appearances in the region. The former, his balloon inflated with town gas, undertook a short flight from Kendal in August 1825.

They variously flew from Preston and Blackburn into Yorkshire and, in September 1826, presumably with her father's permission, carried off the Bolton Gas Works Manager's daughter on a flight to Royton. Over the next two years further ascents were made from Manchester, Stockport and Macclesfield, from Blackburn to Longton near Preston, and from Bury to Edenfield. During some of these flights they safely dropped a variety of animals by parachute.

In 1837 Charles Green made spectacular ascents from Salford in the 62-foot-high *Great Nassau* balloon, so named after his long distance 480 mile flight from London to the German Duchy of Nassau a year before. Many more balloon flights were to take place from North West towns during the remainder of the 1800s, often carrying passengers and sometimes parachutists. It was at a meeting of the British Association for the Advancement of Science held in Manchester in 1861, a choice of venue which itself reflected the region's growing standing in science and industry, that James Glaisher, founder of the Meteorological Office, agreed to make a number of balloon ascents to determine the nature of the upper atmosphere. Glaisher eventually attained a height of 36,000 feet before passing out from lack of oxygen.

The intrepidity of the pioneering balloonists presaged an enthusiasm for matters aeronautical which was to captivate Lancashire and much of North West England for the next two centuries. It would encompass many individual events and feats of skill, endurance and technological achievement of national and international significance, sowing the seeds of a world-scale aircraft manufacturing industry and a regional involvement in virtually every aspect of civil and military aviation.

Resurgence of interest in hot air ballooning in recent years has served to dramatically reinstate the links between the lighter-than-air apparatus of the 'Golden Age of Ballooning' and the awesome products of the aircraft industry of today in the shared skies over Lancashire and the North West.

Chapter 2
Controlled Flight

Having overcome gravity, the pioneers of lighter-than-air ballooning remained acutely aware that, apart from the dangers inherent in their apparatus, ability to control flight was fundamentally constrained by wind force and direction. Various means of steering and propulsion were tried in attempts to produce a navigable airship, or dirigible, including propellers turned by hand, steam, electricity or internal combustion.

But it was not until the latter years of the nineteenth century, when the focus returned to wing-borne heavier-than-air flight and experiments with kites and model gliders incorporating wings or 'planes' began to generate primitive rules of aerodynamics, that ambitions came closer to being realised. The advent of practical and reasonably reliable internal combustion engines capable of marriage to an airframe removed the final obstacle.

The First Aviators

In the USA, Orville and Wilbur Wright built and flew a number of biplane gliders between 1899 and 1903. On 17 December 1903 at Kill Devil Hills, Kittyhawk, North Carolina, Orville became the first to fly a manned, powered aeroplane – the Wright Flyer No. 1. Their series of four sustained, controlled flights took place over soft sands along part of the North Atlantic seaboard with which Sir Walter Raleigh would doubtless have been familiar over three centuries earlier. The historic achievements of the Wright brothers in America were followed in Europe, notably in a France somewhat vexed at the perceived loss of its lead in aeronautical matters, by aviators including Gabriel Voisin, Alberto Santos-Dumont, Louis Blériot and Henry (Henri) Farman. It would be five years after the Wrights first entered the record book before the first official flight was made in Britain – and that by an American cowboy, stage and circus entertainer, Samuel Franklin Cody, a friend of his better known namesake Colonel William F. 'Buffalo Bill' Cody. On 16 October 1908, having tethered his British Army Aeroplane No. 1 to a tree on Laffan's Plain, Farnborough to run up its 50hp French Antoinette engine, Cody cast off and roared into the air. The tree would become an early aviation icon, later to be replicated in aluminium by Farnborough apprentices.

The first officially recognised resident Englishman to make a flight in England was J.T.C. Moore-Brabazon (later Lord Brabazon of Tara) who between 30 April and 2 May 1909 became airborne in his Voisin biplane on three occasions over the Isle of Sheppey. A year later he was awarded the Royal Aero Club of Great Britain's Aviator Certificate No. 1.

Alliott Verdon Roe

A series of short flights – in reality extended jumps into the air – by a Lancashire man, Edwin Alliott Verdon Roe, in his **Roe I Biplane** on 8 June 1908 substantially predated those of Moore-

A.V. Roe and his
Roe I Biplane in
the original
'Avroplane' shed
at Brooklands,
December
1907.

A.V. Roe and his Roe I Biplane in the original 'Avroplane' shed at Brooklands, December 1907.

Brabazon. Roe's biplane, powered by a 24hp Antoinette engine, was built at Putney and flown from the Brooklands motor racing circuit near Weybridge, Surrey. Neither given adequate publicity by Roe, nor attended by official observers, the flights were not formally recognised, a matter which became a source of some irritation to Roe in the years that followed.

Roe was born at Patricroft, near Eccles, Manchester in 1877, one of seven children of a doctor. He was educated in the South of England, at Brooklands, in Buckinghamshire and at St. Paul's School Westminster. He later served an apprenticeship at the Lancashire and Yorkshire Railway Company's locomotive works at Horwich, near Bolton. From there he took a position at Portsmouth Dockyard before going to sea as a marine engineer. His interest in flight emanated from studying an albatross as it followed his ship, a fascination which progressed to designing model aircraft on his return from

sea. In 1906 Roe corresponded with the Wright brothers. That year he submitted a patent application for the improved control of an aeroplane as a result of which, despite later counter-claims by others elsewhere in Europe, he became the accredited inventor of the combined single-lever wheeled control column. It afforded lateral stability and some turning control with fore and aft pitching for climbing and diving. In those early days of aviation lateral control was gained by the flexing or 'warping' of wing surfaces, followed by a gradual transition to partially and eventually fully moveable hinged 'ailerons'. In April 1907, at Alexandra Palace, Roe won a prize in a competition for model aircraft capable of sustained flight, sponsored by that doyen of early twentieth century aviation and proprietor of the *Daily Mail*, Lord Northcliffe. Roe incorporated his patent in the Roe I Biplane, his first full size powered aeroplane which he built at the Putney premises of his brother, Dr. Spencer Verdon Roe. A few weeks after making short flights in this machine on 8 June 1908, Roe was evicted from Brooklands by a management more preoccupied at that time with motor racing than aviation.

If Brooklands had been less than supportive the same could not be said of Mr. J.A. Prestwich, the Tottenham, London manufacturer of JAP engines with whom Roe entered into a short partnership on 15 September 1908 to form the JAP Avroplane Company. It was a JAP 9/10hp engine that Roe fitted in his next aeroplane, the **Roe I Triplane**, built to an entirely different design and employing a tractor rather than pusher propeller. Manufactured at Putney and assembled under railway arches in the Lea Valley near Walthamstow, Essex, the triplane took to the air for short distances on numerous occasions from 5 June 1909. Roe recorded a flight of 100 feet on 13 July and three of 900 feet at an average height of 10 feet on 23 July. Forced eventually to defer to Moore-Brabazon's officially recognised status as the first English resident to fly in England, Roe was nevertheless credited as the first British subject to fly an all-British designed, built and powered aeroplane over British soil. Just two days after Roe's

series of flights in the Lea Valley, on 25 July 1909 Louis Blériot flew across the English Channel.

Facing considerable indifference in the South of England where most of his early experimental work had taken place at Putney, Brooklands and in the Lea Valley, Roe realised the importance of securing longer term financial backing if he was to progress. This materialised in the form of Humphrey Verdon Roe, A.V. Roe's younger brother, already a successful businessman in Manchester. H.V. owned Everard & Co., manufacturers of webbing for 'Bullseye' gentlemen's braces, of Brownsfield Mill, Ancoats. It would appear that more than one form of support was available in Manchester and the South's loss was about to become Lancashire's gain. A partnership was formed and much of 1909 was taken up with discussions of possible financing arrangements.

The Blackpool 'Flying Week' 1909

Meanwhile, concerned that the pace of aeronautical development in Britain was losing momentum to the French following Blériot's spectacular cross-channel flight in July and the success of the world's first

Lancashire Aero Club's grandstand at the Blackpool 'Flying Week' at Squires Gate, October 1909. Col. C.F. Grantham, Hon.Sec., and Mr J. Talbot Clifton of Lytham Hall are doubtless explaining the finer points of aviation. In attendance was the private band of the Club President, the Earl of Lonsdale. *Photo: Blackpool Gazette.*

international aviation meeting at Rheims in August 1909, the irrepressible Lord Northcliffe wrote to the Blackpool Town Council suggesting they organise a 'flying week'. Just as able to recognise a potential visitor attraction in 1909 as they are today, the Council adopted the idea with enthusiasm. Within a matter of weeks, together with the Lancashire Aero Club, they had completed arrangements for the event which was held between 18 and 23 October on hurriedly prepared ground occupying part of a golf course and sand dunes at Squires Gate. Even the United States were unable to hold their first aeroplane meeting until January the following year, at Los Angeles.

A.V. Roe was the first aviator on the programme. His machine was the same 9/10hp JAP-powered Roe I Triplane in which he had made the first 'all British' flights in June and July. The fuselage still bore the name 'Bulls-eye Avroplane', applied whilst at the Lea Valley to advertise the developing connection with H.V. Roe's company in Manchester. But Roe and the giant crowd, variously estimated at over 50,000, were to be frustrated by his inability to take off, the machine only managing a series of unconvincing hops into the air. Generally attributed to an underpowered engine at the time, it was Roe's view that the problem was also rainwater absorption by the 'economy'

Quietly determined, Roe prepares his No. 1 Triplane at Blackpool in 1909. Photo: Blackpool Gazette.

Final adjustments, with the Roe 1 Triplane displaying its 'Bulls-Eye Avroplane' advertising at Blackpool, 1909. Photo: Blackpool Gazette.

paper and open-weave backing fabric with which he had skinned the aeroplane's structure. His aircraft, the original Roe 1 Triplane, was preserved and has been exhibited at the Science Museum, London, since 1925. A replica can today be seen at the Museum of Science and Industry in Manchester. Roe took a second aircraft, powered by a 20hp JAP engine, to the Blackpool event but this was also prevented from flying by the weather.

As a result, it was the next contender Henry Farman in his box-kite biplane who, after successfully circumnavigating the entire two mile course, was credited with performing the first powered flight in Lancashire. Born of English parents in 1874 in Paris, where his father was the London Standard's correspondent, Farman grew up more French than British and later in life adopted French citizenship. Disappointingly for the patriotic Lord Northcliffe and the spectators, it was the French who took most of the honours with flights by the famous high wire walker Louis Paulhan who shared Farman's aeroplane; Henri Rougier, who achieved a height of over 600 feet in a Voisin; and the balloonist Alfred Leblanc in his Blériot. It was left to former big game hunter Hubert Latham in an Antoinette to salvage British pride, awarded the prize for the best flight after amazing the crowd by his ability to fly his machine in strong winds as the weather deteriorated towards the end of the event. Other famous participants included Moore-Brabazon, Fournier 'the racing motorist with nerves of steel', and Suffroy 'the explorer who gave

up wandering the unknown places of the earth to penetrate the virgin spaces of the air'. By the end of the event seven of the twelve aircraft present had flown.

A.V. Roe & Company, Manchester and Brooklands (1)

Alliott and Humphrey Verdon Roe's partnership was formalised on 1 January 1910 by the establishment of A.V. Roe & Co. To keep a closer eye on his investment, Humphrey insisted the factory should be at Manchester where he had spare accommodation in the basement of Brownsfield Mill. In this respect it was Humphrey's influence that drew manufacturing of Roe aircraft northwards to Lancashire, sowing the seeds of what was to become a major growth industry in the years ahead. Initially styled as 'The Aviators' Storehouse', the company advertised itself as the sole maker of the 'Avro' Plane, capable of supplying new and second hand complete Avro Triplanes made in Manchester, engines, propellers and all necessary parts, bolts, screws, wire and wheels required by aviators. But there was no flying ground nearby and in late 1909/early 1910 Roe had to flight test his second Roe I Triplane at Wembley Park, Middlesex, later to become part of the football stadium. For flying purposes the new company then reinstated the link with Brooklands where a new enlightened management had now provided flying facilities inside the racetrack. There, A.V. Roe & Co. offered flying lessons on Triplanes, Farmans or Blériots for £50 inclusive, 'until the full certificate is obtained, at the company's flying ground at Weybridge'. Roe's links with Brooklands can be seen today in the replication of his Avroplane hangar shed and Roe I Biplane at the Brooklands Museum.

In the face of stiff competition from other companies elsewhere, including the Curtiss Aeroplane Company of America (founded in 1907), Short Brothers (registered in 1908) and Handley Page Ltd. (formed in 1909), A.V. Roe & Co. claimed to be the world's first company to be registered as an aeroplane manufacturer. The claim hinges on their establishment as factory production line manufacturers of aeroplanes exclusively, as distinct from a mix of products including balloons, kites, gliders, airships, aeroplanes and various road vehicles as was the case with certain other manufacturers. Short Brothers indeed operated the first aeroplane series production line when they built six Wright biplanes under licence from the Wright brothers on the Isle of Sheppey during 1909/10, but the company also remained much involved with other craft including airships and balloons up to the First World War.

The first aeroplane to emerge from Brownsfield Mill was an improved machine, the 26 ft. - span **Roe II Triplane** powered by a 35hp Green engine. Named *Mercury* at an exhibition organised by the Manchester Aero Club at the White City Stadium, Manchester on 4 March 1910, the machine was further displayed at the London Olympia Aero Show a week later. From there it was despatched to Brooklands to begin a programme of flight trials, progress on which was reported back to the factory by telegram.

A.V. Roe was an airframe designer and builder, not an aero-engine constructor. Sourcing suitable power units for his early machines and his use of a variety of engines ranging in power, bought in from different suppliers, doubtless contributed to his somewhat erratic early flying record. His 1908 partnership with J.A. Prestwich was short-lived and the following year Roe entered into an agreement with the cycle and automobile engineers, Maurice and William Edwards of Bolton, who had designed a novel form of engine 'particularly suitable for aeroplanes'. This was an air-cooled two-cylinder horizontally opposed two-stroke engine working a

9

common crank, to be available in 15-60hp versions, for which the Edwards patents were sealed on 19 May 1910. Edwards engines were manufactured under licence by H.W. Cowley & Co. Ltd. of Bolton and it appears that a business arrangement was entered into between the various parties whereby some were marketed as Avro engines with the Avro name embossed on the crankcase. One such was exhibited on the Avro stand at the 1910 London Olympia Aero Show and, today, a surviving 15hp example is displayed at the Science Museum, London. A second example, believed to have been supplied by Avro to the pioneering Irish aviatrix Miss Lilian Bland in September 1910, is today held by the Brooklands Museum.

A.V. Roe & Co. were quite prepared to construct aeroplanes to the designs of others and in 1910 built a **Farman-type biplane** for Maurice Edwards, powered by one of his own engines. Edwards was a member of a group of enthusiastic aviators including Charles Fletcher, of the Empress Motor Works of Stockport Road, Manchester, who indulged their interests at the Manchester Race Course. Fletcher, probably the first person to fly in Manchester, built two **Empress Monoplanes** of his own design in 1909 and 1910, together with an **Empress Biplane**. One of the monoplanes was exhibited at the 1910 White City event in Manchester. His company also made five and seven-cylinder rotary engines.

In 1908 Fletcher recruited the services of a young mechanic, John William Alcock, who, after spending his childhood years at St. Annes where he attended the Heyhouses School, had moved to Manchester with his parents in 1905. After gaining initial aviation experience with the Manchester group, in 1911 Alcock was detached to Brooklands as mechanic in charge of an assessment of Fletcher's engines being undertaken by Avro. There, he assisted the distributor of French Viale

engines in Britain, Maurice Ducrocq, to install a five-cylinder 35hp Viale air-cooled radial engine in the sixth production Avro Type D biplane. Whilst at Brooklands the young Alcock took the Royal Aero Club Aviator's Certificate and soon came to prominence as an instructor himself. Alcock served with distinction in the First World War, training others and flying both bombers and fighters, before becoming a prisoner of war after being forced down behind enemy lines. After demobilisation Alcock agreed to pilot a converted Vimy bomber which Vickers Ltd. were preparing at Brooklands to attempt the first non-stop crossing of the Atlantic. He was joined by Arthur Whitten Brown, born in Glasgow but who had grown up in Manchester. Brown had also spent time as a prisoner of war, fortuitously putting this to good use by studying navigation. Both were knighted after successfully accomplishing their transatlantic flight in 16 hours 27 minutes on 14/15 June 1919. Sir John Alcock became Vickers' Chief Test Pilot but died only six months later on 18 December in a bad weather flying accident en route to the sixth Paris Air Show.

By 1911 Avro had abandoned involvement in engine manufacturing, their name no longer associated with those of Edwards and Cowley. The same year Fletcher's company ceased trading in the aftermath of a patents infringement case. Thereafter A.V. Roe & Co. variously selected JAP, Green, ENV, Viale, Gnome and other engines to power their forthcoming aeroplanes. Of these, the Roe II Triplane *Mercury* and a new **Roe III Triplane** were flown on numerous occasions at Brooklands in the spring and summer of 1910. The Roe III, flown by A.V. Roe on 24 June, was powered by a 35hp JAP engine and the design incorporated trailing edge ailerons, tail elevators and large rudders. It was on this, the first of four Roe III Triplanes to be built, that A.V. Roe finally found time to take his Royal Aero Club

Aviator's Certificate (No. 18) on 26 July 1910. Although a welcome achievement it was of only limited consolation when, in 1928/29, the Royal Aero Club eventually dismissed his claim to have been the first Englishman to fly from English soil in favour of J.T.C. Moore-Brabazon.

The Blackpool 'Flying Carnival' 1910

The authorities at Blackpool had been determined to improve on the town's 1909 'Flying Week'. A second aviation meeting, the Blackpool 'Flying Carnival', was organised by the Lancashire Aero Club between 28 July and 20 August 1910. A great disappointment to the crowd in 1909, A.V. Roe got off to a potentially worse start in 1910. In transit from Brooklands to Blackpool, his two display machines – the Roe II *Mercury* and a Roe III – were both burned out in a fire on railway trucks between Wigan and Preston, caused by a red hot ember from the locomotive. Not to have participated at Blackpool would have been unthinkable so, in a record four days, Roe and colleagues

assembled a replacement Roe III at Squires Gate from components and structures despatched from the Manchester factory – this time by road. A factory-fresh Green engine arrived just in time. The resulting aircraft, distinguishable from that of 1909 by its two as opposed to four-bladed propeller and an uncovered fuselage (there had been insufficient time to fully clad it) flew on several occasions during the week. Roe even carried passengers. Unfortunately, the stuff of heroes much applauded by the crowd and rewarded by a special prize for merit, ended later in the week in a forced landing when the Roe III was gusted towards a marker pylon.

Spectators at Squires Gate were astonished by the Peruvian pilot Georges Chavez who took his Blériot monoplane to a record breaking altitude of over one mile within 15 minutes of leaving the ground. Otherwise it was the English aviator Claude Grahame-White who dominated the proceedings in his Farman and Blériot machines. An early proponent of the aeroplane's military potential, he was

The Blackpool 'Flying Carnival' of July-August 1910. A.V. Roe shows off the 35hp Green engine and two-bladed propeller of the Roe III Triplane which had superseded the 9/10hp J.A.P.-engined four-bladed unit of the Roe I. *Photo: Blackpool Gazette.*

Success for Roe
and passenger
with the Roe III
Triplane at
Blackpool in
1910, despite
hurried assembly
at Squires Gate
having precluded
cladding the
fuselage.

Rescue following
a later mishap to
the Roe III at
Blackpool in
1910. Man's
earliest form of
transport looks
on, unmoved.
*Photo: Blackpool
Gazette.*

among several aviators at the event who declined to be confined to the official course. In flying over Blackpool he was probably the first pilot to be seen airborne over a Lancashire town. During the Carnival he flew south along the coast to St. Anne's, Lytham, Southport, New Brighton and North Wales. Northwards, from Fleetwood he passed across Morecambe Bay to Barrow-in-Furness, overflying the great shipyards of Vickers Sons & Maxim Ltd. where a number of naval submarines, battle cruisers and a military dirigible airship, the Vickers Naval Rigid **H.M. Airship No. 1**, were under construction. Only two days previously, Grahame-White had shown audacity in buzzing the Home, Atlantic and Mediterranean Fleets assembled in Tor Bay for review by H.M. King George V. In 1910 the distraction of a flying machine cavorting above the greatest show of imperial power in the world – 200 warships with combined tonnage of 700,000 crewed by 50,000 men – was intensely irritating to a navy accustomed to absolute supremacy for nearly a century. Vexation was compounded by the realisation that its great guns would be useless against such a potential threat. All that could be brought to bear on the Farman were the Navy's telescopes. The significance of Grahame-White's exploits at Tor Bay and Barrow, coupled with the accuracy of his subsequent flour-bombing of a target marked out on the ground at Blackpool, was not lost on the Admiralty. But their Lordships' apoplexy would be short-lived: their first airship was already being built at Barrow and within the next two years the aeroplane would start to play a prominent part in naval activities as a result of developments in seaplane and floatplane design in Lancashire and elsewhere.

The Lancashire Aero Club had hoped to return sufficient profits from the 'Flying Carnival' to establish permanent flying facilities at Blackpool but, not for the first time on the Lancashire coast, bad weather struck and the event turned out a financial failure. It nevertheless succeeded in promoting aviation and was an improvement on the 1909 event in that, on the days of settled weather, it allowed British aviators to redeem themselves. Overall it showed how considerably flying had moved on during the intervening nine months. The Manchester Guardian was more pessimistic, commenting that at the end of the event 'the aerodrome lay deserted under an angry copper-tinged sky, and the wind as it rushed over the sand hills, moaned a dirge for the last of the English flying meets.' Indeed the 1909 and 1910 flying events would not be repeated. Local businessmen saw potential for other visitor and leisure attractions on the site and the 1910 Official Programme itself stated that 'Immediately the Flying Carnival is over work will be commenced on laying down a Course to institute a great yearly Steeplechase at Blackpool'. The Clifton Park Racecourse was opened in 1911 but although the successful Coronation Gold Cup event that year attracted 20,000 people sufficient interest could not be sustained; the operating syndicate went into liquidation and horse racing ceased in 1914. After the outbreak of war, in 1915 the land was requisitioned from the Clifton Estate for use by the King's Lancashire Military Convalescent Hospital. 3,000 men were accommodated in temporary buildings erected on the former aerodrome and racecourse, with 1,500 officers in seafront hotels. More than 37,000 wounded servicemen had been treated by the time of the Armistice. But the loss of Blackpool's status as a centre of flying after 1910 would only be temporary.

Soon after the Blackpool Flying Carnival, having placed an order for a Roe III Triplane the Harvard Aeronautical Society invited A.V. Roe to attend its September 1910 flying meeting at Boston in the USA. Roe accompanied the aeroplane on the sea voyage across the Atlantic, together with Claude Grahame-White and his Farman and Blériot aircraft. Both men had discussions with President William H. Taft who visited the meeting.

A.V. Roe & Company, Manchester and Brooklands (2)

Back in Britain the years 1910-14 were busy ones for the new company. Some key appointments were made including the promotion of Reginald J. Parrott from draughtsman to works manager at Brownsfield Mill and, in September 1911, the recruitment of Roy Chadwick to the drawing office as a personal assistant to Roe. Born at Farnworth near Widnes in 1893, having studied at Manchester College of Technology he served his apprenticeship as a draughtsman at the British Westinghouse Electric & Manufacturing Co. Ltd. of Trafford Park, the British subsidiary of Westinghouse Electric Inc. of Pittsburgh, USA, later to be taken over by Metropolitan-Vickers and eventually GEC-AEI. Chadwick would become Avro's chief designer, exercising a profound influence on the firm's future development. A.V. Roe travelled weekly between Manchester and Brooklands where the Avro flying school and flight development facilities provided a shop window for the company's products. Many of its trainees became famous future aviators. Howard Pixton, who later won the Schneider Trophy for Great Britain, gained experience there in 1911 on Roe's final triplane design, the **Roe IV**. Fred Raynham became one of Avro's best known early test pilots. So busy had Brooklands become that in October 1912 Avro moved their flying school to a coastal location at Shoreham in Sussex, where John Alcock became an instructor, the establishment trading as the Avro Flying School (Brighton) Ltd. The base at Shoreham enabled Avro to pursue an interest in floatplane designs in the years that followed.

At Manchester the Avro factory embarked on a prolific output of new aircraft, each pushing the frontiers of technical advance that little bit further. The company's final triplane design, the Roe IV of 1910, was an unsuccessful version with a propensity for crash landing in the Brooklands sewage farm, later inspiring scenes in the 1965 film *Those Magnificent Men in their Flying Machines*. In 1911 it was superseded by the **Avro Type D** biplane with markedly improved performance. Ushering in a link between Avro and the military which was to last for decades, the prototype 'D' was acquired by Commander Oliver Schwann of the Royal Navy. At Cavendish Dock, Barrow-in-Furness, after substituting floats for its wheels, Schwann became the first person to take off in a seaplane from British coastal waters. Further involvement with flying off water also came in 1911 when Avro, still prepared to build to the designs of others, received an order for a Curtiss-type two-seat pusher biplane from Captain Edward W. Wakefield of Kendal. Wakefield fitted floats and operated it from Lake Windermere where it was known as the *Lakes Water Bird*. Another Curtiss-type, the *Lakes Water Hen*, was constructed at Windermere by Wakefield's own company who followed it with a much modified Avro D/E which they named the *Lakes Sea Bird*. The activities of Captain Wakefield and a number of associates led to the establishment of a small-scale, short-lived but significant floatplane manufacturing operation on Lake Windermere which is outlined later.

Avro made an important breakthrough in 1911 by responding to the first military aircraft specification to be issued by the War Office. This was for a two-seat aeroplane capable of meeting a number of performance criteria. The resulting **Avro Type E** was taken by horse-drawn cart from the factory in Ancoats to the London Road (Piccadilly) Station in Manchester for

14

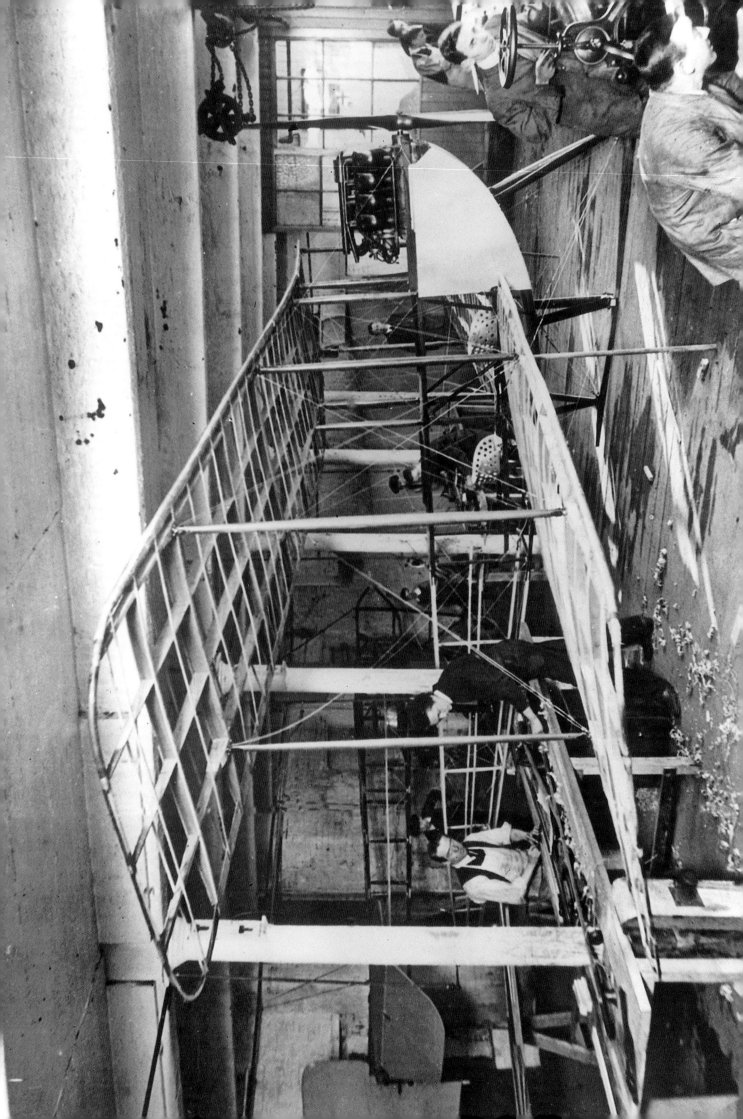

transport by train to Brooklands. It proved an outstanding advance in terms of performance, handling and reliability and, as the **Avro 500**, was the progenitor of a successful series of aeroplanes. The 500 was of immediate interest to the War Office as a training machine and in 1912 three examples were purchased for the newly formed Central Flying School at Upavon in Wiltshire. It was the most successful Avro so far and some 14 were produced for War Office and Admiralty contracts, including a number of single-seater Avro 502s, together with a small number for other customers.

The company started to consider building monoplanes, the first of their own design being the **Avro Type F**, an aircraft also distinguished as the world's first to have a fully enclosed cockpit. The Type F flew at Brooklands on 1 May 1912, to be followed by another monoplane built at Brownsfield Mill that year to the design of Lt. Burga of the Peruvian Navy. Known as the **Burga Monoplane** this flew at Shoreham on 11 November. Avro's alphabetical designation

of aeroplane types terminated in 1912 with the **Avro Type G**, a cabin biplane powered by a 60hp Green engine. This gained a place in aeronautical history when on 25 August its pilot, Lt. Wilfred Parke, established what became the standard technique used by aviators to recover an aircraft from a spin.

With an expanding aviation market, Ministry orders for the Avro 500 and growing sales of components such as the Avro 'strainer' for adjusting the tension of aeroplane bracing wires, the company urgently required further investment to finance its growth. The necessary backing came from the Manchester brewers Groves & Whitnall Ltd. and on 11 January 1913 Avro was registered as A.V. Roe & Company Ltd. with capital of £30,000. Two months later the company opened new premises at Clifton Street, Miles Platting. At that point Mr. James Grimble Groves, Chairman of the brewing company also became Chairman of Avro, with H.V. and A.V. Roe as Joint Managing Directors. With an increasing aircraft workload and continuing responsibilities at Everard & Co., H.V. Roe took in John Lord as a partner at Everards although he too would soon develop a growing interest in Avro. Further orders were received for the 500 and several variants were produced including landplane and seaplane versions of the 501 with 100hp Gnome engines, the 502 and 503. In floatplane form, the latter was sold to the German Navy. The 503 was subsequently manufactured under licence by Gotha and served with the German forces during the First World War.

1913 saw the début of what was to become one of Avro's best loved and most successful aeroplanes, the elegant 80hp Gnome-powered **Avro 504** two-seater biplane. Jointly designed by Roe and Chadwick it proved eminently suitable as a training aircraft and was ordered in large numbers by the War Office. The prototype first flew on 18 September 1913 at Brooklands and performed excellently from the start. After some modifications to wing and control surfaces, the initial warping ailerons being replaced by hinged versions, flying from Brooklands early in 1914 it set a British height record of 14,420 feet having already unofficially exceeded 15,000. In the spring it was purchased by that most enthusiastic and consistent promoter of British aviation, the Daily Mail. Sporting the name of the newspaper along its fuselage and fitted with floats it was used for display flying at towns around the British coast. In its many variants the 504 would be produced in thousands up to 1932, both in land-based form with pronounced and distinctive landing 'skid' and as a floatplane for use off water.

In the months before outbreak of hostilities between Britain and Germany in 1914, Avro introduced the 508 reconnaissance aircraft powered by an 80hp Gnome engine in pusher configuration, the 510 racing/patrol seaplane with large 150hp Sunbeam Nubian engine, and the 511 Gnome-powered 'Arrowplane' scout aircraft. Requiring a longer than average take-off run, in the absence of adequate facilities in Manchester the 'Arrowplane' had to be taken by road to Southport Sands for testing. Avro kept it on the foreshore in a hangar used by local aviation pioneer John Gaunt. Rather less than three years after Roy Chadwick joined the company, a few days before the declaration of war the Avro team was further strengthened by the arrival of Yorkshireman Roy Dobson, appointed initially under Roy Chadwick in the Avro drawing office. Together the two of them would forge the firm's fortunes for decades to come.

Vickers Sons & Maxim Ltd., Barrow-in-Furness

During the years leading up to the First World War, as Avro busily consolidated their manufacturing in the heavily industrialised area of Ancoats, significant developments in aviation were also taking place in what was then North Lancashire but today is in the County of Cumbria. Party to these activities were A.V. Roe & Co., the Royal Navy and several early pioneers of water-based flight using floatplanes. The deep water port of Barrow-in-Furness, sheltered from the Irish Sea by Walney Island, lay on the fringes of the English Lakeland 70 miles to the north west of Manchester. It was the home of the shipyards of Vickers Sons & Maxim Ltd., established as the Barrow Shipbuilding Company Ltd. in 1871 and styled as Vickers Ltd. from April 1911.

Reference has already been made to the first flight of a seaplane – a converted Avro Type D biplane – at Cavendish Dock, Barrow by Commander Oliver Schwann of the Royal Navy in 1911. A notable achievement in its own right, it was in many respects incidental to the main purpose of Schwann's presence in Barrow. For several years the Admiralty had viewed with concern Germany's developing lead in building long range airships to the designs of Count Ferdinand von Zeppelin. In itself this had resulted from Germany's perceived strategic need to compete with the French who had launched the world's first large, fully controllable 'dirigible' airship, *La France*, as far back as 1884. In 1908 their Lordships approached the Vickers shipbuilding and armaments company with a view to them designing a large, British rigid airship. The company had, since 1887, amassed great experience in the manufacture at Barrow of merchant vessels and large warships including battleships and battle cruisers for the Royal Navy and the Imperial Japanese and Russian Navies. Submarines were also a speciality, Vickers having launched the Royal Navy's first, HMS *Holland*, at Barrow in 1901.

Having overcome its initial prejudice against the submarine as an 'ungentlemanly' means of warfare, an increasingly pragmatic Navy saw the potential of the airship – and soon the aeroplane – for fleet spotting and possibly more belligerent activities. *Air-ships* were after all not unlike submarines in shape, although much bigger and quite the equivalent of many capital ships in length. No doubt all this convinced the Admiralty of the logic of selecting Vickers, with proven capacity at Barrow for manufacturing the largest of vessels. At 512 feet in length, 60 feet in diameter and with a gas capacity of 650,000 cu.ft., **His Majesty's Airship *No. 1*** would be nothing if not a large craft. Moreover, in 1910 Vickers had acquired the UK manufacturing rights for the new alloy *Duralumin*. Patented in Germany it combined copper and other elements with aluminium, forming a metal as strong as steel yet, significantly for use in airships, exceptionally light in weight. As a result, despite dimensions similar to those of a large warship, HMA *No. 1* would weigh less than 20 tons.

Following amicable discussions with Zeppelin at Friedrichshafen concerning Germany's experiences of building large

airship assembly halls, a massive 'floating' airship shed capable of completely enclosing HMA *No. 1* during its construction was erected on piles at Cavendish Dock in 1909-1910. This was the structure observed by Claude Grahame-White from his Farman during his excursion from the Blackpool 'Flying Carnival' in August 1910. With work on Britain's first rigid dirigible well under way, in October a naval airship crewing contingent under Commander Maurice Sueter, Inspecting-Captain of Airships, arrived at Barrow in the tender HMS *Hermione* to oversee matters and generally liaise with Vickers. Commander Oliver Schwann was appointed to Barrow as Assistant-Inspecting Captain.

Officially referred to as HMA *Hermione* but satirically dubbed *'Mayfly'*, the airship had a frame made of *Duralumin*, supporting hydrogen-filled gasbags made by Short Brothers who also designed the control surfaces. Skinned overall with aluminium-doped silk, HMA *No. 1* was powered by two 160hp Wolseley engines. The airship emerged completed from its shed on 22 May 1911 but, found to be unacceptably overweight and with a desperate need to conform to Admiralty performance specifications, it was returned to its quarters for essential modifications which took four months. Amongst these, a decision to lighten the airship by removing a 250 ft. triangular-section reinforcing 'keel' from its underside could have been responsible for critically weakening a structure which throughout its manufacture had been plagued by problems of inconsistent quality and tensile strength of the *Duralumin* alloy. Ironically a young draughtsman named Hartley B. Pratt, working in the Submarine Department at Vickers, had taken it upon himself to work out stress calculations which pointed to the risk of a catastrophic structural failure if the keel was taken away. His intervention was unwelcome and went unheeded. On

emerging from its shed for the second time, its diameter reduced to 46 ft., on 24 September the airship broke its back, suffering irreparable damage without having made a single flight. It was reduced to scrap and airship construction at Barrow was halted. The findings of the Court of Inquiry, attended on board HMS *Hermione* by the First Sea Lord Winston Churchill and the Secretary of State for War R.B. Haldane, were never disclosed. Rumours of sabotage by German agents were rife. The most likely explanation was the mishandling by an inexperienced surface crew of an already weakened structure, aggravated by the sideways strain from a hawser applied to prevent a breeze from shifting the airship against dockyard installations. In any event the outcome appears not to have reflected adversely on the long term careers of either Sueter or Schwann. The former became Director of the Air Department of the Admiralty in the years up to the formation of the Royal Naval Air Service and subsequently a Rear Admiral, the latter an Air Vice-Marshal in the Royal Air Force.

Whilst construction of the ill-fated airship had been underway, with Admiralty approval Commander Schwann and other naval colleagues on detachment at HMS *Hermione* had found time to experiment with their modified Avro Type D aeroplane at Cavendish Dock. Among other improvements they redesigned the floats and coaxed more power out of its Green engine. After the failure with HMA *No. 1* it must have been of some consolation to Schwann when he lifted the floatplane off the waters of the Dock on 18 November 1911, albeit briefly. Successful longer flights took place up to the spring of 1912 with Schwann and a new colleague, Sydney Sippe, at the controls. Of an Australian family, Sippe had served an engineering apprenticeship at British Westinghouse at Trafford Park where he became a friend and colleague of Roy Chadwick before

learning to fly at the Avro Flying School at Brooklands in 1911.

Oscar T. Gnosspelius, Captain Edward W. Wakefield and The Lakes Flying Company, Windermere

Twenty miles north east of the bleak waters of Cavendish Dock, in the idyllic surroundings of Lake Windermere, the problems of taking off and alighting on water had also been the focus of attention for another aviation-minded group. Born at Maghull in 1878, Oscar Theodore Gnosspelius of Graythwaite was the son of a Swedish-born Liverpool cotton merchant and stockbroker. Like Captain Edward Wakefield of Kendal, Gnosspelius had been enthused with the idea of flying when visiting the Blackpool Flying Shows in 1909 and 1910. With the relatively sheltered waters of England's largest lake on their doorstep, designing an aeroplane capable of operating off water seemed entirely logical. Moreover, unimpressed with some of the hard landings they had witnessed, if spills were to be as inevitable as thrills, water offered a softer more compliant medium for alighting.

Having qualified as a civil engineer in 1898, Gnosspelius worked on railway, port and mining projects in London, South America and Africa before returning to live with his family at Graythwaite. He experimented with hydroplane models on Windermere in 1909 and designed his **Hydro-monoplane No. 1** on Blériot principles. This was built for him in 1910 with a single central float by the firm of Borwick & Sons, boatbuilders, at their yard at Bowness-on-Windermere. Problems with the float and an underpowered 20hp Alvaston engine resulted in its inability to leave the water. To better equip himself for the task ahead Gnosspelius took lessons at the Avro Flying School at Brooklands during January and February 1911. His re-designed **Hydro-monoplane No. 2** built by Borwicks in 1911 with a more powerful

40hp Clerget engine was airborne briefly in the summer with its designer at the controls, but on leaving the water became immediately uncontrollable ending up on its back in the lake. Recovered, rebuilt and again piloted by Gnosspelius it flew with greater success in February 1912. It was the first locally designed and constructed aeroplane to fly in the area and was frequently airborne over the next two years, often in the hands of pilot Ronald C. Kemp.

Reference has already been made to the two-seat pusher biplane built by Avro to the design of the American Curtiss company for Captain Wakefield. Spurred on by news of the world's first successful flight off water by Glen H. Curtiss at San Diego, California in January 1911, Wakefield ordered the Manchester-built aeroplane which arrived later that year after being tested first as a landplane at Brooklands. On delivery to his lakeside hangar at Hill of Oaks, Wakefield had the wood-framed, fabric-clad aeroplane fitted with a mahogany float designed by Gnosspelius and manufactured by Borwick & Sons. The **Avro-Curtiss** was flown from Windermere on 25 November 1911 by H.H. St. L. Stanley Adams, a former motor racing driver and graduate of the Avro Flying School at Brooklands, and during many successful flights thereafter became popularly known as the *Lakes Water Bird*. At the turn of the year, Wakefield and Stanley Adams jointly founded the Lakes Flying Company, operating a flying school and aeroplane factory from a new hangar at Cockshot Point, near Bowness. Gnosspelius was associated as design engineer.

In 1912 a Gnosspelius-designed **Curtiss-type** aeroplane named the *Lakes Water Hen*, incorporating wings made by Avro at Manchester and floats by Borwicks at Bowness, was built by the Lakes Flying Company. *Water Hen* was an outstanding success, making hundreds of flights over Windermere. Of an entirely different design, the company's third operating aeroplane, *Lakes Sea Bird,* was a two-seat tractor **Hydro-biplane** based on a second-hand Avro Type D/E which had been built originally as a landplane for use at Brooklands by an Australian businessman, John R. Duigan. Having acquired the Duigan airframe, the Lakes Flying Company redesigned and rebuilt it with many modifications including new mainplanes. The resulting machine represented a considerable advance and became a familiar sight above Windermere for several years. Also in 1912 the Lakes Flying Company and Borwick & Sons were contracted by the Admiralty to convert a Deperdussin monoplane to a hydroplane. A new machine was flown to England from France, delivered to Windermere by rail and fitted with a centre float. Following successful trials by Stanley Adams the aeroplane was returned to the Naval Air School at Eastchurch on the Isle of Sheppey, Kent. Later in the year, connections between Windermere and Avro were renewed when Gnosspelius designed the float for an Avro 501 Hydro-biplane built by the Manchester firm to the orders of the Admiralty. This was first flown at Windermere by Stanley Adams in January 1913 and subsequently at Eastchurch.

The first aviator to learn to fly *ab initio* and graduate as a hydroplane pilot from the Lakes Flying Company school was Lt.

Water Hen at Cockshot Point, Windermere, 1912. *Photo: Abbot Hall Gallery via P. Connon.*

J.F.A. Trotter. After obtaining his certificate Trotter requested Gnosspelius to design a two-seat tractor Hydro-biplane which was built by Borwick & Sons in 1913. When first flown by Trotter in September the machine came down heavily in the water and was much damaged. Although repaired and in the air again the following month it proved too heavy and underpowered.

Far more successful was the **Lakes Hydro-monoplane**, also designed by Gnosspelius and built by Borwick & Sons for the Lakes Flying Company in 1913. A two-seat pusher aircraft, along with *Water Hen* and *Sea Bird* it was used extensively for the training of Royal Naval Air Service (RNAS) pilots at Windermere between 1914-16. By then however the Lakes Flying Company had ceased to exist. At the outbreak of war Wakefield sold all its assets including premises and the three aircraft to the Northern Aircraft Company who continued to operate the floatplane training centre. Wakefield rejoined the army and Gnosspelius entered the Admiralty Air Department. Stanley Adams volunteered for service with the RNAS. Lakes pilot instructors Ronald Kemp and John Lankester Parker left to join Short Brothers as test pilots and after the war, following an introduction by Parker, Gnosspelius was appointed head of Shorts' experimental department. There, as his assistant, was Arthur Gouge who later became Chief Designer.

In May 1916 the Windermere training operations at Cockshot Point and Hill of Oaks were re-named RNAS Unit, Hill of Oaks and changed again the following month to RNAS Windermere. The combined efforts of designers, aviators, ship and boat builders-turned aircraft manufacturers at Barrow and Windermere during 1908-14 justify the area's claim to be the birthplace of British naval and civil marine aviation. In the South of England, a naval air school was also established in association with Short Brothers' Eastchurch Works on the Isle of Sheppey in December 1911.

Chapter 3
The First World War
1914-18

Vickers Ltd., Barrow-in-Furness

In September 1911 observers at Barrow-in-Furness witnessing the spectacular failure of **His Majesty's Airship** *No. 1 'Mayfly'* – officially **HMA** *Hermione* – could have been forgiven had they concluded that Vickers' first foray into airship building would also be their last. Certainly the Admiralty and many in government turned cold on the subject of airships for some time. Others, notably Captain Murray Sueter who had been 'rested' after his tenure at Barrow before being brought back to serve as Director of the Air Department of the Admiralty in 1912, continued to keep a close eye on Germany's progress with Zeppelins.

The story of the resumption of airship construction at Barrow little more than two years after the *'Mayfly'* débâcle has many of the ingredients of a ripping espionage thriller. To begin with, airships had greater range, endurance and payload for the delivery of passengers – and potentially bombs – than other contemporary aircraft. Increasingly bellicose statements emanating from the German military left little doubt that the traditional immunity to bombardment enjoyed by Britain as an island might now be a thing of the past. In the perception of many, Zeppelins were the terror weapons of the day, understandably exuding a degree of intimidation consistent with craft the size of naval battleships appearing out of the sky. In time, the ability of airships to fly slowly and remain on station – or in

modern military parlance 'loiter' – for lengthy periods would also prove ideal for reconnaissance over land or sea and for fleet and anti-submarine operations. Even after hostilities broke out, the airship's supposed vulnerability to attack by faster 'heavier-than-air' aeroplanes was not always the case in practice. In the hands of a skilled crew jettisoning ballast at the critical moment an airship might easily outclimb fighter scouts whose engines would be straining to gain height. For many the ultimate Zeppelin menace would be the sound of them rumbling around the night sky apparently at will, dropping their bomb load however inaccurately.

Not surprisingly, for strategic reasons the German Government was disinclined to surrender its lead in the design and manufacture of large rigid airships by making Zeppelins available to other countries such as Britain. The sanction did not initially prevent a German manufacturer of non-rigid airships, Parseval Luftschiffe of Bitterfeld near Leipzig, from supplying one of their smaller craft which was delivered to Farnborough in 1913. As a result of their friendly pre-war contacts with this less sensitive company Vickers expressed interest in building Parsevals under licence and were fully familiar with their design details.

In the meantime, airship intrigue which might have come straight from the pages of the *Boys Own Paper* had already gained local currency in Barrow with suggestions, however improbable, of the involvement of

German agents in the 'Mayfly' episode. In 1912 clandestine activity became fact when during a visit to Germany to evaluate airship development, Captain Sueter and a colleague posed as Americans to secure a flight in a Zeppelin to experience the craft at first hand.

In the aftermath of Sueter's subsequent report the Admiralty requested Vickers to design another large rigid airship and the company reinstated its Airship Department at Barrow. As Chief Draughtsman, Airships, Vickers brought back Hartley Pratt, the young designer who after making himself unpopular by warning of the structural weakness of 'Mayfly' had left to work for the shipbuilding company J. Samuel White & Co. on the Isle of Wight. There, Pratt had been impressed by a colleague, Barnes Neville Wallis, whom he now recruited as his assistant. Both were initially installed at Vickers' design offices in London. For Wallis it was the start of an association with the company that was to span six decades and involve a number of connections with Lancashire and the North West of England.

There was yet more intrigue in April 1913 when a Zeppelin made a forced landing at Lunéville in France and, whilst ostensibly providing hospitality for its crew, the French authorities used the opportunity to take detailed photographs which were subsequently made available to the British Government and Vickers. In a more remarkable episode still, during a business visit to Parseval in 1914 shortly before the outbreak of war, Hartley Pratt personally took pencil rubbings of details of Zeppelin framework girders which he spotted on railway wagons in transit to Friedrichshafen.

Possessing all the necessary information, Vickers proceeded on the designs for the airship requested by the British Government, accorded the designation **HMA** *No. 9*. Go-ahead for its construction had been given at the end of 1913 and

initial work commenced in the shed originally built for 'Mayfly'. At 526 feet in length and 53 feet in diameter, with a gas capacity of nearly 850,000 cu.ft., HMA *No. 9* was even larger than her predecessor and a decision was taken to build a new two-bay shed on Walney Island. Yet again, in another strange twist of circumstances, the only firm able to design such a vast structure capable of withstanding the wind strengths associated with Morecambe Bay was the German company which had advised on the Zeppelin sheds at Friedrichshafen. Somewhat surprisingly – maybe intentionally to monitor what the British were up to – they were allowed to supply the designs and the civil engineering was able to proceed. Construction of HMA *No. 9* ran into 1914 when four 180hp Maybach engines were delivered to Barrow in yet another late pre-war liaison with Germany made all the more bizarre by the abrupt return home of the firm's technical representatives as the international situation deteriorated. Meanwhile, the German Parseval non-rigid airship which had come to Britain in 1913, designated **HMA** *No. 4,* had proved so successful that three more were ordered. The outbreak of war precluded any further deliveries and the three craft which had been intended for Britain were subsequently diverted to the German Navy. HMA *No. 4* was used by the RNAS to carry out patrols over the Thames Estuary, was refurbished at Barrow by Vickers in 1915 and later used to train crews for rigid airships. Holding all the necessary constructional details, Vickers stepped into the breach by building three Parseval-types at Barrow, designated **HMA** *Nos. 5, 6 and 7.* These were 304 feet in length with a capacity of 364,000 cu.ft. and variously powered by two 180-240hp Wolseley/Maybach and Renault engines. It was 1917 before all three were in service, to be used mainly for training future rigid airship crews and for mine hunting before being dismantled in 1918-19.

Airship work was well under way at Barrow when on the afternoon of 29 January 1915, in probably the only closely targeted enemy action taken against an aircraft factory in the North West during the First World War, the German patrol submarine *U-21*, 650 tons, Kapitan Otto Hersig, surfaced off Walney Island and opened fire on the new airship shed with her 88mm deck gun. Clearly, the German Naval High Command knew all about the large installation at Barrow and its contents. On being invited to withdraw by the Walney Island Coastal Battery, with no damage sustained onshore, the 210-foot-long *U-21* slipped beneath the waves to resume her more conventional and successful duties of sinking shipping in the Irish Sea and Scottish waters. The brief action served to underline the need to expedite production of airships to protect coastal waters and vital shipping lanes.

Hersig, with *U-21* and her complement of 35 crew, became one of the most successful submarine commanders. Over three years they sank 36 ships including, ironically, the Barrow-built 12,000-ton battleship HMS *Triumph* in the Dardanelles off Gallipoli on 25 May 1915. On 7 May 1915 the submarine's sister ship *U-20* was responsible for sinking the 31,500-ton Cunard Liner RMS *Lusitania*, en route from New York to Liverpool, off the Old Head of Kinsale on the south coast of Ireland. Amongst 1,198 passengers and crew lost were 124 American citizens, a major contributory factor to the USA's eventual entry into the war.

The threat posed by submarines generated an Admiralty specification of February 1915 for a class of small, non-rigid airships capable of no more than 40-50mph but, equipped with radio and a 160lb bomb load, able to fly low, slow and remain stationary on lookout for mines, periscopes and surface oil traces from submarines in coastal waters. It further required that they be capable of easy

manufacture in significant numbers. The result was the Sea Scout, otherwise Submarine or Sea Searcher **'SS' Class** of hunter airship, some 143 feet in length and up to 30 feet in diameter. They were controlled by a crew of two – a pilot and observer/WT operator – from an aircraft fuselage 'car' suspended beneath a 60-70,000 cu.ft. envelope. Up to 10 of a total of some 50 'SS' Class airships produced at a number of centres throughout the country during the war were made at Barrow during 1915-16. Most of the Barrow-built versions were fitted with B.E.2c aeroplane fuselage 'cars' with propellers in tractor configuration although some had Farman fuselages with pusher propellers. The majority of the Barrow 'SS' Class remained in Irish Sea waters, serving with Royal Naval Air Stations at Luce Bay in Dumfries and Galloway, Anglesey and at Barrow itself.

Such was the importance attached by the Government to combating the U-boat menace that in March 1915 the First Lord of the Admiralty, Winston Churchill, ordered the suspension of work on the HMA *No. 9* rigid in favour of concentrating efforts on getting the 'SS' Class non-rigids into service. With design work subordinated to relatively prosaic series manufacture of the simpler, smaller Parsevals and 'SS' Class, Hartley Pratt and Barnes Wallis left Vickers forthwith to enlist in the Artists' Rifles. Within two or three months of their departure renewed

'SS' Sea Scout non-rigid airship undergoing trials with a new type of mooring mast in Vickers' huge Walney Island erecting shed, Barrow-in-Furness, 1918.

concerns about the Zeppelin threat forced a government re-think and work on HMA *No. 9* was started up again in June. Also in the summer of 1915 non-rigid production got into its stride and SS*17* – the first Barrow Sea Scout and the first Barrow airship to fly successfully – took to the air in July. SS*18* duly followed in August when Vickers were also invited to design a new, larger version of HMA *No. 9*, completion of which was itself to be expedited. The new design envisaged a rigid airship 535 feet in length with a capacity of 942,000 cu.ft., powered initially by four 250hp Rolls-Royce Eagle engines giving a useful available or 'disposable' lift of 6 tons compared with the 3.8 tons of HMA *No. 9*. It would be designated **HMA *No. 23***, the first of a proposed new **Class 23** type. An order for the new airship was received from the Admiralty in October and construction commenced in March 1916 alongside HMA *No. 9* in the double shed at Walney Island. By that time airship work at Barrow had grown to the extent that two large ballrooms in Douglas on the Isle of Man were taken over by the Vickers subsidiary the Ioco Rubber & Waterproofing Company for the production of rubberised airship fabric and inflation testing of gasbags.

With work on military airships of all types once again high in Government priorities, the service careers of Hartley Pratt and Barnes Wallis were peremptorily ended within months of their enlistment. Commissioned briefly in the RNVR, prior to being civilianised once again both were returned to airship work, Pratt at RNAS Kingsnorth in Kent and Wallis in charge of construction at Barrow. During the next five years, whilst living at Kents Bank near Grange-over-Sands, Wallis was to develop a lifelong affinity for the hills and lakes of Cumbria.

Owing much to the Zeppelin which the French had secretly photographed in 1913 HMA *No. 9* was eventually completed in

November 1916, over three years after she had been ordered. With the experience of HMA *No. 1* still fresh in minds she had been very strongly built and as a result was overweight as well as overdue and outdated. Nevertheless, HMA *No. 9* was the first British rigid airship to fly and her disposable lift performance was improved after a number of modifications including the fitting of revised engines. Again with HMA *No. 1* in mind these were carried out with the utmost care. HMA *No. 9*'s subsequently short career prior to deletion in June 1918 was spent mainly with the Rigid Trials Flight at RNAS Howden, Yorkshire. With the airship off their hands at last, Vickers were able to make a start early in 1917 on the second '23' Class to be built at Walney Island, **HMA *No. 26***, which had been ordered twelve months earlier.

November 1916 also brought an Admiralty order for the proposed Zeppelin-type **Class 33** airship *R.37*, with an envelope length of 672 feet, diameter of 79 feet and a capacity of 1,950,000 cu.ft., to be powered by five 240hp Sunbeam engines. Because even the Walney Island shed was too small for a craft of this size it was decided that a third shed 900 feet in length should be constructed. A site was chosen near Flookburgh on the more sheltered Cartmel peninsula projecting into Morecambe Bay some ten miles east of Barrow. The new building was to be part of a comprehensively planned community including houses to accommodate airship assembly workers with a rail link to the Barrow main line. Even though considerable progress was made, adverse ground conditions and an horrendous seven-fold increase in costs caused development to be abandoned in September 1917. Officially the decision was attributed to shortage of constructional steelwork. The contract for *R.37* and all the parts made by Vickers for the airship up to that date were handed

over to Short Brothers at Cardington. *R.37* was destined never to be completed. The Flookburgh site lay derelict until 1941 when the RAF opened it as a temporary fighter station. As Cark Airfield, it remains in limited use for private aviation to the present day.

September 1917 also saw the trial flight of HMA *No. 23* at Barrow, that of the virtually identical HMA *No. 26* coming six months later in March 1918 following a rapid acceleration in the production programme. After entering service with the RNAS both were to overfly the surrender of the German submarine fleet off Harwich on 20 November 1918. Otherwise their disposable lift of 6 tons compared with the 30 tons of a Zeppelin restricted the use of Class 23 airships mainly to training and experimental purposes. In the case of HMA *No. 23* the latter included successful trials involving release of Sopwith Camel fighter scouts carried beneath the airship. HMA *No. 26* was deleted from service in March 1919 and *No. 23* in September.

Meanwhile, Barnes Wallis had been working on a radical new design for another rigid airship to be built at Barrow. At last he was given a completely free hand, the only constraint imposed on him in the aftermath of the decision not to proceed further with the Flookburgh shed was that the airship should be no longer than could be accommodated at Walney Island. His plans were given Admiralty approval in November 1917. Designated **R.80**, the new airship was 535 feet in length with a width of 70 feet, a gas capacity of 1,200,000 cu.ft. and powered by four 230hp Wolseley-Maybach engines. Two of these were coupled to a single pusher propeller behind the forward control car, the others housed in two power-cars amidships. *R.80* was a triumph of aesthetic design, her elegantly tapered fully streamlined profile contrasting markedly with the bluff, parallel lines of her predecessors. She was completed in October 1918 and first flown the following month when a rapid ascent due to overheating of the envelope caused some structural damage to her girders. Subsequent repairs and alterations requested by the Admiralty took until 1920 to complete. During this period Barnes Wallis' health broke down as a result of overwork but towards the end of his convalescence he was back at Barrow to see *R.80's* successful second flight trial in July 1920.

R.80 was to be the last of Barrow's rigid airships. Despite being as advanced as the latest Zeppelins, with a top speed of 60mph and a disposable lift of 17.8 tons, the timing of her completion just after the First World War resulted in her being surplus to requirements. The Air Ministry took delivery in February 1921, *R.80* flying over Barrow in final salute before setting course for Yorkshire. There, at Howden and later at Pulham in Norfolk she was used on just a few occasions for the training of American airship crews before being deflated, tested to destruction and finally scrapped in 1925. Vickers' 12-year involvement with airships at Barrow was concluded in 1921 when the company completed a one-off order for a Parseval-type non-rigid for the Japanese Imperial Navy.

The scaling down of the airship programme in the immediate aftermath of the war precipitated the closure of Vickers' Airship Department at Barrow. Initially, Barnes Wallis was kept on a retainer basis, taking up a post teaching mathematics in Switzerland. When interest in airships was revived once again in 1923-4 the Vickers design team was re-established as the Airship Guarantee Company at Howden in Yorkshire and Wallis was appointed Chief Designer. In charge of structural calculations was Neville Shute Norway, better known later as the author Neville Shute. The outcome was Wallis' magnificent **R.100**, a 709-foot-long five million cu.ft. 100-passenger airship with a top speed of 70mph. In designing the *R.100* Wallis used the principle of the

geodesic, the shortest distance between two points on a curved surface, by spirally winding wires to form a geodetic cylindrical mesh structure for containment of the gasbag. It enabled a remarkable 95 per cent of the *R.100's* volume to contain gas.

Conceived to pioneer Empire air routes and despite making a number of successful flights including a return crossing of the North Atlantic to Canada, *R.100* was not to be allowed to develop its full potential. Following the catastrophic accident in 1930 involving her sister craft the Cardington-built Government Airship *R.101*, designed and built on different principles to Wallis' *R.100*, all airship work was brought to a complete halt.

Barnes Wallis remained with Vickers who transferred his talents to aeroplane design at Vickers Aviation, Weybridge, Surrey in 1930. There, his use of geodetic structures would come to the fore once again, with subsequent recurring links between his work and aircraft produced in Lancashire and the North West.

At the end of the First World War the newly formed Royal Air Force had over 100 airships remaining on strength out of a total of more than 200 of all types which had been built by firms including Vickers at Barrow, Beardmore at Inchinnan, Renfrew, Armstrong Whitworth at Barlow, Yorkshire, Shorts at Cardington and Royal Naval Air Stations in various locations. Vickers and their associated companies had become the second-largest manufacturers of airships in the world after Zeppelin.

A.V. Roe & Company Ltd., Manchester and Hamble

At Manchester, despite their move from Brownsfield Mill in Ancoats to larger premises at Clifton Street, Miles Platting, A.V. Roe & Co. Ltd. still entered the First World War with inadequate production space for the upsurge in orders for the **Avro 504**. Twelve had been ordered by the War Office during the summer of 1913 and were delivered prior to Great Britain's declaration of war on Germany on 4 August 1914. The Admiralty followed with an order for seven for the RNAS. Fortuitously, only a mile from Clifton Street a large extension had been built to the Newton Heath Works of the textile engineers Mather & Platt, but not yet occupied. By agreement between the two companies this was taken over by Avro who also acquired adjacent land for expansion. To be known as the Park Works, Newton Heath, the new factory was supplemented by the nearby Heath Works and the Empire Works in Failsworth. Clifton Street was retained as the company's woodworking department.

Avro 504s were on the strength of No. 5 Squadron of the Royal Flying Corps, one of the first contingents to cross the Channel on 13 August and were soon in the thick of things over France and Germany. One of them had the unfortunate distinction of being the first British aeroplane to be shot down in the conflict when hit by ground fire on 22 August. In October, under conditions of great secrecy, a special flight of four RNAS Avro 504s was formed in Manchester for the purpose of attacking the Zeppelin sheds at Friedrichshafen on the Bodensee (Lake Konstanz). The aircraft were crated to a French airfield at Belfort, 125 miles from the target. Three of them, each loaded with four 20lb Hales bombs, made the attack on 21 November 1914 flying at low level on the approach over the lake. Significant damage was sustained by the Zeppelin works. One of the pilots on the epic four-hour return flight, the first ever strategic bombardment attack by a formation of aircraft, was Flt. Sub-Lt. Sydney Sippe who was awarded the DSO. A graduate of the Avro Flying School at Brooklands and, with Commander Oliver Schwann a fellow pilot of the Avro 'D' floatplane at Barrow-in-Furness, Sippe's close links with Avro aircraft were further renewed by the Friedrichshafen raid. In

another action, on 17 May 1915 Avro 504s carried out the first aerial interception of a Zeppelin which was forced down behind German lines in Belgium.

But as the hothouse of war forced development of more powerful, faster aircraft it was as a trainer that the Avro 504 entered series production on a large scale. The War Office and Admiralty virtually competed with each other for every batch produced. The 504's advantages for training included a lower wing staggered two feet behind the upper, giving the front seat pupil or observer a good view of the ground. A prominent front landing 'skid' averted risk of 'digging in' by the ten-foot propeller. In flight the 504 was noted for its stability, manoeuvrability and the lightness and precision of its controls. With an almost absurdly low landing speed of 37mph it could be put down safely in the smallest of fields anywhere. Such was its popularity amongst pilots, particularly in 'J' and 'K' versions, that it was probably the first aeroplane to justify the description ubiquitous, recognisable worldwide by the trademark of the Avro 500 Series – a tail rudder distinctively shaped like a fat comma in profile. One of many eminent personalities who learned to fly on the legendary Avro was HRH Prince Albert, later King George VI, who qualified in a 504J at Croydon in 1919.

By 1916 Avro 504s streaming off the Park Works production line were towed through the streets, wingless but on their own wheels, to the railway for despatch and final assembly at a number of Government Aircraft Acceptance Parks (AAPs) around the country. Lack of decent flying facilities at Newton Heath prevented all but a few from being flown from the works themselves although from 1915 some were delivery flown from a temporary field at Ashburton Road, Trafford Park, also used by Avro for production test flying. Between 1911 and 1913 it had been operated as Manchester

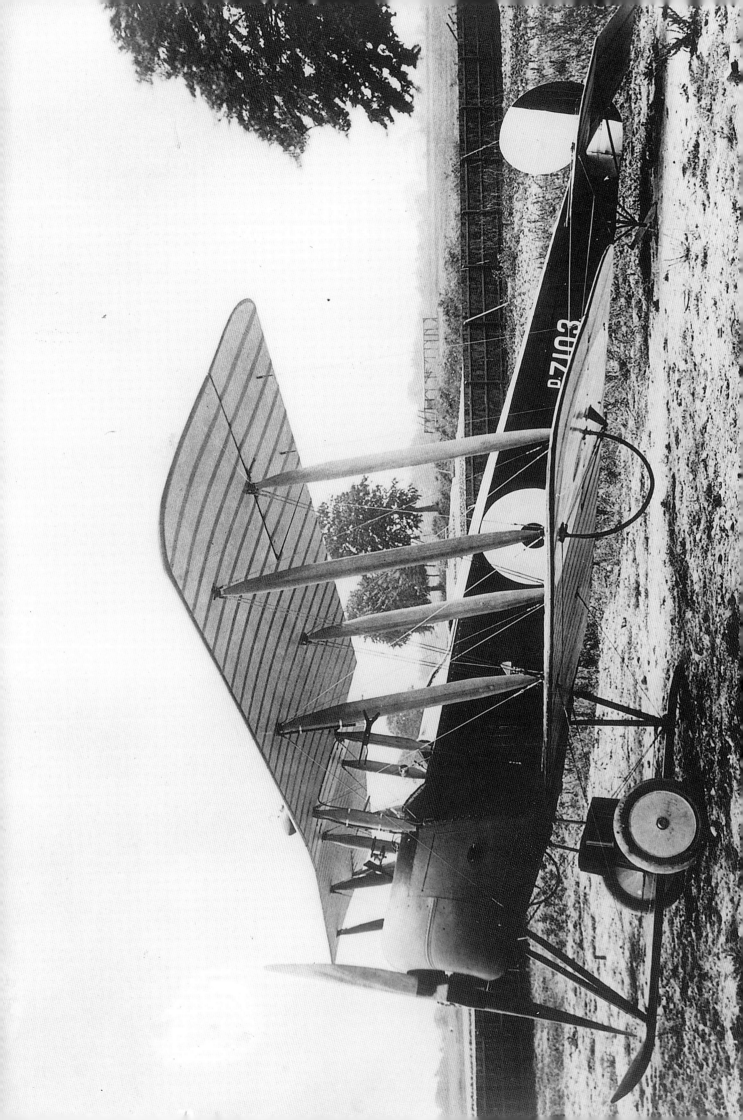

Aerodrome Ltd. Towards the end of the war Avro despatched aircraft to No. 15 (Manchester) Aircraft Acceptance Park, established by the War Department at Hough End Fields, Alexandra Park, in Didsbury in the winter of 1917-18. No. 15 AAP was set up primarily to receive aircraft from National Aircraft Factory (NAF) No. 2 at Heaton Chapel, Stockport and flight test them prior to delivery to their units.

Although born in Lancashire, Alliott Roe had spent most of his early years in the South of England. Financial circumstances had dictated the choice of Manchester as the initial location for his company but, with profits accruing during the war years, he began to consider expanding operations in less congested more rural surroundings. The Avro Flying School had been based on the South Coast at Shoreham, near Brighton, from 1912 and in 1916, on a motor tour of the South with his wife, he found a 300 acre site at Hamble with foreshore to Southampton Water which he persuaded the company to buy. His plan was to build a new factory and houses in a 'garden city' environment, boosting production and focusing on the development of seaplanes for which he foresaw great future demand. The full realisation of his grand design was to be frustrated by the wartime shortage of building materials, but not before a large building had been erected prominently displaying the Avro name. Architecturally reminiscent of a Lancashire cotton mill it was used for final assembly of Avro aircraft made at Manchester, as a design and technical centre and the company's Experimental Department. Reluctantly Roe had to accept that the new site would have to operate in tandem with operations in Manchester rather than superseding them as originally intended. Some Avro 504s would be produced at Hamble but its principal role under R.J. Parrott as General Manager was the design, manufacture,

assembly and testing of prototypes in which capacity it led to the termination of the company's activities at Brooklands. Roy Chadwick and the Avro Design Team moved down to Hamble where Chadwick's father Charles, formerly of British Westinghouse, was Works Manager for a period during the war. Roy Chadwick was appointed Chief Designer at Hamble in 1919. At Manchester Roy Dobson succeeded R.J. Parrott as Works Manager.

Government sought more direct involvement in aircraft production in 1916 and the Society of British Aircraft Constructors was established to represent the industry as a whole. Demand for Avro 504s appeared insatiable and some 18 subcontractors around the country were appointed to build them. Countless others were engaged to manufacture components in a programme which provided both Avro and Government with invaluable experience over two decades later when aircraft production was once again essential for national survival. During the last twelve months of WWI the combined production of Avro 504s by all manufacturers exceeded 5,000. Avro themselves were turning out over 200 each month. A figure of 8,340 is often quoted as the total wartime output of all types of 504, comprising 3,696 by Avro and 4,644 by subcontractors, exceeding that of any other British aircraft. It is possible, however, that these include elements of post-war production but in any event there is broad agreement that a grand total of some 10,800 was built before production finally ceased in 1932. Production levels of such magnitude placed tremendous pressure on aero-engine manufacturers and explain how the 504 came to be fitted with a universal engine mounting capable of accommodating some 20 different types of engine. After the war it was stated that Avro 504 production alone had consumed a third of the country's supply of silver spruce.

Opposite:
'K' version of the Avro 504, arguably the world's first 'classic' aircraft which first flew in its original form in September 1913. In total, 10,800 Avro 504s of all types were produced worldwide up to 1932.

Small numbers of nine further types of experimental fighter, reconnaissance and bomber aircraft were made, assembled and tested variously at Manchester and Hamble up to the end of the war. Significant among these were the **Avro 523 Pike**, the **Avro 529**, and the **Avro 533 Manchester** three-seat twin-engined bomber, Avro's first 'twin'. As the war drew to a close none was produced in quantity. Of the two Pikes made at Manchester one was crated down to Hamble for assembly and testing, the other erected on Southport Sands from where it was flown to Hamble.

Having been closely involved in founding the aircraft industry in Lancashire before the war, Humphrey Verdon Roe bought back the Groves family shareholding in Avro in December 1916, selling the shares to other members of his family before leaving the company in 1917 on receipt of a commission in the RFC. After the war he married the sociologist and British pioneer of birth control Dr. Marie Stopes. On Humphrey's departure Alliott Verdon Roe became Avro's Managing Director. Of the other brothers, Everard Verdon Roe succeeded R.J. Parrott as General Manager at Hamble and later became Vicar of Hamble Parish Church.

Vulcan Motor & Engineering Company (1906) Ltd., Crossens, Southport

Geoffrey de Havilland, British pioneer aviator, aeroplane designer-constructor and a contemporary of A.V. Roe, founded the de Havilland Aircraft Co. Ltd. at Stag Lane Aerodrome, Edgware, Middlesex in 1920. Before doing so he had designed some of the best known military aircraft of the First World War, including the **B.E.2, D.H.4, D.H.9** and the **D.H.10 Amiens**, a range of single and twin-engined biplane fighters and bombers.

The initials B.E. represented Blériot Experimental, denoting de Havilland's development of French designs which progressed into the B.E.2 of 1912. One of the first aircraft to be built at the Royal Aircraft Factory at Farnborough, Hampshire, the B.E.2 was also the first British aircraft to see service in France in 1914. Noted for its stability rather than performance and manoeuvrability, a characteristic which made it eminently suitable for reconnaissance and bombing, the B.E.2 suffered appalling losses at the hands of German fighter aircraft. During the so-called 'Fokker Scourge' over the Western Front in 1915-1916 it earned the chilling sobriquet 'Fokker Fodder'. Though lacklustre as a fighting aeroplane, the docility of the B.E.2d made it ideal as a trainer in dual-controlled form.

Well over 3,500 B.E.2s were built, requiring the services of subcontractors around the country. One such was the Vulcan Motor & Engineering Company, a manufacturer of motor cars who had switched over to volume production of lorries and ambulances at the onset of war. Their reputation for quality and output was such that the Government's Air Board awarded them contracts for aircraft production, commencing with 100 B.E.2d and 200 B.E.2e versions. Vulcan were reputedly the first aircraft industry 'outsiders' to be awarded such work.

De Havilland's D.H.4/9/10s were initially built by the Aircraft Manufacturing Co. Ltd. (Airco) of Hendon. Excellent handling and performance made the D.H.4 day bomber an immediate success in service. But in the D.H.9A, the newly formed Royal Air Force, resulting from the amalgamation of the RFC and RNAS on 1 April 1918, received one of its most outstanding aircraft. Powered by 375-465hp engines such as the Rolls-Royce Eagle, Napier Lion and American-built Liberty, D.H.4/9/9As were used extensively over the Western Front and in bombing raids on Germany. The D.H.10 came too late to see service in the war. Post-war duties of all of them extended to 'policing' roles in the Near and

Middle East including Iraq, with 'tropicalised' D.H.9s also deployed in India over the North West Frontier. In Britain in 1919 a D.H.9 established a world altitude record of over 30,000 ft. – remarkable progress only 10 years after the Blackpool 'Flying Week'. In 1920 in the USA, Charles Lindbergh, later to undertake the first solo crossing of the North Atlantic, flew D.H.4s to pioneer transcontinental mail route services.

Such was wartime demand for the D.H.4 and D.H.9 that, among a number of other subcontractors, the Government turned again to the Vulcan Motor & Engineering Company. Around 100 of each type were made at Southport, whilst 350 D.H.9As were also ordered but not necessarily all completed before hostilities ceased.

In common with the Fylde Coast to the north, much of the West Lancashire Coast between the Mersey and Ribble estuaries, from Waterloo near Liverpool and Freshfield near Formby, as far as Southport, had been the scene of a number of pre-war flights by pioneer aviators. One of them, a Liverpool electrical engineer named Henry Melly, built two hangars on the sands at Waterloo, which were later used by the RNAS. Robert Fenwick, an associate of Melly, in conjunction with a colleague Sidney Swaby and two local companies, Planes Ltd. of Birkenhead and the Mersey Aeroplane Company of Freshfield, designed and built the alliteratively named *Mersey Military Monoplane*. Despite showing initial promise the aircraft crashed during military trials on Salisbury Plain in December 1912, killing Fenwick. Early in 1910, with an eye on activities at neighbouring Blackpool, Southport Council also determined to provide facilities for aviation and a hangar was erected on the foreshore at the northern end of Hesketh Road. The location adjoined '40 square miles of hard sand, and a plain of more than 900 square miles to fly over'. The hangar became the operating centre for Southport Sands (Hesketh Park) Aerodrome on a 'Site acknowledged by Experts to be the finest Flying Ground in the North of England'. Initially the hangar was used by local aviator-constructor John Gaunt and later by the Yorkshire pioneer Harold Blackburn. In 1911 Gaunt removed to another hangar nearby which was also used by Avro for testing the Avro 511 'Arrowplane' scout.

During the early war years the Hesketh Park facilities were used by Vulcan Motor & Engineering for the re-erection of B.E.2d/e aircraft built nearby at Crossens, prior to being test flown from the foreshore by pilots from the 'parent' manufacturer, the Royal Aircraft Factory at Farnborough. In 1917 the RNAS built two 12,500 sq.ft. Bowstring Truss hangars capable of accommodating small coastal patrol non-rigid airships and the aerodrome was designated by the Government as Aircraft Acceptance Park No. 11 (Southport) for the reception of D.H.4 and D.H.9 aircraft from the Vulcan works. After flight testing these were flown on to the appropriate service units. It is believed that a number of the aircraft made by Vulcan were also crated to Russia for use by the Imperial Air Corps.

National Aircraft Factory (NAF) No. 2, Heaton Chapel, Stockport

In 1917 the Government decided to exercise even closer control of aircraft production by establishing three National Aircraft Factories under the Ministry of Munitions: No. 1 at Waddon, near Croydon, Surrey for D.H.9s and, in the

De Havilland D.H.4 of the type made by the Vulcan Motor & Engineering Company Ltd., Crossens, Southport.

Top left:
Workforce of NAF No. 2, Heaton Chapel, Stockport, gather in front of the first (D1001) of 444 D.H.9s which they produced in 1918. The aero-engine is a six-cylinder 236hp Siddeley-Deasy Puma.

Top right:
D.H.9 assembly at NAF No. 2 in 1918, with a single D.H.10 visible in the distance. A notice suspended from the roof read 'Remember a hidden mistake may cause a brave man to lose his life'.

Bottom:
One of only seven twin-engined D.H.10 heavy bombers, out of 200 ordered, completed at NAF No. 2 before WW1 ended.

North West of England, No. 2 at Heaton Chapel for D.H.9s and D.H.10s, and No. 3 at Aintree for Bristol F.2B Fighters.

The Gorton, Manchester firm of Crossley Bros. Ltd., who from 1906 had made engines and motor cars, expanded into additional premises at High Lane, Heaton Chapel. By the mid-point of the war they were supplying large numbers of personnel carrier 'tenders' to the RFC and during 1917-18, manufacturing Beardmore and Bentley aero-engines. In November 1917, as Crossley Motors Ltd., they were appointed to manage NAF No. 2 extending over 15 acres of adjoining land.

Commissioned in only nine months the new factory had a workforce of 2,500, many of whom were women from the textile industry who had received instruction in aircraft building at a Government Aircraft Construction Training Centre at the Belle Vue Pleasure Ground in Manchester, where initial production of D.H.9 parts commenced. Of 500 D.H.9s ordered, some 444 were delivered in 1918 but with the ending of the war only seven of the larger twin-engined D.H.10 bombers out of a contract for 200 are believed to have been completed.

Parkland known as Cringle Fields adjoining the factory was requisitioned for flight testing and delivery of aircraft produced at NAF No. 2 although most were towed to nearby sidings for transport by rail to Aircraft Acceptance Parks. These included No. 2 (Northern) AAP near Sheffield and No. 15 (Manchester) AAP at Alexandra Park, Didsbury.

National Aircraft Factory (NAF) No. 3, Aintree, Liverpool

The open expanse of Aintree Racecourse was the scene of some of the earliest flights in Lancashire. Following the Doncaster Aviation Meeting in October 1909, S.F. Cody had his huge 'Flying Cathedral' biplane, developed from that in which he had made the first flight in Britain a year before, transported in sections for re-erection at Aintree in November. There, he flew it before large crowds on several occasions up to January 1910 in a number of abortive attempts to win a cash prize for the first flight from Liverpool to Manchester.

Land which the Government acquired for strategic wartime purposes adjoining the racecourse was by 1916 used for munitions, aircraft storage and preparation. In February 1917 discussions took place between the Ministry of Munitions Aeroplane Construction Department and the Cunard Steamship Company when it was proposed that in order to further boost aircraft production for the war effort, Cunard should manage the erection and operation of a National Aircraft Factory in the locality. The vast Cunard organisation had interests worldwide and was considered to be well up to the task. Moreover, in addition to its marine engineering expertise it had a large Furnishing Department engaged on fitting out ship interiors involving extensive woodworking operations. Initial preparations commenced at Cunard's Pier Head offices in Liverpool and a contract

was received for the manufacture of 500 **Bristol F.2B Fighters**. Designed for the Bristol & Colonial Aeroplane Company of Filton, Gloucestershire by Frank Barnwell, the two-seat reconnaissance fighter was another successful WW1 aircraft demand for which outstripped the capacity of its parent manufacturer. Initially it was the subject of heavy losses in combat over the Western Front. But the situation changed dramatically once pilots learned to make full use of its manoeuvrability and performance by flinging it headlong into the mêlée as they might a single-seater, rather than flying straight and level as a platform for the rear gunner. Indeed 'Biffs' established such a reputation that German pilots were often reluctant to engage them.

The contractors Trollope and Colls began work on the Aintree factory, to be designated NAF No. 3, in October 1917. Despite adverse weather and a shortage of labour, the factory, considerably in excess of half a million square feet, was completed in February 1918 on land to the west of the racecourse bounded by Ormskirk Road, the Leeds and Liverpool Canal and the Lancashire and Yorkshire Railway to which rail sidings were provided. Large machine and erecting shops were built and, with some fuselage, wing and control surfaces work subcontracted to other firms on Merseyside and elsewhere, aircraft production at Aintree started in March. Employing over 2,600 men and women NAF No. 3, managed by Major C.K. Butler-Stoney, turned out its first Bristol Fighter in June. From October, after various organisational disputes, Cunard handed over control of NAF No. 3 to the Ministry of Munitions. Production was terminated in January 1919 when only 126 aircraft had been completed. Mostly powered by 200hp Hispano-Suiza engines (about three were fitted with Sunbeam Arab units of similar power) or the more powerful Rolls-Royce 250/280hp Falcon, the aircraft were test and delivery flown from land laid out as an airfield to the north of the factory, or crated for despatch by rail to destinations including Queensferry Aircraft Acceptance Park. The balance of the contract for 500 was cancelled, as was a later order for 500 Sopwith Snipe single-seat fighter scouts placed at the beginning of November 1918 and rescinded at the end of the month. By the end of the war Bristol and their subcontractors around the country had delivered a total of 3,100 'Biffs' and by the time the 'Brisfit', as it became known, ended its RAF service career in 1932 no less than 5,308 had been built by eleven firms. After hostilities ceased, NAF No. 3 was redesignated No. 4 Aircraft Salvage Depot which stored several thousand surplus aircraft and aero-engines and was operated by the Aircraft Disposal Co. (Airdisco) of Croydon, an offshoot of Handley Page Ltd. These uses ceased around 1925 when the British Enka Co., later part of Courtaulds, occupied the former aircraft factory to make rayon 'artificial silk' and, later on, parachute material in WW2. After the First World War the adjoining Aintree Racecourse was used for civil aviation from 1919 until around 1926.

The Oldham Aircraft Factory

Continuing bombing raids on British towns and cities by Zeppelins and Gotha aircraft of the German Military Air Service brought calls in 1917 for a heavy bomber capable of taking the war to Germany by attacking principally industrial targets. The outcome was the **Handley Page 0/400,** an improved version of the earlier 0/100, a three-seat twin-engined biplane with a wingspan of 100 feet, contemporarily described as 'a bloody paralyser of an aeroplane', designed and built initially at Cricklewood, London. Capable of delivering a 1,650lb bomb, the heaviest to be dropped in the conflict, 0/400s proved highly effective elements of Major-General Trenchard's Independent Bombing Force.

The American Expeditionary Forces in France had no equivalent aircraft and in 1917 arrangements were hurriedly made for the manufacture of 1,500 of the 0/400 by the Standard Aircraft Corporation of America. The intention was to crate these over via the Port of Liverpool for assembly in Britain and onward delivery to the Night Bombardment Section of the US Air Service. Consideration was given to erecting the aircraft as close as possible to the port of entry but, with potential facilities such as Hooton Park on the Wirral earmarked for training purposes, the search for an assembly base was instigated over a wider area.

The success of the German U-boat campaign had by 1916-17 starved many Lancashire cotton towns of imported raw cotton. Mills and workers were under-employed and, working with an American liaison officer, the Ministry of Munitions identified Gorse Mill No. 2 at Hollinwood, Chadderton, to the west of Oldham, as suitable for conversion for assembly of aircraft. Adjoining land offered potential for the erection of large single-storey assembly sheds with provision for an aerodrome and hangars. Lilac Mill at Shaw was also selected for related production. Work on the 'Government Factory for Assembling American Aircraft, Hollinwood, Oldham' began on 1 March 1918 by civil engineers Trollope & Colls Ltd. who were also engaged on NAF No. 3 at Aintree. German prisoners of war were employed on site works for the adjacent American Aircraft Acceptance Park airfield. In April the Ministry of Munitions appointed a subsidiary company of Waring & Gillow Ltd., the Alliance Aeroplane Company Ltd., to manage the factory. Waring & Gillow themselves made wings and propellers for D.H.9s at their Lancaster furniture works. Former cotton workers were re-trained at the Belle Vue, Manchester aircraft component factory and training centre. Rapid progress on the buildings enabled assembly of 0/400s to begin in July 1918 but, with deliveries still subject to disruption at sea, only 130 incomplete sets of airframe components and considerably fewer engines had been received by the time of the Armistice. Much work still remained to be done on the aerodrome.

The Oldham Aircraft Factory had been on the verge of making a strategic contribution to the war effort on behalf of the American forces but as the war ended, with British requirements for the 0/400 satisfied, the Ministry of Munitions had no need for any more of the heavy bombers. As a result instructions were given for the ten aircraft which are understood to have been substantially completed to be dismantled and all components returned to America. Repatriation of all materials was completed by January 1919.

The Oldham facility lay only two miles from the Newton Heath Works of A.V. Roe & Co. and had the war continued longer the output of both, together with NAF No. 2 at Heaton Chapel, could have generated considerably more air traffic for No. 15 (Manchester) AAP at Alexandra Park. Indeed, extensive hangars were built at the AAP large enough to accommodate 0/400s. The AAP was operational from May 1918 but, there also, all development ceased abruptly at the end of the war. Unlike Oldham however, which was given over to other uses post-war, Alexandra Park Aerodrome as it became known was to remain in aviation use for some years for civil air services. A.V. Roe & Co. occupied a hangar at Alexandra Park during the war and retained it as a test-flying base for a number of years after.

Dick, Kerr & Company Ltd., Preston and Lytham

The origins of aircraft manufacturing and assembly in Central Lancashire during the First World War can be traced to the conflict at sea, particularly the threat posed by German submarines in British home and coastal waters. Whilst Vickers and other manufacturers countered the peril by producing 'SS' Class hunter airships, there emerged also the need for long range patrol, reconnaissance and anti-submarine flying boats for general fleet co-operation duties.

That both Preston and Lytham should enter the aeroplane industry by producing large flying boats was the result of a complex association between a number of long established companies and their links with early aviators. Wartime exigency and the desperate need to expand production by identifying companies with the capability to act as efficient contractors were principal determinants. Intertwined with all these factors was that adventitious element of chance which has often influenced the location of 'new' industries not otherwise dictated by raw materials or other fixed resources.

During the latter part of the nineteenth century Preston was a major centre of the cotton textile and engineering industries. In 1897 the enterprising engineering firm Dick, Kerr & Co. Ltd. of Kilmarnock acquired a disused factory on the east side of Strand Road, Preston, with an open aspect towards the newly constructed Albert Edward Dock to the west. The factory had previously been occupied by the North of England Railway Carriage & Iron Co. dating back to 1863. Dick, Kerr had prospered as makers of railway and tramway equipment. At the turn of the century, now with a factory in England, they were poised for greater success as suppliers of electrical traction equipment to municipal authorities around the country who were about to convert tramways from horse-drawn to electric power.

In 1898 the Electric Railway & Tramway Carriage Works Ltd. was established as a subsidiary to run the factory which after considerable modernisation and extension was soon turning out 800 tramcars per annum. A year later a new factory was built on the opposite side of Strand Road on reclaimed marshland created by the diversion in 1892 of the River Ribble to create the new dock. This was occupied by the English Electric Manufacturing Co. Ltd., producers of generators, tramcar motors and controllers. Hitherto, motors for electric tramcars had to be imported from the United States but synergy between the two Strand Road factories soon enabled powered tramcars and complete tramway systems to be offered to a growing market at home and overseas. Further changes came in 1903 when Dick, Kerr took over the English Electric Manufacturing Co. Two years later the Carriage Works became the United Electric Car Co. Ltd., retaining their separate identity until 1917 when Dick, Kerr took complete control of all the Strand Road operations.

At the outbreak of war Dick, Kerr 'Preston' tramcars were in ubiquitous service all over the country and in addition to their civil and electrical engineering commitments the factories were awarded important armaments contracts for shells and artillery pieces.

In 1916 Dick, Kerr gained control of the Rugby firm of Willans & Robinson, makers of steam engines for coupling to dynamos generating electric power. Willans & Robinson were in turn associated with the Phoenix Dynamo Manufacturing Co. Ltd. of Bradford. Phoenix were early providers of munitions for the war effort but matters took a dramatic turn in 1915 when the Ministry of Supply appointed them as manufacturers of aircraft, beginning with Type 184 patrol seaplanes subcontracted by Short Brothers. Remarkably, with no previous aircraft experience Phoenix delivered their first aeroplane in just over six months, in January 1916. In September, as production continued, the company established its own aircraft design department headed by Lt. William Oke Manning, resident Admiralty technical officer at the works, who was released by the Admiralty for the purpose.

Before being commissioned in 1914 Manning had been a notable aeroplane designer with two other companies. As early as 1908 he had been an associate of Howard T. Wright Brothers Ltd., later Warwick Wright Ltd., engineers, motor car manufacturers and pioneer aviators of London. Together they designed a number of successful aircraft some 35 of which were built between 1907 and 1911. J.T.C. Moore-Brabazon was a co-director of the company. Other associates included T.O.M. Sopwith, founder of the Hawker Company and Marcus D. Manton, English Electric's Chief Test Pilot in the 1920s, both of whom learned to fly on 1910 Howard Wright biplanes. The 'English Wright brothers' as they are sometimes referred to were amongst those, including Shorts, Handley Page and, in America, Glen Curtiss, who could challenge A.V. Roe & Co. as being the first manufacturers of aeroplanes although only the latter was established exclusively for that purpose.

When the Coventry Ordnance Works acquired the Wrights' aircraft interests in 1911 they gained not only Wright the constructor but also Manning the designer and Sopwith as Chief Pilot. But Wright went soon afterwards to manage the Isle of Wight firm of boat and aeroplane makers J. Samuel White & Co. who had employed Hartley Pratt and Barnes Wallis. In 1917-18 Wright played a leading role as technical adviser to the Air Ministry in the establishment of the Handley Page 0/400 assembly factory at Oldham. W.O. Manning left Coventry in 1914 to join the RNVR, taking up his position with Phoenix two years later.

Manning proved to be an exceptional designer employing what, in 1916, were advanced and rigorous calculation techniques for estimating the weight of a new design in order to extrapolate required wing size. He developed statistical analysis of weight and performance data as input to the final design and detail stressing.

Phoenix also continued to manufacture to the design of other companies and received further orders for Short seaplanes. Those produced initially were delivered to Royal Naval Air Stations such as Great Yarmouth, and later ones to Blackburn Aircraft at Brough on the Humber estuary, for final assembly. Some land-based aircraft were flown directly from the Phoenix works by pilots including John Lankester Parker (later Short Brothers' Chief Test Pilot) and Rowland Ding of the Blackburn Aircraft Co., both former instructors at the Northern Aircraft Company at Windermere.

Late in 1917 an order was placed with Phoenix for 50 **Felixstowe F.3** flying boats, to be followed by a further 120 F.3 and F.5 versions. These were large, four-seat twin-engined patrol, reconnaissance and anti-submarine biplanes designed by Squadron Commander John Porte of RNAS Felixstowe in 1915. In taking as his basis the wings and tail of the Curtiss H-4, Porte improved on the American flying boat by designing a new hull more suitable for operations in the hostile waters of the North Sea. With a wingspan of 102 feet, length of 49 feet, height of 19 feet and a maximum take-off weight of over 13,000lb, Felixstowes were very large aircraft for their day. The basic airframe structures were made of wood and surfaces skinned

with wood and fabric, whilst extensive use of bracing wires in the wing and tail units made an immensely strong aircraft. Two Rolls-Royce Eagle VIII 345hp engines gave them a top speed of 93mph with an endurance of six hours on patrol. Armament comprised four Lewis machine guns, two in the open front 'bow' position, with four 230lb bombs carried on racks beneath the wings.

The first Phoenix F.3 flew at Brough in February 1918 and subsequent aircraft entered service on anti-submarine duties along the East Coast. The F.5 was a slightly larger version with up-dated engines: too late to see service in the war it became the standard RAF flying boat between 1918-25. W.O. Manning designed an experimental development designated the **P.5 Cork**, two of which were built but despite their superior performance the ending of the war precluded the type from entering production.

In Lancashire Dick, Kerr were already contracted to supply petrol-electric locomotives for hauling ammunition trains to the Front, shells, artillery and other munitions, when in 1917 they were requested to manufacture flight structures – wing and tail units – for Felixstowe F.3s. Doubtless their proven capability in large scale manufacturing and craftsmanship in the fabrication of wooden-bodied vehicles,

N4230, the first Felixstowe F.3 made at the United Electric Car Co. 'Carriage Works', Messrs. Dick, Kerr & Co., Strand Road, Preston in 1918, here reassembled at South Shields.

Felixstowe F.3
flying boat on
patrol.

Felixstowe F.3
N4259 was built
at the
United Electric
Car Works
in 1918. Both
scimitar-bladed
propellers
were set for
opposite,
outwards
rotation.

working with large quantities of high quality seasoned timber, commended them to the authorities as potential flying boat builders. Work on the F.3 started at the United Electric Car Co. late in 1917. Responsibility for hull construction was entrusted to other contractors and the first Preston-built aircraft, with wings and tail married up to a hull received from Messrs. Boulton & Paul of Norwich, was completed by February 1918. Other hulls were supplied by the Bowness boat and floatplane manufacturer Borwick & Sons. These were

towed down Windermere to Lakeside to be transferred to Preston by rail.

After completion, Felixstowes were transported in dismantled form by a fleet of steam lorries operated by Strand Road haulage contractors H. Viney & Co. on a 150 mile journey to South Shields on Tyneside. There Dick, Kerr fitted out hangars on the shoreline for final assembly and flight testing. 35 Felixstowes undertook the tortuous three-day road journey. In 1918 the unsatisfactory delivery arrangements caused the government to requisition from the Clifton Estate land between Lytham Green and the Dock, fronting the Ribble Estuary, for the establishment of a flying boat assembly works with direct access to open water. Two large hangars were built with concrete apron and slipway. Dick, Kerr received a second contract for another 50 F.3s, later amended to include 32 F.5s. Of these only 11 of the former and two of the latter were completed before the contract was terminated after the Armistice. It is possible that up to 28 Felixstowes from the two contracts, 26 F.3s and the two F.5s, were completed at Lytham to be delivery-flown from the Ribble. In a 'wings over the Ribble' scenario, it is interesting to speculate whether, in the latter stages of the war, a Felixstowe taking off from the Estuary might on occasion have shared airspace and exchanged greetings with a late production Vulcan Engineering D.H.9 or 9A, up from Hesketh Park aerodrome (AAP No. 11, Southport) to the south.

In 1918, one final wartime aircraft project remained on Dick, Kerr's order books. The previous year, the Admiralty had issued **Specification N.4** for an even larger flying boat for fleet co-operation and open sea reconnaissance. Three were ordered, two from the Fairey Aviation Co. of Hayes and one from Phoenix at Bradford. Capacity problems caused Fairey to subcontract one of the aircraft to Dick, Kerr who named it *Atalanta*. The Preston factory produced the necessary drawings for the flight structures of both *Atalanta* and her Phoenix sister boat *Atalanta II.* Everything for *Atalanta* except the hull was manufactured at Strand Road and conveyed to Lytham by lorry. The hull was built by May, Harden & May at Southampton to the patented stressed-skin flexible structure devised by Lt. Linton Hope of the Admiralty, a former yacht

designer. This arrived at Lytham also by road in 1919 for marriage with the wings and tail. Not completed until 1921 the aircraft was then dismantled – essential merely to get it out of the tight confines of the Lytham Works. In that form it was taken by road for reassembly at the Isle of Grain Marine Aircraft Experimental Establishment (MAEE) where it eventually flew in 1928. *Titania*, the Fairey-built N.4, flew at Felixstowe in 1925 but the RAF decided the type was too large and no longer required. *Atalanta II* was completed by Phoenix but never flew and in the absence of further orders the Phoenix aircraft department at Bradford closed in 1919.

The N.4s were very large aircraft with a 139-foot wingspan, powered by four Rolls-Royce Condor engines in tandem pairs with tractor and pusher propellers. Their armament of 1,000lb bomb load and six machine guns resulted in an all-up weight in excess of 30,000lb. Endurance of nine hours was accompanied by a top speed of 115mph.

Best available information suggests that some 60 aircraft of various types had been built in factory or series production in Lancashire and the North West between 1909 and the outbreak of war in 1914. By the time of the Armistice, little more than four years later the total stood at around 4,500. Reflecting the efforts of aircraft companies and contractors all over the country, even after a huge rate of attrition the Royal Air Force ended the war with a remarkable 22,500 aeroplanes and 100 airships on strength, 3,300 of which had front line operational status.

Chapter 4
The Inter-war Years
1919-39

The Great War had stimulated phenomenal mass production of aircraft, some estimates putting total British output at 55,000 units during the period of hostilities. Of 4,500 built in the North West, over 3,000 were Avro 504s which by 1918 were rolling out of the Manchester factory at 200 per month. The target of 500 a month at the Newton Heath Works, where a major new factory was completed in 1919, was abandoned after the Armistice.

Victory rendered such levels of production and the maintenance of the RAF's force of 22,500 aircraft unsustainable. A shock wave of cancellations swept through the new aircraft industry, contractors and munitions manufacturers throughout the country. Government committees were established to advise on the reorientation of industry and labour to peacetime conditions, with particular reference to the new centres of aircraft manufacturing. The urgent priority was to regain, expand and diversify into pre-war markets at home and overseas.

At first the universal hope amongst the aircraft industry was that the rescinding in 1919 of the five-year national ban on non-military flying would unleash a whole new civil aviation market for their products. In the event much of this would be satisfied by the disposal of vast stocks of surplus aeroplanes already in service, stored at Aircraft Acceptance Parks or still at the factories. At Manchester, A.V. Roe & Co. offered to buy back surplus Avro 504s but

the Government's Disposal Board initially began to auction stocks of 504s, D.H.4s and D.H.9s before deciding to place all of them with the Aircraft Disposal Co. Ltd. of Croydon, a subsidiary of Handley Page Ltd. Many were sold to governments overseas but most found their way onto the civil market.

The majority of the 50 or so companies around the country who had built aircraft during the war would lose all such business in its aftermath. Concerned to prevent excessive loss of capacity the Government ring-fenced a select group of 16 who were allowed to compete for vastly reduced military contracts and such civil business as they could attract. Otherwise Government support was limited to a few flagship projects such as the development of Empire air routes and the abortive airship programme.

In the North West, only A.V. Roe & Co. at Manchester would maintain continuity of aircraft production during the next two decades and even they found it necessary to explore other markets as well. At Preston and Lytham, Dick, Kerr and their successors kept a foothold in flying boat production until the mid-1920s before being compelled to revert entirely to traditional markets. Otherwise, aircraft manufacturing was either summarily halted or limped on for a short period into peacetime.

Work at the Oldham Aircraft Factory and NAF No. 3 at Aintree was terminated and the buildings were given over to other

Opposite:
Dick, Kerr-built
Fairey N.4
Atalanta in the
Lytham hangar
around 1920 –
a tight fit with
wingspan of
139ft. and length
of 66ft.

industrial uses. Vickers Ltd. at Barrow-in-Furness remained involved with airships on a reducing scale until 1921 by when they were fully engaged on merchant shipbuilding to replace the tonnage lost at sea during the hostilities.

At Crossens, Southport, the Vulcan Motor & Engineering Co., having made large numbers of lorries and ambulances in the war as well as aircraft, returned to production of motor vehicles including commercials and buses. The next 20 years were difficult times for Vulcan who remained at Crossens until 1938 when, as part of the Tilling Stevens Group, production was moved to Maidstone in Kent. The long established Vulcan name was finally extinguished after takeover in 1951 by the Rootes Group who required an open field for marketing their own Commer-Karrier commercials.

Termination of aircraft production at NAF No. 2 at Heaton Chapel was not quite so precipitate but had certainly petered out in 1919 when Crossley Motors Ltd. took up their option to purchase the factory at 45 per cent valuation. Traditionally, like Vulcan, Crossleys were makers of road vehicles and they established a new Anglo-American subsidiary company, Willys-Overland-Crossley, to manufacture cars and trucks based on chassis imported from Willys-Knight in the USA.

Dick, Kerr & Company Ltd./ English Electric Company Ltd., Preston and Lytham

At Preston where Dick, Kerr's workforce had increased fourfold to 8,000 during the war, response to post-war conditions was immediate. The company already controlled the United Electric Car Co., Willans & Robinson and the AEG Electric Co. Discussions were held with Phoenix Dynamo and Coventry Ordnance Works, all the companies deciding to amalgamate as the English Electric Co. Ltd. on 14 December 1918. The head office of the new company was located in London.

Aircraft continued to feature amongst a wide range of electrical and mechanical engineering and in 1920 W.O. Manning was appointed Chief Aircraft Designer. At Bradford he had designed a large, passenger-carrying flying boat, the abortive and clumsily named English Electric Eclectic. In London he started to design a small single-engined experimental Fleet reconnaissance and coastal patrol flying boat for gunnery and spotting operations, the **English Electric M.3 Ayr**. A contract was secured for two prototypes.

Manning also took a fresh look at the Bradford-built Phoenix P.5 Cork which had shown considerable potential as a successor to the Felixstowe. Its original Rolls-Royce Eagle engines were replaced by 450hp Napier Lions and after successful trials a contract was awarded in January 1923 for a derived prototype coastal patrol and anti-submarine flying boat to be known as the **English Electric P.5 Kingston**.

In complete contrast, having attended a gliding competition on the Sussex Downs in 1922, Manning saw the need for a small ultra-light monoplane, powered by the lightest possible engine, as a training aircraft. He persuaded the Air Ministry to issue a contract for a prototype to be built for £600 specifying a 30-minute endurance. The resulting aircraft would become the **English Electric S.1 Wren**.

Flying boat work at Preston and Lytham drifted on after the war with final deliveries of Felixstowe F.3s and F.5s taking place in 1919. But it was 1921 before the large N.4 *Atalanta* quit the Lytham hangar. With no further work at that time, the site reverted to the Clifton Estate. Aircraft work at Strand Road, Preston was suspended until the beginning of 1923 when, with contracts secured for the Ayr, Kingston and Wren, the Aircraft Department was reinstated. Later in the year the Lytham flying boat base and hangar were brought back into use.

Work on the Wren began at Strand Road

on 5 February 1923 and remarkably the prototype – the first aeroplane to be designed and manufactured by the English Electric Co. – flew just two months later to the day. Its maiden flight was from the Dick, Kerr sports field at Ashton Park in Preston but thereafter trials took place from the sands near the Lytham hangar. Of wooden-frame box-girder plywood and fabric construction, powered by a 3hp ABC flat twin 398cc motorcycle engine, the 37 ft.-wingspan Wren was in effect a motor glider. Weighing only 232lb empty, it flew at between 25 and 50mph. Two production Wrens were entered in the 1923 Daily Mail Light Aeroplane Competition, one achieving 87.5 miles per gallon to be declared joint winner. A fourth example is believed to have been built for display at the British Empire Exhibition, Wembley, in 1924. But the Wren failed to catch on. In

the hands of a skilled, preferably lightly-built pilot, it could give exciting displays but its minimal power, limited speed and frail structure offered few reserves of safety for less accomplished aviators. In 1954 a surviving example was restored to flying condition at Warton and today resides with the Shuttleworth Collection of aircraft at Old Warden, Bedfordshire.

Government requirements for a large flying boat to replace the Felixstowe resulted in the Kingston being prioritised ahead of the smaller Ayr. Detailed design was undertaken at Preston where construction of the prototype's Linton Hope-type hull began in 1923 by a team of boatbuilders recruited from Scottish shipyards. It was the company's first hull to be made 'in-house'. The completed structures were taken by road for final erection at Lytham where, in the hands of Maj. H.G. Brackley and a crew of two, the 85ft.-wingspan 15,000lb aircraft rolled down the slipway on 22 May 1924. After taxiing trials the Kingston was powered for take-off but almost at the point of becoming airborne it struck flotsam, possibly a baulk of timber from Lytham or Preston Docks, coming to a dead halt in a cloud of spray. Sinking at the nose but

English Electric S.1 Wren, in 1923 the company's first entirely new aircraft design, with the Strand Road 'West Works', Preston, in the background.

English Electric's third Kingston Mk.I, N9710, enters the water at Lytham for its first flight on 13 November 1924 in the hands of Maj. H.G. Brackley and subsequent delivery to Calshot.

A photograph to silence complaints from 'ground crews' for all time, as Kingston Mk.I N9710 taxies into deeper water at Lytham under its own power, 13 November 1924.

The fifth and final Kingston Mk.I N9712 stands outside the Lytham Works at the top of the slipway to the Ribble Estuary in February 1925, displaying its immaculate Linton Hope-type timber hull and fuselage.

Opposite: After N9712's hull was commandeered for structural testing at Farnborough its serial number was allocated to an experimental metal-hulled Kingston Mk.II, seen here outside the Lytham Works in March 1925.

remaining afloat vertically in the water, aircraft and crew were rescued, the Kingston subsequently being repaired and delivered to the Admiralty.

Despite the inauspicious start the Air Ministry ordered four more Kingston Mk.Is, the hulls for which were laid down side by side at Lytham and the superstructures built at Preston. The first was completed in autumn 1924 but was taken in dismantled form by rail to Felixstowe, which had taken

over from the Isle of Grain as the MAEE, for its first flight. The next two were flown at Lytham by Maj. Brackley and English Electric's newly appointed test pilot, Marcus Manton. Both aircraft flew from Lytham to Calshot, near Southampton, around the turn of the year. Manton piloted the final Mk.I at Lytham early in 1925 but this was dismantled and transported to Farnborough for structural testing of its hull.

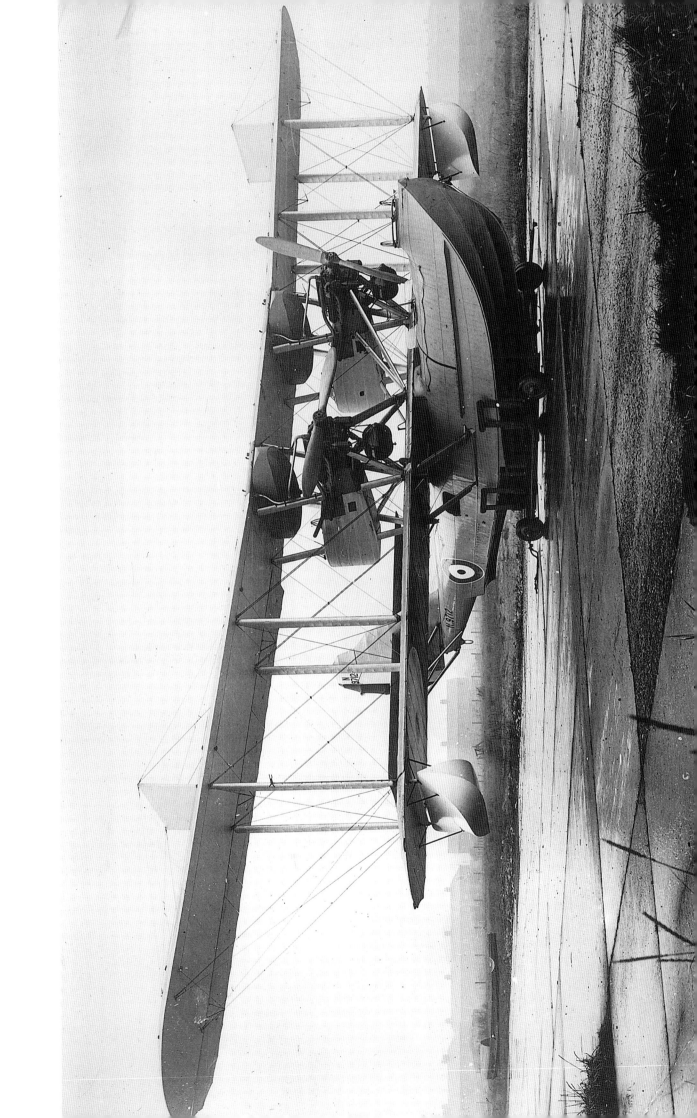

By the time
Kingston Mk.II
N9712 took to
the water the
'ground crew'
had apparently
been issued with
a dinghy.

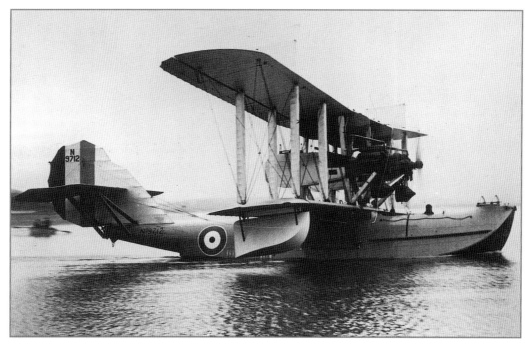

The sixth Kingston was a one-off Mk.II with a fluted metal hull of *Duralumin*, otherwise built to Linton Hope principles at Preston in 1925. Assembled at Lytham it was flown to Felixstowe in December. In subsequent testing it was found that the Mk.Is had satisfactory air performance but take-off and alighting characteristics were less so. The metal-hulled Mk.II was heavier, had an inferior performance and suffered 'porpoising' on take-off. As a result English Electric reverted to wood for the hull of the seventh and final Kingston to be produced at Lytham, the Mk.III. Although of conventional material, the hull was of a new experimental design and profile. The Mk.III was completed early in 1926.

Meanwhile, work had continued on the two Ayr prototypes whose Linton Hope hulls were built at Preston. Only one of the Ayrs was completed in final assembly at Lytham. This was an experimental biplane flying boat with a 46 ft. wingspan, powered by a single 450hp Napier Lion. Swept back lower wings with pronounced dihedral were rooted at the waterline to act as buoyant sponsons. When launched in March 1925 a predictable tendency to lean over to left or right in the water, rolling

from one sponson to the other, made taxiing difficult. More serious was the drag-induced bow wave and spray which held the lower wings firmly down in the water. Unable to take off, the Ayr was transported to Felixstowe for further testing and it is believed that both hulls ended up at RAE Farnborough for structural examination.

The departure of the Kingston Mk.III from Lytham to Felixstowe on 16 March 1926 left English Electric with no further aircraft work. On that very morning the company announced the closure of its Aircraft Department. Direct representations made by the Mayor of Lytham St. Anne's in a telephone call to the Air Minister concerning the effect on the local economy were to no avail. The Lytham hangars were vacated for a second time, the West Hangar being leased to the Parkstone Film Company and subsequently purchased by a well-known local bakery. The Aircraft Department at Strand Road, Preston was given over to railway locomotive work. In London the English Electric aircraft design team was disbanded in April and W.O. Manning made redundant although he continued to serve the aircraft industry in other capacities for another 20 years.

The first English Electric Ayr (foreground) and prototype Kingston under construction at the Dick, Kerr Preston 'East Works'. In 1923 electric locomotives were being built in the shop to the right of this photo.

Kingston Mk.I, probably the first N9712, stands at the head of the slipway, with Ayr N148 to the right, Lytham Works, February 1925.

The elegant but soon to be proved impractical English Electric Ayr at Lytham, February 1925.

Ironically, the Kingston Mk.III proved to have the best performance of all the Kingstons but it would be another 12 years, in 1938, before aircraft work returned to Preston.

A.V. Roe & Company Ltd., Manchester, Hamble and Woodford

When restrictions on civil flying were lifted at Easter 1919, A.V. Roe & Co. were straight off the mark with the formation of the Avro Transport Company. For the preceding 18 months they had had access to hangarage at No. 15 (Manchester) AAP at Alexandra Park, Didsbury. Immediately the military opened it up for shared civil use, in May, using three-seater Avro 504Ks, the company inaugurated daily return flights to Blackpool Sands at the Starr Gate Inn, via Southport. The five-guinea single, nine-guinea return trips constituted Britain's first scheduled domestic air service. Avro also continued to use Alexandra Park as their northern production test flying centre for the next five years, with Hamble fulfilling that role in the south.

Joyriding flights proved so popular at Hamble that they were extended to northern seaside locations including Blackpool South Shore, Southport Sands, Birkdale, Fleetwood, Morecambe, Liverpool Waterloo, the Isle of Man and to Alexandra Park itself. Charges were one guinea basic

or two guineas to 'loop the loop'. With the daring exploits of Great War aviators still fresh in mind, spiced further by Alcock and Brown's Atlantic crossing in June, public demand was insatiable throughout the summer of 1919. The 'blowing sands' of the Lancashire coast were made to blow all the more by the lusty revving of Gnome, Le Rhône and Clerget engines in war-surplus Avro 504s piloted by heroes of the RFC, RNAS and RAF. Long queues of people excitedly clutching pound notes and shillings formed at ticket cabins on the Lancashire beaches. By August 10,000 people at Blackpool alone had gained their first experience of flight, in the capable hands of pilots including a former RNAS flyer Capt. H.A. 'Sam' Brown. In the south, Hamble-manufactured 504L seaplanes and a three-seat 504M enclosed cabin landplane known as the 'Avro Limousine' were used for flights along the coast and over London.

Briefly that summer, pre-war links between Avro and the Lake District were renewed when the Avro Transport Company leased the Cockshot Point hangar on Windermere. Two 504K floatplanes were operated by Avro pilot Howard Pixton for pleasure trips over the Lakes and also to undertake newspaper deliveries from the railhead at Windermere to Douglas, Isle of Man. Pixton had been Avro's chief flying instructor at Brooklands and tutor to a number of pre-war Lakes aviators including Oscar Gnosspelius, Ronald Kemp and Sydney Sippe.

It was ironic that the opening in November 1919 of Avro's large new factory at Newton Heath, planned during the later stages of the war to meet anticipated demand for five hundred Avro 504s per month, came at a time when the downturn in orders began to bite. Moreover, the first signs of economic depression were starting to dent optimism for civil aviation's prospects. Luckily some production of the 504 was still required, but after a short yet exciting interlude the Avro Transport Company was wound up in

1920. Having provided useful cash flow if not spectacular profits, it had certainly promoted public awareness of aviation.

Managing Director A.V. Roe and Works Manager John Lord were determined to secure survival in the lean years that followed. Even with money in the bank, dwindling aircraft orders made diversification essential. Some of their new product lines must have been bitter pills for the company to swallow, including tin baths, bassinets, billiard tables, children's toys – and even coffins using the company's considerable woodworking capacity. Roe was a prolific inventor in many fields outside aviation and, leaving aircraft in the hands of Roy Chadwick, now Chief Designer, he proceeded to develop a motor car. In 1919 he acquired patent rights for an epicyclic gearbox which he fitted in the Avro '12' three-seater saloon car built with a wooden body from Avro 504 materials mounted on a pressed steel chassis. Four years later he also designed the Monocar, an enclosed motorcycle fitted with small 'outrigger' stabilising wheels incorporating some of the ideas he had already used to 'weatherproof' his own motorcycle on which he travelled extensively between Manchester, Brooklands and Hamble.

Avro Transport Company 504Ks, fitted with floats and still bearing manufacturer's serial numbers and military insignia, outside Capt.E.W. Wakefield's pre-war hangar at Cockshot Point, Windermere, leased by Avro in 1919.

Only a few Avro '12's had been made when, amidst a number of factory lay-offs as trade deteriorated further, Avro were approached by Crossley Motors of Gorton, Manchester and Heaton Chapel, Stockport, who were interested in entering into collaborative arrangements for joint manufacture and marketing of their own cars. It is possible that Sydney Sippe, who had joined Crossleys as their Sales Manager at the end of the war, acted as broker in the matter. In any event their discussions went beyond the original proposition to the extent that in May 1920 Crossley Motors, under William (later Sir William) Letts, achieved a 68 per cent controlling interest in A.V. Roe & Co. The Avro '12' was discontinued and the Newton Heath Works turned to making bodies for Crossley cars and reconditioning war surplus Crossley tenders for use as commercials. Under the agreement reached, A.V. Roe & Co. retained separate identity and, in August, Newton Heath became the company's head office. A.V. Roe was Chairman, John Hubble was appointed General Manager by Crossleys and Roy Dobson was Works Manager. 1920 ended with Roe's appointment to the OBE for services to aviation.

Roy Chadwick, Chief Designer from 1919, together with most of the Avro design team had spent the latter part of the war at Hamble, the company's South of England design, experimental and test flying centre between 1916 and 1928. Chadwick was responsible for all the later variants of the 504 and was prolific in generating new designs. His first post-war project was the **Avro 534 Baby** of 1919, a tiny 25 ft.-span biplane with a 20-30hp engine, which reflected Roe's particular interest in light aircraft. About 12 were built at Hamble where Chadwick, having learned to fly there, nearly lost his life when he crashed the second in the series. The aircraft was rebuilt as G-EACQ and bought in 1920 by H.J. 'Bert' Hinkler, an Australian former RNAS flyer who had joined Avro as a test pilot. After shipping it to Australia Hinkler flew the aircraft on an epic 700 mile flight from Sydney to his home town of Bundaberg where he taxied along the main street to his mother's house before returning to Britain to be appointed Avro's Chief Test Pilot.

Chadwick's next design, the **Avro 536**, was a derivative of the 504 with a widened fuselage accommodating four passengers. Used for pleasure flights by the Avro Transport Company, twelve were built at

Manchester, ten at Hamble and four elsewhere. The 504K remained in production at both Manchester and Hamble. Overhaul and modification of 504s disposed of by the Government to the Dominions under the Imperial Gift Scheme provided important business for the Newton Heath factory in the 1920s. Hamble played a major role in the design, manufacture and testing of other types including the **539 racing floatplane**, the **547 commercial triplane** and **548 passenger biplane.**

Avro's first new post-war military aircraft was Chadwick's 68 ft.-span **549 Aldershot** long-range bomber, then the largest single-engined bomber in the world. 17 were made at Hamble but were frequent visitors to Alexandra Park Aerodrome at Manchester. 15 saw service with the RAF between 1924 and 1926. Most were powered by 650hp Rolls-Royce Condor III engines but one of the prototypes, fitted with a Napier Cub, was Avro's first aircraft to use an engine of 1,000hp and at that time the world's most powerful bomber. The Aldershot represented a distinct technological advance in aircraft

construction. RAE Farnborough had been experimenting with metal spars and ribs in Avro 504 wings to substitute for scarce wood which itself could be of variable quality. The Aldershot was the first Avro machine built with a metal fuselage of steel tube with pin-jointed struts, albeit still covered by fabric and plywood. A later experimental version also had steel wings. For the first time it was necessary to employ fitters specially trained in lining up and accurate assembly.

A consequence of the new technology was the realisation, as described by C.E. (Teddy) Fielding (Pioneering Years 1918 to 1961 – pub. British Aerospace PLC, 1982) who had joined Avro's materials testing department in 1918, that as aircraft became more complex there would be a need for more effective manufacturing, inspection and parts control systems. The days of furniture factory technology with traditional methods geared to wood, wire, glue, fabric and dope were fast receding in the aircraft industry.

Aldershot technology was carried over in 1921 to Avro's next large aircraft, the notoriously ugly **555 Bison**, an entirely

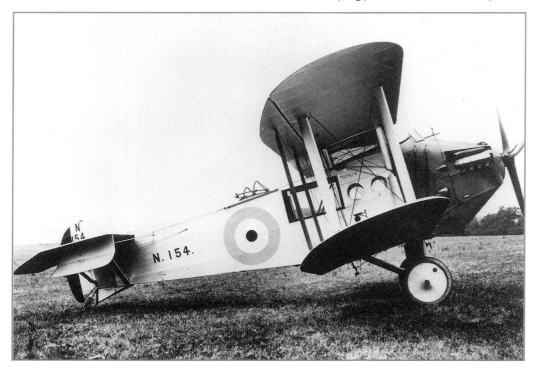

Second prototype Avro 555 Bison of 1922, built at Hamble. A roomy, enclosed cabin with radio, navigation and plotting table facilities lay between the open cockpit and rear gunner's position. All 53 production aircraft were made at Manchester and Woodford.

functional single-engined deck-landing machine for maritime reconnaissance. Three prototypes were built at Hamble but it was the Newton Heath factory that discharged the production order for 53 aircraft for service in both the RAF and Fleet Air Arm. It signalled the reintroduction of large scale manufacturing of new designs at Manchester.

Alexandra Park at Didsbury was the focus of considerable aviation activity in the early 1920s and was used by both Avro and the Lancashire Aero Club. The latter, established in 1922 by Mancunian John F. Leeming, assumed the mantle of Britain's oldest civilian flying club after the pre-war demise of the similarly titled Blackpool-based organisation that had run the 1909 and 1910 flying meetings at Squires Gate. Also in 1922 Britain's first scheduled *airline* service was established by Daimler Airways, using a de Havilland D.H.34 plying between Alexandra Park and Amsterdam via Croydon, with a connection to Berlin. Manchester Corporation, desperate to win the race to secure Britain's first municipal aerodrome, were keen to acquire the site. Fast approaching however was the expiry, due in 1924, of the Air Ministry's lease from the landowner, Lord Egerton of Tatton Hall. His subsequent decision not to allow continued aviation activities, preferring recreational and housing uses, left Avro, the Lancashire Aero Club and Manchester Corporation all seeking alternatives.

The Corporation opted for land to the west of the city at Barton Moss where the scale of site preparation works threatened to delay their plans. Not to come first in the municipal aerodrome stakes was unthinkable so, whilst proceeding with Barton, Manchester kept the initiative by hastily opening a temporary aerodrome at Wythenshawe in 1929. Barton superseded it in 1930.

A.V. Roe & Co. secured land to the south of Manchester at New Hall Farm, Woodford, near Bramhall in Cheshire.

There, some 16 miles from the Newton Heath factory, amidst green fields overlooked by hills rising towards the Peak District, they re-erected several hangars removed from Alexandra Park. Woodford also offered a lifeline for the Lancashire Aero Club, whom Avro allowed to share the site.

With Woodford still being prepared, in February 1925 the first deliveries of the Avro Bison were made from Newton Heath for final assembly and flight testing at RAF Sealand near Chester, prior to Service acceptance trials at Farnborough. By spring, with the grass airfield operational and final assembly taking place in the recently erected flight shed, Bisons were being flown from Woodford to Sealand. Some subsequently served on the carriers HMS *Furious* and *Eagle* in the Home and Mediterranean Fleets. In August, Woodford was the venue for an air pageant attended by 25,000 people, the first of many Woodford Air Displays to come.

The remarkable Avro 504 continued to enjoy further lease of life. Hitherto fitted with various types of rotary engines, all sharing the same characteristic of relative thirstiness, later versions were powered by newer in-line and radial units which offered greater economy in fuel and oil consumption. Curtiss, Renault, Airdisco and Wolseley Viper in-line engines, the latter available cheaply and in quantity from the Aircraft Disposal Company, were used in the **Avro 545, 548 and 552**. Installation of powerful radial engines such as the Lucifer, Mongoose and Lynx produced the last major 504 variant, the **504N**. Although the 'N' first flew at Hamble in 1919, it later generated a huge Air Ministry order for 511 aircraft, all of which were built at Manchester between 1927 and 1932. Popularly known as the Avro Lynx, the 504N incorporated a reinforced fireproof bulkhead to cope with its radial engine, together with a much stronger undercarriage. Late production machines used welded steel tube in fuselage construction. It was in a 504N that F/O Frank Whittle, later to be associated with the North West of England with the development of his jet engine by Rover, Lucas and Rolls-Royce at Clitheroe and Barnoldswick, demonstrated the art of 'crazy flying' at the 1927 Hendon Air Display.

The ultimate radial 504 was the **504R 'Gosport'**, a lightweight version with excellent handling and performance powered by the 100hp Avro Alpha five-cylinder engine built in Manchester in limited numbers by Avro's parent company, Crossley Motors Ltd.

To maintain public interest in aviation, in 1926 the Director of Civil Aviation, Sir Sefton Brancker, suggested a daring feat involving landing an aeroplane on a mountain summit. The idea was taken up by Bert Hinkler of Avro and J.F. Leeming, Chairman of the Lancashire Aero Club. Helvellyn, at 3,118 ft. England's highest mountain, was decided upon. Their aircraft would be a Manchester-built Gosport, fitted with a strengthened 504N undercarriage. On the mountain in the early afternoon of 22 December, a solitary fell walker, Professor E.R. Dodds of the University of Birmingham, was surprised to hear the sound of an approaching aeroplane. Surprise turned to astonishment as the Gosport landed before him at the summit. The pilots were delighted to encounter so worthy a witness. The Professor signed a brief statement on a scrap of paper verifying the first landing of an aeroplane on a mountain in Great Britain. With only 30 yards to take off before the precipice above Red Tarn, full power was applied and the Gosport shot out above the abyss, dropping slightly as it clutched the air, before gaining speed and returning safely to Woodford. It was a crowning moment for the Avro 504, Lancashire-built and engined, flown by a Lancastrian and an Australian. Their exploit was symbolic of an era of

record-breaking aviation achievements and epic flights.

Designs continued to pour off the drawing boards of Roy Chadwick's team at Hamble throughout the 1920s. Most were produced in small numbers or even as one-off prototypes. They included light sporting aircraft and an elegant fighter biplane, the **566 Avenger**, demonstrated at an air display held at Squires Gate, Blackpool in 1928. Two **557 Avas**, 95 ft.-wingspan coastal defence aircraft with vast biplane tails and twin rudders were built between 1924 and 1927, the second of them being of metal construction. The RAF's need to replace D.H.10s on the Cairo-Baghdad desert air route gave Avro the opportunity to supply three **561 Andover** transport and ambulance aircraft carrying 12 passengers in wicker seats with the pilot still in an open cockpit.

In Spain, the aviation pioneer Juan de la Cierva spent much of the early 1920s developing a rotary wing aircraft which he reasoned would be incapable of stalling at low speed. Moreover he believed that given adequate forward motion, rotating wings would generate lift without motorised drive, using the same principle as the sycamore seed. He termed his concept of automatic rotation the 'Autogiro'. After a number of setbacks he achieved success in 1924 with his **C.6A/B Autogiro** which used the fuselage of an Avro 504K with a 110hp Rhône engine for tractor power. Spinning the four-bladed 36 ft.-diameter rotor by ropes was found to shorten the required take-off run. After a

Avro 586 (Cierva C.8V) two-seat Autogiro at Hamble, September 1927. It was an experimental conversion of a conventional Manchester-built 504K biplane previously completed as a 552A with a Wolseley Viper 180hp in-line engine. It was restored to its original form in 1930.

Outside the Hamble Works in 1927 with the prototype Avro 581 Avian G-EBOV are, left to right, Roy Chadwick, Bert Hinkler and Reg Parrott. Hinkler made his epic flight to Australia in this machine in February 1928. Manchester and Woodford turned out 345 Avians.

demonstration at Farnborough in 1925 the Air Ministry ordered two from A.V. Roe & Co. When these were built at Hamble in one and two-seater versions they marked the start of a 12-year association with the Cierva Autogiro Co. Ltd., founded in 1926 with design offices at Bush House, London and at Hamble. Cierva supplied the rotor assemblies and Avro the fuselages. When a C.12/17 hybrid version, fitted with floats and known as the Hydrogiro, flew from Southampton Water it became the world's first rotary-winged seaplane.

A further Air Ministry Autogiro order of 1926, stipulating the incorporation of a purpose-designed fuselage, gave Avro the opportunity to use the new fuselage also in the **Avro 581 Avian**, the first of a new series of conventional biplane light aircraft that would transform the company's future over the coming years.

In 1929, abandoning his previous use of 'lash-ups' of assemblies from conventional aircraft, Cierva applied a completely new design integrity to produce the two-seater C.19 which had a new rotor system with automatic 'windmilling'. 28 were built at Hamble and others under licence in France and Germany. Although Hamble had featured principally in the Autogiro programme so far, in the 1930s Avro's Manchester factories would engage in

significant production of its ultimate development – the **Avro Rota**.

Avro Chief Test Pilot Bert Hinkler had continued to nourish an ambition to fly all the way to Australia. In 1927 he bought the Avro Avian prototype G-EBOV for £750, resigned from the company and began his preparations. Flying alone he departed from Croydon on 7 February 1928 and in an epic journey packed with incidents and hazards, including crossing the shark-infested Timor Sea, arrived in Darwin to a rapturous welcome 11,000 miles and 15½ days later. He had shattered the previous record of 28 days set in 1923 by a much larger twin-engined Vickers Vimy. Sadly Hinkler died in a similar bid in 1933 when his de Havilland Puss Moth aircraft crashed in the Italian Appennines. A legacy of his achievements is the display to the present day of the Avian, alongside the Avro Baby which he flew in Australia in 1920-21, at the Queensland Museum, Brisbane.

Hamble was the principal centre for development and production of the Avian prototype and its Mk.II/III versions, totalling 45 aircraft. Some 345 later versions were manufactured at Manchester and Woodford up to 1933 and it was from the latter aerodrome, as production gathered pace, that in 1927 the Irish aviatrix

Mrs Sophie Elliott-Lynn, flying an Alpha-engined Avian II and carrying a passenger, reached an altitude of 19,200 ft.

Small numbers of two other Avro types were produced at Hamble, the **Avro 584 Avocet** fighter of 1927, the company's first biplane of all-metal stressed-skin construction and, in 1928, the **Avro 604 Antelope** day bomber of all-metal *Duralumin*.

1928 was a momentous year for A.V. Roe & Co. Crossley Motors Ltd. experienced a slump in their share price and in May agreed to sell Avro to the Armstrong Siddeley Development Company owned by the forceful industrialist John D. Siddeley who, with aero-engine and motor car interests in the Midlands, also controlled Sir W.G. Armstrong Whitworth Aircraft at Coventry. Siddeley may well have seen an opportunity to terminate development of the promising Avro Alpha engine manufactured by Crossley, a potentially damaging competitor for his own company's radial engines such as the Lynx and Genet. At a stroke he was able to expand the market for such engines by requiring volume-producing Avro to install them. Certainly work on the Alpha ceased

soon after his acquisition.

Whilst eliminating Crossley as potential aero-engine competitors, Siddeley was astute in recognising the value of retaining the world-renowned Avro name. Once again, as under the Crossley regime, A.V. Roe & Co. were allowed to retain separate identity. But Siddeley considered Hamble too peripheral for Avro operations and in a complete reversal of Alliott Verdon Roe's 'grand design' of 1916 he concentrated all Avro activities – design, experimental, production and flight testing – back at Manchester and Woodford. In 1929, after nearly 13 years in Hampshire, Roy Chadwick and his design team found themselves back in Manchester alongside production personnel. Some Avro work continued at Hamble but in 1931 the site was reassigned to Armstrong Whitworth and Air Service Training in whose hands it remained until 1960.

Relieved though they were to learn of Siddeley's commitment to retaining the Avro name, the Newton Heath Works were shocked when Alliott Verdon Roe tendered his resignation to Siddeley in October 1928. Roe's long-standing interest in seaplanes and flying boats had compelled him to negotiate a controlling investment in the boat-building firm of S.E. Saunders Ltd., of Cowes, Isle of Wight, establishing a new company, Saunders-Roe Ltd. After taking Avro colleagues John Lord and Harry Broadsmith with him, they produced aircraft such as the Saro Cutty Sark amphibian, Cloud and London flying boats. In the Second World War they built Walrus and Sea Otters, and converted American Catalina flying boats at Beaumaris, Anglesey. Exciting later projects included the world's first jet-engined flying boat fighter, the SR.A/1, the world's largest passenger flying boat, the 220-seat SR.45 Princess, and rocket-assisted interceptor fighters. Saunders-Roe purchased the Cierva Company in 1951, gaining an entrée to the light helicopter market. Awarded a contract to develop hovercraft, Saro built the world's first – the SR-N1 – in 1959.

Edwin Alliott Verdon Roe OBE was knighted in the New Year's Honours List of 1929 for his pioneering work and services to aviation. Having slightly modified his name by deed poll, Sir Edwin Alliott Verdon-Roe assumed the Presidency of Saunders-Roe Ltd. in 1933, serving in that capacity until his death in 1958 at the age of 80. Although born in Lancashire he spent much of his later life in Hampshire at Hamble and Rowlands Castle. His achievements in early flight, in designing,

manufacturing and flying the first all-British aeroplane and in forming A.V. Roe & Company in Manchester in 1910 were instrumental in establishing the aircraft industry in Lancashire and the North West of England. Of all the eminent, worthy personalities in the history of aviation he was the true, all-round pioneer of the British aircraft industry.

Foreseeing great demand throughout the Empire for a large rugged transport aircraft, in 1928 the two 'Roys' – Dobson and Chadwick – visited the Dutch Fokker factory at Amsterdam to examine the highly successful **Fokker F.VII** cantilever-winged tri-motor transport. This employed an advanced welded – rather than pin-jointed strut – steel tube fuselage structure. At home the Air Ministry was sceptical, requiring welded joints to be 'normalised' by heat treatment to refine the grain structure of the metal and eliminate stresses. At the same time, despite their most strenuous efforts, they had failed to break an F.VII 'demonstrator' which they had obtained in 1926. As a result, having negotiated a licence to build the aircraft, Avro were able to persuade the authorities that given consistent metallurgical and jig control, certification could be granted without normalisation. The technology was extended to the **Avian IVM**, the 'M' signifying metal frame.

The sixth Avro 618 Ten, G-AASP *Achilles* joined Imperial Airways in April 1931, serving on charter patrol of desert pipelines in Iraq and later on European passenger services.

Avro 618 Ten wing construction at Newton Heath.

Avro 642/2m G-ACFV was delivered to Midland and Scottish Air Ferries Ltd. on 5 April 1934 and named *Marchioness of Londonderry* by the Prime Minister Ramsay MacDonald in a ceremony at Liverpool's Speke Airport. Wrecked in a crash, rebuilt and sold to other operators she found her way to the Far East and was destroyed by Japanese action in 1942.

14 of the Dutch-designed three-engined transports were produced as **Avro 618 Tens**, ten-seater monoplanes with all-wood plywood covered wings remarkably thick in section, spanning 71 ft. and high-set on fabric-covered welded steel tube fuselages. Several gave sterling service in the Middle and Far East and Australia. Nine other variants ranged from smaller five/six-seat tri-motor **Avro 619/624s** to the larger two and four-engined **Avro 642/2m** and **4m** with shoulder mounted wings. Bearing little

resemblance to their Dutch progenitor, the 642s represented Avro's first venture into modern aerodynamic monoplane designs. All 23 of the series were built at Newton Heath and flown from Woodford. In 1933 an Avro Ten further reduced the flying time from England to Australia to under seven days.

The imported technology more than proved its worth. Welded tubular steel structures were stronger than wood, did not warp and were not as vulnerable to

The sole Avro
642/4m *Star of
India* became
the personal
transport of the
Viceroy, Lord
Willingdon, in
1934. It was
dismantled at
Delhi in 1940
after a wing was
found to be
infested by ants.

Avro 626 for
the Brazilian Air
Force on a flight
from Woodford.
The engine is a
260hp
Armstrong
Siddeley
Cheetah V.

Opposite:
G-ABBY, one
of three
Manchester-
built Avro 624
Six aircraft, was
registered in
1931. In May
1933 it was
modified as a
hybrid Five/Six
with two of its
three Armstrong
Siddeley 105hp
Genet Major
engines slung
below and clear
of the wing. It
was used by Air
Service Training
Ltd. and No. 11
Air Observer &
Navigation
School before
being scrapped
in March 1941.
Here it flies near
the confluence
of the Hamble
River and
Southampton
Water, the
Hamble Works
being behind the
aircraft. *Photo:
Aeroplane.*

internal corrosion as had been feared.
They offered clear advantages for use in a
wide range of climatic conditions, amply
demonstrated by the worldwide success of
the Avian IVM. In 1929 Chadwick had no
hesitation in using welded steel in a new
two-seat basic biplane trainer, the **Avro 621
Tutor**, which was adopted as the standard
RAF trainer in 1932 when production of
the venerable 504N finally came to an end
at Newton Heath and Woodford. The
Tutor and later Avro 636 were the first
Avro aircraft to employ metal wing
structures in series production. 795 Tutors,
including 394 for the RAF, were built at
Newton Heath between 1930 and 1936, all
powered by Armstrong Siddeley Mongoose

or Lynx engines. Another 60 were licence-
built in South Africa and Denmark. Many
entered the civil market at home and
overseas, with civil and military orders
received from Australia, Canada, Greece,
Poland, Eire and China. Output of such
magnitude required the introduction of
mass production techniques which would
serve Avro well in future years.
Substantially completed, Tutors were towed
by lorry to Woodford for final assembly,
where a new Chief Test Pilot, Capt. H.A.
'Sam' Brown, formerly of the Avro
Transport Company, was now in charge of
flight testing.

A special version of the Tutor, the **Avro 626**, was designed in 1930 for smaller overseas air forces requiring a versatile aircraft which, sold with conversion kits, could be adapted for training, bombing, reconnaissance, night flying or even seaplane use. A third cockpit offered an optional gunnery position. 206 were made between 1930 and 1940, exported to 15 countries worldwide. During a sales tour of South America in 1931 the works' demonstrator was pressed into service by the Argentine military to assist in putting down a local insurrection. It was so successful that they ordered a further 14. The RAF trainer version was known as the **Prefect**.

But Avro were still prepared to consider small-series production or even one-offs. In 1930 they responded to a Canadian requirement for a **mail plane** by fitting out a previously uncompleted Antelope airframe with a 40 cu.ft. fire and waterproof mail compartment. Unfortunately, the project foundered in Canada and the aircraft was returned to Avro who used it for demonstration and as an engine test bed.

Significantly greater success was enjoyed by the Genet-engined **Avro 631** and **643 Cadets**, smaller versions of the Tutor built in 1931 for air club and private use. 104 were made, many for Air Service Training at Hamble who also used the Tutor, and for the Royal Australian Air Force. A further 27 variants including the **Club Cadet**, **Cabin Cadet**, and **Cadet three-seater** also contributed to Avro's prodigious output of light and training aircraft at Newton Heath and Woodford during the 1930s. Six larger streamlined versions, **Avro 641 Commodores**, offering comfortable cabin accommodation for two pilots and three passengers were built at Avro's Failsworth works in 1934, to be flown from Woodford.

Armstrong Siddeley influence, previously limited to the use of their engines by Avro, went considerably further with the company's next product, a two-seat fighter trainer of 1935. Designed as the **Avro 636** by Roy Chadwick in conjunction with Armstrong Whitworth's Chief Designer John Lloyd, it was recognisably AW in morphology. Moreover its metal wing and tailplane structures were made by Armstrong Whitworth at Coventry using the company's riveting process. The 636 was also noteworthy for its exceptionally advanced single strut oleo leg undercarriage, designed by George Dowty who worked for Avro at Hamble during the 1920s before going on to establish the world-renowned eponymous landing gear company. Four 636s were supplied to the Irish Air Corps.

The emergent 1930s design trend in America for fast, twin-engined low-wing passenger monoplanes such as the Boeing Model 247 prompted discussions in 1933 between Imperial Airways and Sir John Siddeley. The airline's requirement for a long range four-passenger charter aircraft was met by Roy Chadwick's design of the **Type 652**, a 56 ft.-wingspan machine powered by two 270hp Cheetah engines capable of cruising at more than 150mph over 600 miles. Chadwick developed further the now tried and tested Avro-Fokker technology by repositioning the one-piece plywood-covered wooden mainplane low down on a welded steel fabric-covered fuselage. A retractable undercarriage was deemed essential to meet performance specifications. Imperial Airways signed a contract for two aircraft at the Newton Heath Works in 1934, the first of which took to the air at Woodford in January 1935, piloted by Deputy Chief Test Pilot F.B. Tomkins. From such modest beginnings, no-one could have foreseen at the time the impact that the initial design would have on Avro's order books in the years to come.

Also during 1934, with tension building in Europe, the Air Ministry invited Avro to tender for a twin-engined coastal patrol aircraft so similar in basic specification to the 652 that it was relatively simple for Chadwick to 'militarise' the original design. Bill Thorn flew the prototype at Woodford in March 1935 and Geoffrey Tyson the first of 174 ordered for the RAF, with provision for gunnery and bombing equipment, in December. Subsequently named the **Anson Mk.I**, it was a potent fighting aircraft in its day, the RAF's first monoplane to enter service and their first with a 'retractable' undercarriage. The fact that in retracted position the wheels still projected beneath the engine nacelles proved indirectly to be an advantage in service use: 'wheels up' rolling landings for whatever reason were possible with little or no damage to the airframe. In fact, the perspiration-producing 140 turns by hand of the crank-operated chain-driven undercarriage mechanism encouraged many crews to fly wheels down for much of the time.

1934 also saw further involvement with the **Cierva Autogiro** project when Avro obtained a licence to build entirely the 'ultimate' **C.30A** two-seat version including now the rotor system. Contemporary company advertising stressed its simplicity of operation: 'The new direct control Autogiro makes flying as safe and simple as driving a motorcar. It is impossible either to stall or spin. Its cruising speed is 95mph and landing speed nil'. After three pre-production examples, 12 were delivered to the Air Ministry in 1934-5 for Army co-operation assessment, becoming known as **Avro 671 Rota Is**. Another 66 were built, powered by Genet engines, for civil use and export as far afield as Russia, India and China before production ceased at Newton Heath in 1938. Some were fitted with Cierva's Autodynamic rotor head which, with the aircraft at rest and blades at zero incidence, could speed them up to

'beyond take-off' revolutions. Application of the positive pitch control would then generate sufficient lift to pluck the aircraft 20 feet into the air, reducing the take-off run to some 36 feet or less. All were distributed via the Cierva company base and Autogiro flying school at Hanworth, near London, established in 1932.

To the surprise of most of those concerned, in June 1935 Sir John Siddeley (later Lord Kenilworth) sold his interests in Armstrong Siddeley to Hawker Aircraft Ltd. A new holding company, Hawker Siddeley Aircraft Co. Ltd. was formed which included Hawker, Gloster, Sir W.G. Armstrong Whitworth, Armstrong Siddeley Motors, Air Service Training and A.V. Roe & Co. In bringing together the names Roe and Whitworth it revived links between Manchester and Sir Joseph Whitworth, a native of Stockport who had established his world famous engineering and machine tool company in Manchester during the previous century. In 1897 he had joined with the armaments and shipbuilding entrepreneur Sir W.G. Armstrong of Tyneside.

In 1934 the British Government had announced its intention to build up the strength of the RAF which after years of peace, economic crisis and intermeddling by the League of Nations had slumped to abysmal levels. From 22,500 aircraft on strength in 1918, the RAF in 1933-4 had just 850 in the front line and remained entirely a biplane force. When Hawker Siddeley came into existence in 1935, the Hawker production lines were fully engaged on turning out obsolescent Fury, Hind and Hart fighter-bomber biplanes but starting to gear up for mass production of the RAF's first fighter monoplane, Sydney Camm's Hurricane. The company had insufficient capacity to complete orders for its **Audax** army co-operation and training biplane, 287 out of a total of 624 supplied to the RAF as a result being subcontracted to Avro. Others were built by Bristol,

Gloster and Westland. With fuselages of steel tube and riveted joints, and wings of fabric-covered metal, subcontractors were allowed to compensate for differing cumulative variations by adjusting the length of a single strut. Avro also developed a more powerful version, the **Avro 674**, using a 750hp Armstrong Siddeley Panther engine in place of the original 530hp Rolls-Royce Kestrel. 24 were supplied to the Egyptian Air Force in 1937-8.

For the third time in its then 25-year history, a change of control allowed Avro to retain its own operating identity. But at the same time the company benefited from access to Hawker Siddeley Group resources for investment in plant and buildings, gaining approval in 1935 for a 250,000 sq.ft. extension to the Newton Heath Works. Three further flight sheds were erected at Woodford, taking the total to five. Against a background of RAF Expansion Schemes and, from 1936, a programme of shadow factory construction to vastly increase aircraft production, Avro also gained a major new 600,000 sq.ft. assembly hall at Woodford, completed in under six months and opened in December 1939. Manufacturing at Newton Heath was complemented by final assembly, production flight testing and experimental activities at Woodford where, in the late 1930s, there were so many overlapping projects that company test pilots were leaping between Avians, Tutors, Cadets, Autogiros, Audaxes and Ansons to pack in as many 30-minute pre-delivery test flights as possible.

Barton Aerodrome, F. Hills & Sons Ltd.

In April 1929, with work proceeding on the proposed permanent site at Barton Moss, Manchester Corporation won the race for the establishment of Britain's first municipal aerodrome by the expedient of opening temporary facilities at Wythenshawe. Barton, with a large new hangar, superseded it as Manchester Municipal Airport in 1930 under the management of Northern Air Lines (Manchester) Ltd.

Manchester's first scheduled airline service since the demise of the Alexandra Park Daimler Airways flights was inaugurated by Imperial Airways in June. Despite subsidies the Croydon-Birmingham-Manchester-Liverpool service was disappointingly short-lived although Barton was kept busy by other operators such as Railway Air Services and Hillman Airways, general aviation and a series of public air displays including those of Sir Alan Cobham and his Flying Circus. But it was the critical assessment of the airport by KLM-Royal Dutch Airlines pilot Captain Ivan Smirnoff in January 1934 that effectively terminated Barton's ambitions for attracting international services. Once the airfield had been deemed too small and ill-drained for larger aircraft, Manchester Corporation

were compelled to examine further alternatives as a result of which in July 1934 they resolved to develop a much larger site to the south of the city at Ringway.

In spite of the setback Barton continued as an aerodrome and became a significant centre for the manufacture of light aircraft during the 1930s and the Second World War. The Lancashire Aero Club, Britain's oldest flying club, relocated from Woodford to Barton in 1946 and the airfield remains busy for private and club flying to the present day.

During 1935 the French amateur aviator Henri Mignet published designs, promoted by the Daily Express to popularise aviation, for a unique ultra-light aircraft which using a motor-cycle or light car engine could be amateur-built at home. At £70, cheap to erect, fly and maintain it was known as the 'Pou du Ciel' or **'Flying Flea'**. Having failed to master the controls of conventional aircraft, Mignet dismissed them as over-complicated. Dispensing with a tailplane elevator which he considered illogical, he sought to control pitch by pivoting the forward of two wings of almost equal size. Under certain circumstances this proved inadequate to raise the nose and at maximum incidence could result in airflow over the closely-mounted rear wing which had the effect of control reversal. As a result, in the hands of the very amateurs for whom it was intended, the 'Flying Flea' had potentially lethal characteristics not least of which was difficulty in pulling out of a shallow dive.

After a number of fatalities Mignet, visionary to some, crackpot to others, saw his design banned in France and grounded in Britain where construction of up to 1,000 is believed to have commenced. A number were built in the Manchester area, including one by employees of the Durham woodworking firm F. Hills & Sons Ltd., who in 1935 had moved into the former Ford Motor Co. Model 'T' factory at Trafford Park. The tandem monoplane, or super-staggered tailless biplane depending on preference, is believed to have flown at Barton Aerodrome to the intense fright of all concerned, before being allowed to pass into history. Today, an example is on display at the Museum of Science and Industry in Manchester.

On a more positive note, the 'Flying Flea' episode had alerted Hills' Director W.R. Chown to the potential demand for a small, inexpensive light aircraft and the firm opted for the safer course of building under licence the Czechoslovakian all-wood two-seat **Praga E114 'Air Baby'**. Powered by 36hp Praga engines built by Jowett Cars Ltd., between 1936 and 1938 some 35 were completed at Trafford Park as **Hillson Pragas**, retailing at £385. These were flown from Barton Aerodrome where a number were operated by the Northern Aviation School and Club Ltd. established there by Chown. Single examples of two developments designed by Norman Sykes, the **Hillson Pennine** and **Helvellyn**, were built in 1937-8 and 1939 respectively. Despite the erection of a hangar at Barton by Hills in 1938, production of complete aircraft was curtailed for a while when the company concentrated on the manufacture of aircraft-quality plywood, components for Avro Ansons and, through a new company Hills-Jablo Propellers Ltd., composite wood, rubber and metal airscrews.

At the outbreak of WW2 the Ministry of Aircraft Production requisitioned the facilities at Barton Aerodrome and Hills relocated to Ringway to become involved once again in making aircraft, later returning to Barton in the same capacity.

Fairey Aviation Company Ltd., Heaton Chapel, Barton and Ringway

In 1933/34 C. Richard Fairey, distinguished founder of the Fairey Aviation Co. Ltd. of Hayes, Middlesex, anticipated the coming need for more production space for bomber aircraft by acquiring the 560,000 sq.ft. Willys-Overland-Crossley factory, formerly National Aircraft Factory (NAF) No. 2, at Heaton Chapel, Stockport. Having languished during the slump, the Crossley Motors associate company had finally entered into liquidation in December 1933 when Crossley vehicle production was retrenched at the main factory in Gorton, Manchester and at their original High Lane, Heaton Chapel works adjoining the former NAF.

Harold Ingham, of Poulton-le-Fylde, recalls starting his career in the aircraft industry in January 1935 as a 16-year-old apprentice at the Fairey factory, one of the first people on site after the company took over the Heaton Chapel works in 1934. Only wings for the Fairey Hendon night bomber were made there to begin with and one of his first jobs was fitting the stringers. Women formed a large part of the early workforce, combining their experience of the textile industry with dexterity in the sewing together of sheets of canvas for airframe cladding. With work on wing build well advanced, pressures on Fairey to discharge orders for the Hendon intensified in 1935 when the company received a much larger order for the Battle day bomber. Production lines were laid out and the Heaton Chapel plant, by then employing around 750 people, was incorporated in February 1936 as the Stockport Aviation Company Ltd. Major Thomas Barlow, Fairey's Chief Engineer, was appointed Managing Director.

The **Fairey Hendon** was a large, 101 ft.-wingspan twin-engined cantilever monoplane heavy bomber dating back to a specification issued in 1927. An ungainly affair, the prototype first flew at Fairey's Great West Aerodrome, now part of Heathrow, in 1930. Extensive areas of canvas cladding led to its nickname 'The Cloth Bomber'. It required so many modifications that production of 14 Hendon Mk.IIs was not sanctioned until 1934. Even as the RAF's first monoplane heavy bomber it was quite obsolete when it entered service in 1936-7. Before production started the prototype was ferried to Heaton Chapel as a pattern aircraft. With no landing ground adjoining, it was flown in March 1936 by company test pilot Duncan Menzies to the Avro aerodrome at Woodford to be dismantled and transported to Heaton Chapel by road. Given that Avro were then flight testing early production 'state of the art' Ansons, it is possible to imagine some critical stares from the ground as the cumbersome Hendon, with fixed undercarriage enveloped in huge 'spats', lumbered into the circuit. Was this the best that the new competitors ten miles up the road had to offer?

In 1935 Manchester Corporation had refused to allow Fairey use of part of the proposed new airport at Ringway for final assembly and production test flying. Instead, Fairey's attention was drawn to the underutilised Barton Aerodrome to where the first production Hendon, completed at Heaton Chapel in August 1936, was taken by road for final assembly in the main hangar. The first two aircraft were flown from Barton to Fairey's Great West Aerodrome but the remaining 12 were collected direct from Barton by RAF crews. An order for a further 62 was cancelled in anticipation of the entry into service of the Vickers Wellington bomber.

Fairey shared the misgivings previously expressed with damning effect by Captain Smirnoff concerning the limitations of Barton for large aircraft. They finally got their way in 1937 when Ringway was made available to them and the first of a number of Fairey hangars came into use there in June, a year before the airport opened for civil use. It marked the beginning of a huge aircraft production programme by Fairey in the Manchester area during the war that was soon to follow. Portending this was the formation of No. 613 City of Manchester Squadron of the Royal

Auxiliary Air Force at Ringway in February 1939 and No. 14 Ferry Pool of the Air Transport Auxiliary (ATA).

Hooton Park Aerodrome, Comper Aircraft Ltd.

After horse racing ceased at the Hooton Park Club Race Course, between Ellesmere Port and Bebington on the Wirral Peninsula in Cheshire, in August 1914 the site was requisitioned for army training purposes. In 1917 three large Belfast Truss hangars were built for flying training by the Royal Flying Corps. A subsequent proposal that they be used for the assembly of American-built Handley Page 0/400 heavy bombers imported in kit form through Liverpool did not materialise and, as previously described, instead the scheme went ahead almost to the point of completion at the Oldham Aircraft Factory.

Training continued at Hooton Park until 1919 but thereafter little happened until 1927 when a local businessman, George Dawson, acquired most of the Hooton Park Estate with a view to developing it as the principal airport for the North of England. Hooton Park Aerodrome became the home of the Liverpool and District Aero Club, a centre for popular light aviation, a staging post for King's Cup Air Race events and preceded Speke as Liverpool's first official commercial aerodrome.

In March 1929 Dawson assisted Flt. Lt. Nicholas Comper to establish Comper Aircraft Ltd. in one of the hangars. A former student of aerodynamics, working with colleagues at the Cranwell Light Aeroplane Club, Comper had designed a series of ultra-light sporting parasol monoplanes. Comper's **C.L.A.7 Swift**, a distinctive open cockpit design with a 24 ft. wing set at pilot's eye level, entered production in 1929. Of wood construction with plywood and fabric covering, the Swift used a braced parasol wing and a fuselage made in three sections, bolted together.

The wings folded back allowing the complete aircraft to be stored in a garage. First flown in January 1930, the Swift was offered with optional 34hp A.B.C. Scorpion two-cylinder opposed or 50hp Salmson A.D.9 nine-cylinder radial engines at prices ranging from £400-£475.

Comper persuaded a former Cranwell colleague and aero-engine designer, Capt. Douglas Pobjoy, who had established Pobjoy Airmotors & Aircraft Ltd. in Surrey, to set up an engine plant at Hooton Park. The Pobjoy 'R' was a seven-cylinder single row air-cooled radial unit of remarkable power to weight ratio. From 1931, when fitted to the seventh and subsequent aircraft, it proved ideal giving a top speed of 145mph – almost equal to contemporary RAF fighters.

That year, Comper also started to build an aircraft to the general design of Cierva's Autogiro. Using a Swift fuselage off the production line, he added a rotor pylon with experimental balsa blades, short wings, a conventional tail and Pobjoy 'R' engine. Comper fitted mechanical means of starting the rotor. Known as the **Cierva C.25** it was first flown, by Cierva himself, at Hooton Park in March 1932 but was badly damaged in a heavy landing. Extensively modified it later flew with greater success but although one of the fastest of the autogiros it never went into production.

In the meantime, in 1930 Comper had assembled two – some reports suggest three – **Ford 4-AT-E tri-motor** transports at Hooton Park as a preliminary to such aircraft being erected at Ford in Sussex.

Comper Swifts proved outstanding as single-seat high performance sports and touring aircraft, making numerous epic flights to South Africa, Australia and even a return crossing of the Andes. No less than eight entered the 1932 King's Cup Air Race. Some, fitted with D.H. Gypsy engines were reputedly capable of 185mph. Despite such successes the economic

conditions of the thirties precipitated a fall in demand and when Comper's lease at Hooton Park expired in March 1933, having secured new financial backing he relocated to Heston, near London, the national centre for light aviation. 41 Swifts were produced between 1930 and 1933, over 30 at Hooton Park and the rest at Heston where Comper's activities were later absorbed by the Heston Aircraft Company.

During the 1930s Hooton Park Aerodrome was also the base of the Martin Hearn Aircraft Company. The eponymous founder, an aero-engineer, pilot and celebrated 'wing walker' with Sir Alan Cobham's Flying Circus, established a general aviation business with joyriding and barnstorming flights using Avro 504s. Hearn's company at Hooton Park – and at Hesketh Park, Southport – made a major contribution to aircraft assembly during the Second World War. Amy Johnson was among famous pre-war aviators associated with Hooton Park.

Speke Airport, Liverpool

The origins of aviation at Speke, five miles north east of Hooton Park on the Lancashire side of the River Mersey, date back to 1928 when Liverpool Corporation acquired the 2,200 acre Speke Estate with the intention of developing 400 acres as an airport. Speke shared in the short-lived Imperial Airways service to Croydon via Manchester (Barton) and Birmingham. Blackpool and West Coast Air Services operated to Blackpool and the Isle of Man. In 1933 Speke took over from Hooton Park as Liverpool's official airport, with KLM, Aer Lingus, Railway Air Services and Hillman Airways offering services from 1934. That year, the Liverpool and District Aero Club transferred from Hooton Park. No. 610 (County of Chester) Squadron of the Royal Auxiliary Air Force formed at Hooton Park in 1936, with 611 (West Lancashire) Squadron at Speke.

The American aviator Dick Merrill, accompanied by Harry Richman in 1936 and Jack Lambie in 1937, made Speke the base for two record-breaking transatlantic flights using a Vultee V-IA *Lady Peace* and Lockheed 10 Electra respectively, but had to use the firmer Southport Sands as the actual point of departure for their heavily laden aircraft. For their first attempt they packed the wings with 40,000 table tennis balls as a contingency floatation device. Charles Lindbergh visited Speke briefly in 1937. At the outbreak of war, levelled out, drained and with full facilities including control tower, terminal and hangars, Speke had become the second busiest airport in the country and was poised to make a major contribution to wartime aircraft production.

Moss Brothers Aircraft Ltd. (Mosscraft), Chorley

Leisure flying between the wars led to the establishment of Moss Brothers Aircraft Ltd. of Moor Road, Chorley, in 1937. William Henry Moss, Managing Director of the firm's parent company H.S. Moss Ltd. Paint & Varnish Works of Chorley, was one of five aviator brothers. Together they built two single-engined two-seat all-wood light monoplanes, low wing designs spanning 34 ft. Produced in 1937 and 1939, the **Mosscraft M.A.1** and **M.A.2** respectively were powered by 95hp Pobjoy Niagara III and 90hp Blackburn Cirrus Minor I engines. Work on building second examples of both was terminated by the war and was never to be completed.

Early in 1940 the M.A.2 was evaluated as an army air observation post aircraft, a requirement for which was subsequently met by the metal-frame, high-wing British Taylorcraft Auster. The M.A.2 was then shipped to Canada where, fitted with an enclosed cabin, in a transcontinental flight in stages between Vancouver and Toronto it achieved the distinction of becoming the first aircraft of below 100hp to cross the Canadian Rockies.

Both aircraft were back on the post-war British air circuit including King's Cup Air Races, often to be seen at Barton and Squires Gate. Both were lost in crashes, that of the M.A.1 costing the life of its designer in 1950. During the war, W.H. Moss was extensively involved with aircraft production at Speke.

Squires Gate and Stanley Park Aerodromes, Blackpool

After the pioneering events of 1909 and 1910, aviation returned to Blackpool in 1919 with the use of the sands at South Shore by the Avro Transport Company. But when the Military Convalescent Hospital at nearby Squires Gate closed in 1924 and the site was handed back to the Clifton Estate, it was deemed safer than the sands as a flying ground. Once again Squires Gate echoed to the sounds of aero-engines, becoming the base of the Lancashire School of Aviation.

In 1927 Blackpool Corporation, one of a number of local authorities around the country gripped by the fever of establishing municipal airports, engaged Sir Alan Cobham to advise on the most suitable site. Rather than opting for Squires Gate, most of which lay in Lytham St. Anne's close to noise-sensitive residential areas, instead he recommended land east of Stanley Park at Marton held by Sir John Bickerstaff who was considered a more amenable landowner than the Clifton Estate. The Corporation accepted Cobham's report and proceeded with a two-year £39,000 programme to drain and level the 120 acre site, lay out four grass landing strips between 1,200 and 2,000 feet in length and build a Belfast Truss hangar and clubhouse. Cobham himself inaugurated services by piloting the first passenger flight – from the Isle of Man – in August 1929. Operation of the aerodrome was leased to National Flying Services Ltd., the Lancashire School of Aviation relocated from Squires Gate and services were provided to the Isle of Man by British

Saro A.17 Cutty Sark G-ABBC of British Amphibious Air Lines Ltd. comes ashore at Blackpool's South Shore, 1932/33.
Photo: Blackpool Gazette.

Amphibious Air Lines Ltd. The latter company, established by Flt. Lt. R.H.C. Monk in 1932, operated one of the first aircraft produced by Saunders-Roe Ltd. at Cowes, Isle of Wight, after A.V. Roe's resignation from Avro in 1928. During 1932-33 its Saro A.17 Cutty Sark amphibian G-ABBC plied between the Blackpool foreshore and Douglas Bay, with the ability to land alternatively at Stanley Park and Ronaldsway if the sea state required. Stanley Park Aerodrome was opened officially by Prime Minister Ramsay MacDonald in June 1931.

But other aviators and operators still favoured Squires Gate which was used for the Blackpool Air Pageant and RAF Show in July 1928. In 1932 Blackpool and West Coast Air Services established a rival service to the Isle of Man. Significantly, Imperial Airways also preferred Squires Gate. With activity growing faster there than at Stanley Park, in 1934 the Clifton Estate offered to sell some 460 acres comprising the aerodrome, a golf club and greyhound stadium to Blackpool

Corporation for £175,000. Agreeing to purchase, the Corporation then found itself responsible for two aerodromes. With its lease at Stanley Park set to expire in 1937, it sought advice from the Ministry of Transport who recommended concentrating aviation at Squires Gate which offered greater potential for the 5,000 ft. runways and night flying facilities then being required by modern aircraft.

To make the necessary improvements at Squires Gate all operating companies and aviation activities there had to be temporarily relocated to Stanley Park. Although the latter was effectively closed once Squires Gate reopened, a large Empire Air Day display was held at Stanley Park a few months before the outbreak of war. Thereafter, both sites would make a vital contribution to Britain's aircraft production war effort.

Chapter 5
The Second World War
1939-45

Expansion and the Shadow Factories

Germany's rearmament during the 1930s, particularly in air strength with the cynical development of 'civil' aviation and aircrew training having started even during the 1920s, fortunately did not go entirely unheeded. The collapse of the League of Nations Disarmament Conference in June 1934, following the German walk-out, propelled Britain reluctantly at first but with increasing resolve to embark on the re-equipment of its own armed forces. Only half of the RAF's front line strength of 850 aircraft was at that time available for home defence and it remained entirely a biplane force. The Government announced an RAF Expansion Programme to ensure parity with the air strength of any potential European aggressor. In Germany it was stated in 1935 that the Luftwaffe, which was supposed to have formally existed only for a matter of weeks, had already attained equivalent strength to the RAF. An arms race was inevitable.

Proposals for 'Shadow Factories' were announced in 1936, part of a five-year series of expansion schemes to boost the output of the parent aircraft and aero-engine factories by harnessing the mass production expertise of motor vehicle and related industries such as electrical engineering. Funded by Government but project-managed by industry, they were strategic also in terms of dispersing production to areas less vulnerable to air attack, including regions of high unemployment resulting from the decline of traditional industries such as textiles, coal and heavy engineering. Moreover they freed up capacity at the established aircraft factories for vital new experimental and design work.

The impact of the programme on Lancashire and the North West would be to dramatically accelerate the establishment of a number of major new aircraft, aero-engine and component factories. Indeed, many of the decisions taken to provide modern 'state of the art' production facilities in the late 1930s would be the principal determinants of the scale and location of the region's aircraft industry not just during the Second World War but post-war and to the present day.

In one of the earliest initiatives, in 1936 the Government proposed that the the de Havilland Airscrew Company of Stag Lane, Edgware, Middlesex should erect a factory for the large scale manufacture of propellers in an area of high unemployment remote from the risk of air attack. On the advice of a senior company manager, who was a Lancastrian, a site was chosen at Lostock to the west of Bolton. Construction was completed in 1937 and the additional capacity enabled de Havilland to assemble and repair over 200,000 propellers during the war for aircraft including Spitfires, Hurricanes and Lancasters.

Rolls-Royce Merlin and Bristol Hercules engines were to become the standard workhorses for the RAF during World War

Two. Although entirely dissimilar in design, the former an in-line V-12 and the latter a 14-cylinder radial, both were immensely powerful and during their lifetime would be developed to double their initial horsepower. Under the auspices of the Air Ministry work began in July 1938 at Crewe, Cheshire on a factory to augment production of the Merlin at Rolls-Royce's Derby plant. Completed in twelve months and managed by Rolls-Royce themselves very much as an extension of Derby, the Crewe factory produced over 26,000 Merlin and 2,200 Griffon engines. Yet even in 1939 it was far from certain that Derby and Crewe together would be capable of meeting the demand. Accordingly the Government invited the Ford Motor Company, vastly experienced in mass production techniques, also to set up facilities for manufacturing Merlin engines. This Ford did with a new factory built in 1940 at Trafford Park near Manchester where the company had made Model 'T' cars by the thousand from 1912 until they relocated to Dagenham, Essex in 1929. The first of over 30,400 'Ford' Merlins came off the new line in 1941, most intended for Lancaster and Mosquito factories. Between them, Rolls-Royce at Crewe and Ford at Trafford Park turned out a staggering 56,400 Merlins on behalf of the North West.

Clayton-le-Moors near Accrington was selected as the location for a vast factory built by the Government in 1939/40, subsequently occupied by the Bristol Aeroplane Company to shadow its principal plant at Filton in the manufacture of Hercules engines. Nearly 14,400 Hercules were made at Clayton-le-Moors for installation in Lancaster, Halifax, Stirling, Wellington and Beaufighter aircraft, together with a small number of its more powerful development, the 18-cylinder Centaurus.

In 1939 the complex 24-cylinder Napier Sabre was the world's most powerful aero-engine. Its manufacturers D. Napier & Son Ltd. lacked capacity at their Acton, London factory resulting in the Government financing a new plant for the company at Walton, Liverpool. Completed in 1941, with the Standard Motor Company engaged to advise on mass production methods, the first of 3,400 Sabre engines was turned out early in 1942. But the Sabre initially proved difficult to engineer as a reliable engine, delaying the entry into service of Typhoon and Tempest aircraft. The English Electric Co. were invited in as 'trouble shooters' and in December 1942, with the approval of the Ministry of Aircraft Production (MAP), took over the Napier company. The Sabre-Typhoon-Tempest combination eventually proved a hard-won success.

Of huge significance for the long term was the work carried out from the late 1930s by Metropolitan-Vickers at Trafford Park on the development of the axial turbojet engine. Equally, from 1940 the Rover Company and Lucas – and from 1942/43 Rolls-Royce – were heavily engaged on the development and manufacture of Frank Whittle's centrifugal turbojet at Clitheroe and Barnoldswick.

The wider story of the region's major contribution to the development and production of aero-engines from the early years of the twentieth century to the present day is told in *Classic and Modern Aero-Engines associated with Lancashire and the North West of England*, published by Lancashire County Council in 1999.

If the North West's contribution to aero-engine production was impressive, its role in wartime manufacture and assembly of complete aircraft was nothing less than breathtaking. As early as 1935 Air Marshal Sir Hugh Dowding, Air Member for Research and Development, intimated to Roy Fedden, Chief Designer for Bristol's Engine Division, that Bristol had been selected as the first aero-engine company to be 'shadowed'. When seven large motor companies were approached only one, the Rootes Group, showed initial enthusiasm. The others would follow suit later, but to begin with it was the determination of the industrialist William 'Billy' (later Lord) Rootes that drove the early stages of the shadow programme. A Rootes-managed shadow factory at Ryton, Coventry, was soon producing Mercury and Hercules engines although the Bristol Company's own plant at Accrington would eventually be the largest of all Bristol shadow engine factories.

Perhaps it was no surprise that when a large shadow factory for the manufacture of Bristol Blenheim bomber aircraft was proposed and a site selected adjoining Speke Airport near Liverpool, an area of high unemployment, it was Rootes Securities who were entrusted with its construction and management. Started in 1937 and opened in 1938 the Speke plant is generally regarded as the first of Britain's shadow aircraft factories.

Expansion and dispersal of Bristol aircraft production had further implications for the North West. In 1938 the Government acquired the remaining Crossley factory at Heaton Chapel for refurbishment and extension as the Errwood Park Shadow Factory. This lay adjacent and to the east of the former WW1 NAF No. 2 plant that the Fairey Aviation Company had bought from Crossleys in 1934. It was logical that Fairey, now making Battle aircraft at Heaton Chapel, should also manage the Errwood Park factory where in 1939 they contracted to manufacture Bristol Beaufighters.

At the Vickers Aviation factory at Brooklands, near Weybridge in Surrey, the Wellington bomber first took to the air in June 1936. It was evident that Vickers lacked the production capacity for the anticipated level of orders and approval was given in September for construction of a shadow factory. Vickers began evaluating possible sites in the North West and the

bordering area of North Wales in 1937. A site was chosen to the west of Chester, between Hawarden and Broughton, which had partly been used as a relief landing ground for RAF Sealand near Queensferry. Administratively it lay just inside the County of Flintshire in Wales. Site preparation began in December 1938 and building works were completed in September 1939. Adjoining the factory an airfield designated RAF Hawarden was laid out for joint use by the RAF and Vickers-Armstrongs. Such was the scale of the RAF's requirement for the Wellington that it was soon realised that even the Weybridge and Chester facilities would be inadequate. Authority was obtained in December 1939 to establish a second shadow factory for which land at Squires Gate Aerodrome, Blackpool, was selected. Work started at the beginning of 1940 and the resulting factory – larger even than that at Chester – was completed during the summer. Vickers-Armstrongs would manage both.

In a post-war account by the English Electric Company of its contribution to the war effort it stated: "In the Spring of 1938, as a result partly of our personal observations on the Continent, we felt that circumstances had arisen which made it the duty of this Company, as of every important engineering concern, within the limits of its possibilities, to place its accumulated experience and engineering organisation at the disposal of the Government to help in this vital purpose of expediting the defence programme".

No doubt someone at the Air Ministry recalled the involvement of the company and its predecessors Dick, Kerr & Co. in the production of Felixstowe and Kingston flying boats at Preston and Lytham between 1917 and 1926. Accordingly it was decided that English Electric at Preston should be requested to re-enter the aircraft building industry, manufacturing the Handley Page Hampden bomber to supplement production at the parent factory at Radlett, Hertfordshire. Subsequent events unfolded rapidly with reciprocal visits by Frederick (later Sir Frederick) Handley Page and George (later Sir George) Nelson, Chairman of English Electric, to Preston and Radlett. With orders placed, the immediate priorities for English Electric involved alterations and extensions to their Strand Road premises at Preston together with the identification of a suitable site for an aerodrome for final assembly and pre-delivery flight testing. After considering land at Freckleton, Squires Gate and Samlesbury, with strenuous lobbying by Preston and Blackburn Councils, the Air Ministry selected the latter. Situated mid-way between the two towns, land at Samlesbury had already been compulsorily acquired by the two councils during 1935-37 for potential development as a shared municipal aerodrome.

Of all the existing and proposed new centres of aircraft manufacturing in the region, only one company – A.V. Roe & Co. at Manchester and Woodford – had experienced continuity of production from the earliest days of flight. After incorporation into Hawker Siddeley in 1935 the Newton Heath Works had already been extended by a quarter of a million square feet when, on a visit to the plant in August 1938, the Secretary of State for Air, Sir Kingsley Wood, announced the Government's decision to charge the company with responsibility for the erection of a completely new £1 million aircraft factory. A large site at Greengate, Chadderton near Oldham was soon identified and by March 1939 work was sufficiently advanced to transfer certain personnel, materials and equipment from Newton Heath. Operational arrangements were to remain as before with major aircraft sub-assemblies transported from Chadderton and Newton Heath for final assembly and flight testing at Woodford. Moreover the final assembly lines at

Woodford would also start to receive sub-assemblies from yet another new centre of aircraft production, that of Metropolitan-Vickers at Trafford Park. Though not formally requisitioned by the Government, Manchester's new airport at Ringway, where the Fairey Aviation Company occupied hangars from June 1937, would also provide important wartime assembly, flight testing and experimental space for Avro as well as facilities for use by the armed forces.

With investment on this scale in place, the region was poised to make a vast contribution to national aircraft and aero-engine output. Allied air strength would derive even further benefits from the assembly of aircraft 'kits' from the United States, together with general aircraft repair and flight test facilities at other centres in the North West including Burtonwood, Warton, Ringway, Speke, Hooton Park and Hesketh Park to be described later.

Fairey Aviation Company Ltd., Heaton Chapel, Errwood Park and Ringway

At the outbreak of war the Fairey Company had occupied the former NAF No. 2 at Heaton Chapel, Stockport for five years, having completed small scale production of the irrelevant Hendon bomber there in 1937. Between 1937 and 1940 the plant was engaged exclusively on the manufacture of the company's next aircraft, the single-engined **Fairey Battle** monoplane bomber. Conceived in response to a 1932 specification for a day bomber, it originally represented a quantum leap beyond the RAF's biplanes, capable of carrying three times their bomb load 70mph faster. When the prototype first flew at Fairey's Great West Aerodrome in March 1936, although the 'launch aircraft' for Rolls-Royce's new 1030hp Merlin engine and Fairey's first of all-metal stressed-skin construction, delays over design changes had already eroded much

of its technological advantage. As a result it was verging on obsolescence when it entered service in 1937.

Production orders for an initial 155 Battles were placed in May 1935 and, as with the Hendon, the Battle prototype was taken to Heaton Chapel for reference as a pattern aircraft. The first production example emerged from the factory to be flown from Barton Aerodrome by test pilot Duncan Menzies in April 1937, thence to Fairey's Great West Aerodrome in May. The next four, together with the reassembled prototype, also flew from Barton but all subsequent machines were transported by road from Heaton Chapel to the company's new facilities at Ringway for final assembly, flight testing and delivery.

A total of 1,171 Battles was produced at Heaton Chapel and Ringway up to the end of 1940, mostly as Battle I bombers but including some 200 built as dual, separate-cockpit trainers. A further 1,029 were built by Austin Motors at Longbridge. At Manchester refurbishment work on the Battle, by Fairey at Ringway and David Rosenfield Ltd. at Barton, continued up to 1943.

With over 1,000 Battles on RAF strength at the declaration of war, ten squadrons were immediately despatched to France as the Advanced Air Striking Force. Their deployment was a reprise of the response of 1914 when Manchester-built Avro 504s were amongst the first detachment of the RFC to be sent across the Channel. The

first Luftwaffe aircraft to be shot down by the RAF in WW2, a Messerschmitt Bf 109E, fell to the gun of an RAF Battle on 20 September 1939. Thereafter however, the Battle's Achilles' heel was to prove its retention of the defensive armament of a 1930s biplane, namely a single rearward-firing 0.303 machine gun with a huge blind spot astern and below. It was a weakness later exploited ruthlessly by German fighters.

When the main German advance started on 10 May 1940, Fairey Battle and Bristol Blenheim squadrons were ordered to mount low level attacks on armoured spearheads and key road bridges at Sedan and over the Albert Canal at Maastricht. They proved to be virtually suicide missions, carried out with exceptional heroism by the RAF crews. On 12 May F/O D.E. Garland and Sgt. T. Gray, flying a Heaton Chapel/Ringway-built Battle of No. 12 Squadron were killed at Maastricht. They were awarded the first two RAF Victoria Crosses of the war. Intense ground fire reduced the bomber force from 135 to 72 over two days. In four actions involving Battles, 60 out of 108 aircraft were lost, a monstrous 55 per cent loss rate. But at least it contributed towards slowing down the German advance in the days leading up to the evacuation of the British Expeditionary Force from Dunkirk later in the month. By late 1940 the lessons had been learned and the Battle was demoted to second-line duties in which it provided useful service as a trainer for pilots converting to Merlin-engined Spitfire and Hurricane fighters, and as a target tug.

The Royal Navy had been pressing for modern high performance fighter-bombers for the Fleet Air Arm from the mid-1930s. Early in 1937 Fairey produced two prototypes of the P.4/34 light bomber, similar in appearance but slightly smaller than the Battle. Stressed for dive-bombing and with minor modifications, Fairey convinced the Admiralty that the new aircraft would meet the specification issued in 1938 for a two-seat carrier-borne fleet fighter. The second prototype flew at Fairey's Great West Aerodrome in April 1937 and in 1938 was modified as a flying mock-up for the production aircraft, which was to be known as the **Fairey Fulmar.** Like the Battle it was powered by a 1,030hp Merlin engine, but differed in its armament of eight Browning machine guns mounted in the leading edge of wings that folded for carrier operations.

Orders were placed and in what had become a familiar routine Duncan Menzies flew the mock-up Fulmar to Ringway in August 1939 to enable the Heaton Chapel production staff to get their hands on it. The first of 250 production Fulmar Mk.Is was test flown from Ringway in January 1940 and deliveries to the Fleet Air Arm started in early summer. From the end of the year Heaton Chapel was engaged on the manufacture of 350 Fulmar Mk.IIs with more powerful 1300hp Merlins. The factory also had to contend with refurbishing 100 Fairey Swordfish biplane torpedo bombers whilst Fulmar production was under way.

The Fulmar served with distinction in support of naval operations in theatres as varied as the Malta and Russia convoys, Norway, the Mediterranean and in the Indian Ocean. Production ceased in December 1942 with the 600th example being elivered early in 1943.

In 1939 Fairey had received an order to build 500 **Bristol Beaufighters** at the Errwood Park Shadow Factory adjacent to their Heaton Chapel plant. To cope with the increased output, in 1940 the MAP erected a further flight shed and two assembly hangars for Fairey's use at Ringway. The Beaufighter was the latest in a series of Bristol-designed twin-engined strike aircraft that had included the Blenheim and Beaufort bomber and torpedo attack planes. It proved to be one

of the most potent and effective 'multi-role' aircraft of WW2. A large 57 ft.-span, 7-10 ton heavy long range fighter, it was armed to devastating effect with – at last – four Hispano 20mm cannon and up to six 0.303 machine guns. Two hefty Bristol Hercules radial engines propelling it most usefully to over 300mph brought the aircraft's centre of gravity forward to the extent that it had to be compensated by a characteristic snub nose. Not for nothing was it described as 'two ruddy great engines hotly pursued by an airframe'.

A total of 498 Beaufighters was turned out by Errwood Park between December 1940 and May 1943. The first 25 were Mk.IF night fighters, the RAF's first really effective aircraft of that type. The fact that radar experts had been able to shoehorn bulky A.I. Airborne Interception radar into a fighter was to remain unknown to the Luftwaffe for two years, one of Britain's best kept secrets of the early war years.

Production continued with 300 Mk.IC long-range Coastal Command maritime patrol fighters and 173 Mk.VIC aircraft with more powerful engines. Some Errwood Park Beaufighters were despatched to Australia where another 374 were built to counter the Japanese threat from the north.

Such a heavy, powerful aircraft was not the easiest to handle, with a pronounced tendency to 'swing' on take-off and landing. Early in its service life the probably apocryphal story circulated that some

Bristol Beaufighter production at Errwood Park. The mighty Hercules engines generated considerable centrifugal swing on take-off and landing.

76

pilots were on the verge of refusing to fly it, their dissent being instantly silenced when it was reported that women delivery pilots of the ATA were experiencing no particular difficulties. On 12 June 1943 a Stockport-built Beaufighter IC of 236 Squadron, flown by Flt. Lt. Gatward and Sgt. Fern at low level to Paris, deposited French tricolores on the Champs-Elysées and the Arc de Triomphe and from rooftop height raked the city's Kriegsmarine and Gestapo HQ with cannon fire. Of little strategic gain, as an act of outstanding airmanship and heroism it was a huge morale booster for Parisians and earned the crew the award of DFC and DFM respectively.

Overlapping the contract for Beaufighters at Errwood Park was that placed with the Fairey Company for construction of **Handley Page Halifax** four-engined heavy bombers, production of which started in October 1942. During the next three years, up to October 1945 the plant made a total of 661 Halifaxes comprising 325 B.Mk.III, 246 B.Mk.V and 21 B.Mk.VII bombers together with 69 A.Mk.VII glider-towing variants, all powered by Hercules engines.

By 1943 Heaton Chapel and Errwood Park had become the nucleus of Fairey's two million sq.ft. North West Group operations with ancillary and repair facilities at Reddish, a requisitioned former bus depot at Parrs Wood, Stretton and a former shirt factory at Warrington. The company also managed a repair depot at

Burtonwood until this was taken over by the USAAF in 1943. Altogether Fairey employed 16,000 people in the Manchester area during the wartime peak. This was in addition to the parent factory at Hayes, Middlesex and operations at Heathrow and Heston Aerodromes engaged on aircraft including the Albacore and Firefly.

The huge Fairey empire presented enormous management challenges, not helped by the essential absence in the United States of its forceful yet patrician Chairman and Managing Director, C.R. Fairey. For most of the war he was responsible for co-ordinating procurement and production of American aircraft for the RAF as Deputy Director-General and Controller of Production for the Air Section of the British Purchasing Mission in New York and later Director-General of the British Air Commission in Washington. At home, conflicting priorities, emphasis on fighter production, manufacturing and supply chain blockages were seriously delaying Fairey's new Barracuda and Firefly aircraft to the extent that the Minister of Aircraft Production, Sir Stafford Cripps, instigated a restructuring of the company's management and organisation including the introduction of American-style project team working.

Production of the **Fairey Barracuda** three-seat carrier-borne torpedo and dive-bomber finally got under way at Heaton Chapel in May 1942. Five years of gestation with indecision over the power plant – eventually a low output version of

Handley Page Halifax production at Errwood Park.

Fairey Barracuda production at Heaton Chapel.

the Merlin was selected – resulted in an aircraft ordered in 1939 not entering service until July 1942. It was to prove an effective, if not aesthetic aircraft. A shoulder-position wing, providing a good view for the observer/navigator, necessitated a long undercarriage massively strengthened for repeated deck landings. Together with the large flaps, it required a powerful hydraulic system. Overall ungainliness was completed by a high-set braced tailplane, resulting in an aeroplane whose lines went all over the place. It was said to have prompted an American General, having walked all round a Barracuda, to comment: "That sure is the finest flying machine I've ever seen, but it'll never replace the airplane!".

But the Barracuda had not been designed to impress either allies or enemies with its aesthetics. Most notably it proved its worth on 3 April 1944 when a force of 42 aircraft crippled Germany's last surviving battleship the 52,600 ton (l.w.) *Tirpitz* in the Kåfjord inlet of the Altafjord in northern Norway, leading to events in which it was finally sunk at Tromsö on 12 November.

A total of 1,160 Barracuda Mks.I/II/III/V emerged from Heaton Chapel and Ringway where production and development continued up to 1947. The Fairey Aviation Co. also used two hangars at RNAS Stretton, south of Warrington, to prepare Barracudas. Altogether, Fairey's North West Group contributed nearly 4,000 new-build Battles, Fulmars, Barracudas, Bristol Beaufighters and Handley Page Halifaxes to the war effort. Additionally, they serviced, repaired, overhauled and modified a further 2,000 of these aircraft and 100 Fairey Swordfish.

A.V. Roe & Company Ltd., Newton Heath, Chadderton, Woodford, Ringway and Yeadon

Metropolitan-Vickers Ltd. (Metrovicks), Trafford Park

The opening of Avro's 750,000 sq.ft. Chadderton factory in April 1939 was followed in December by that of a new assembly building almost as large at Woodford where it dwarfed the existing four flight sheds. At that point the total floorspace controlled by Avro amounted to 2.28 million sq.ft. Continuous expansion thereafter would see this figure rise to over 6 million sq.ft. by the war's end. In another significant development, with winter rains regularly reducing the grass airfield at Woodford to a quagmire, work began early in 1940 on the construction of 'hard' runways which were largely completed by the autumn.

Roy Chadwick and his team had some impressive new designs on the drawing board although several Avro products of the 1930s were still in evidence and would see service in the forthcoming conflict. Even the Audax biplane, built at Newton Heath and Woodford in 1937-8, remained in RAF service as a training and communications aircraft in the early war years, seeing action in Africa and the Middle East. At home, the Avro Rota Autogiro made between 1934-8 performed a vital role throughout the war in maintaining the country's radar defences. The Rota's ability to slowly orbit a fixed point out at sea made it an ideal ranging 'target' for radar calibration. A special RAF Autogiro squadron was formed and every radar station from the Orkneys to the Isle of Wight benefited from the Rota's unique capability. Calibration flights were considered so vulnerable to attack as to merit fighter escorts.

By September 1939 no less than 760 Avro Ansons were in service with ten squadrons of Coastal and 16 of Bomber Command. The Anson saw immediate action when on 5 September it became the first British aircraft of the war to attack a German U-boat. In another famous action a single Anson pursued by three Messerschmitt Bf 109s destroyed two and damaged the third by the expedient of throttling back and opening fire as they overshot. Considered highly potent at its introduction, the Anson soon became outclassed as a fighting aircraft and it was as a crew training aircraft for navigation, bombing and gunnery, and as a transport, that it proved exceptional in the long term. So much so that when production finally ceased in 1952 a total of 11,020 had been built, 8,118 by Avro in Britain and 2,902 in Canada. In the course of its long 18-year production life modernisation of the Anson included the introduction of metal wing structures, moulded plywood fuselage cladding and the substitution of its extensive 'glasshouse' windows by oval 'portholes'. Only the Spitfire, Hurricane and amongst multi-engined aircraft the Wellington, were built in greater numbers.

Still fondly remembered as 'Faithful Annie', its enduring image as a trusty 'hack' belies the Anson's original aggressive purpose.

As the military incarnation of Imperial Airways' 1933 requirement for a small airliner, development of the Anson was paralleled in 1934 by calls for a fast transport 'plane from Lord Rothermere, proprietor of the ever aviation-minded Daily Mail. His requirement for a two-crew, six-passenger aircraft coincided with the Bristol Aeroplane Company's Type 142, then on the drawing board. When this first flew in 1935, powered by two Bristol Mercury engines, it proved 50mph faster than contemporary RAF biplane fighters. Rothermere handed the machine over to the Air Ministry forthwith for military evaluation. Developed subsequently as the **Bristol Blenheim** light day bomber it generated orders of such magnitude that could only be met by setting up additional production lines. The first of these was the Bristol shadow factory at Speke, erected and managed by Rootes Securities from 1937, but in May 1938 A.V. Roe & Co. were also requested to undertake production

Built at Newton Heath and Woodford in the summer of 1939 Avro Anson Mk.I N5331, with early 'glasshouse' windows, is pictured on a training flight in Canada early in 1942. It served with No. 10 Flying Training School RAF which was relocated from Tern Hill, Shropshire to Moose Jaw, Saskatchewan in 1940 under the British Commonwealth Air Training Plan. Wear and tear have added to the effectiveness of the Anson's camouflage. *Photo: Aeroplane.*

initially of 250 Blenheim Mk.Is alongside the Anson in their extended Newton Heath factory. Over the coming months both types could be seen being transported by road for final assembly at Woodford where the first 'Avro' Blenheim was lifted off the grass by Sam Brown in September. Blenheim production also started at the new Chadderton factory the following year where the first product was therefore of *Bristol* and not Avro design. The 200,000 sq.ft. Ivy Mill at Failsworth, acquired by Avro in 1936, supplied both plants with Anson and Blenheim components. During the 1930s Avro pioneered the design of stretch forming machines which became universally adopted by the industry for building all-metal aircraft. The Blenheim was the first all-metal stressed-skin aircraft to be built by Avro, providing experience they would soon employ in the mass production of aircraft of their own design. Avro's initial Blenheim order was followed in 1940 by one for 755 Mk.IVs, the first of which Brown flew from Woodford in March. Avro's production of a total of 1,005 Blenheims was completed in November 1941 but over two-and-a-half times that number were produced by Rootes at Speke where production also terminated in November.

During the summer of 1940 Woodford was also engaged on the conversion to RAF standards and pre-delivery test flying of 20 American Martin Maryland 1 bombers, part of a consignment of 50 originally intended for the French Air Force. They had been crated to Burtonwood after the collapse of France.

With Woodford's new runways still to be constructed, in May 1939 Avro located its Experimental Flight Department at Ringway in a hangar adjoining the 1938 Airport Terminal. It would remain there for the rest of the war with both A.V. Roe and the Fairey Aviation Company expanding their assembly and flight facilities at Ringway throughout the period of hostilities. In

February and March 1942 Avro were once again involved with American aircraft when at Ringway they converted a number of Douglas DB-7 bombers, initially destined for the Belgian Air Force, into Bostons and Havocs for use by the RAF.

In the meantime Roy Chadwick had been designing a new aircraft to meet an Air Ministry specification of 1936 for a heavy bomber, powered by two Rolls-Royce Vulture engines, capable of carrying an 8,000lb bomb load with a crew of six. Designated Type 679 and named the **Avro Manchester**, in 1939 two prototypes made at Newton Heath were taken to the company's new Experimental Flight Department at Ringway for reassembly and engine fit. They were a far cry from their namesake, the twin-engined Avro Manchester biplane bomber of 1919. Weighing up to 25 tons laden, the new all-metal light alloy stressed-skin Manchester employed elaborate hydraulic and electrical systems and was Avro's largest and most powerful aircraft so far. To facilitate construction and repair the fuselage comprised five major sub-assemblies built and equipped separately for bolting together on the production line. Each was provided with plug and socket connectors and pipeline joints for easy coupling of services.

Sam Brown made the first of a series of test flights from Ringway on 24 July 1939. These revealed all sorts of problems involving hydraulics and airframe but, most seriously of all, with the Vulture engines. Basically the Vulture was an extremely powerful and complex 24-cylinder 1800hp unit comprising two V-12 Peregrine engines in 'X' configuration driving a common crankshaft. Overheating and lubrication problems led to piston seizures, con-rod and big-end failures. Chadwick's fundamentally excellent airframe was easily modified by redesigning the original twin-fin tail to include a centreline third fin, a feature retained well into production until

retrospectively replaced by an enlarged version of the original twin-fin arrangement. The wings were strengthened and extended slightly. But engine problems would bedevil the Manchester throughout its life. Wartime priorities for Merlin and Griffon engines meant that Rolls-Royce were never able to devote sufficient development time to the Vulture. Nevertheless it was ironic that they were well on the way to sorting it out when it was cancelled in 1942. Perhaps its very name had condemned it from the start ...

Desperate to take the war to Germany after victory in the Battle of Britain, the authorities were impressed by the Manchester's range and bomb load and rushed the aircraft into production and service with the minimum of proving. Avro had received a contract for 200 in mid-1937 and two years later the Air Ministry ordered another 100 from the new works of the Metropolitan-Vickers Co. Ltd. at Mosley Road/Westinghouse Road, Trafford Park and 150 from the Fairey Aviation Co. at Stockport. Altogether orders for 1,200 were mooted.

The first four Avro production aircraft were assembled and test flown at Ringway. Thereafter, from November 1940 sub-assemblies were taken to Woodford where the aircraft were flight tested from the brand new 'hard' runways. The RAF received its first deliveries that month. Metrovicks' Manchesters were delivered to Avro for final assembly at both Woodford and Ringway but production initially suffered a serious setback when on 23 December the first 13 aircraft on the Trafford Park production line were destroyed in an air attack. The first Metrovicks-built machine flew from Woodford in July 1941. Short flights from Woodford to Ringway for final 'mods' were a feature of Manchester production up to 1942 until curtailed by the demise of the Vulture engine. Including the prototypes, 159 were made by Avro and 43 by Metrovicks.

In service, pilots appreciated the Manchester's handling if not its reliability. Despite several 'groundings' of the Manchester force, with losses deemed to result more from mechanical malfunction than the enemy's air defences, the aircraft nevertheless played a significant part in Bomber Command operations until it was withdrawn from front line duties in July 1942. On the night of 30-31 May 1942, 46 Manchesters participated in the first thousand-bomber raid on Cologne. Afterwards Flt. Lt. Leslie Manser was posthumously awarded the Victoria Cross for keeping his crippled Manchester airborne long enough, on only one engine, to enable his crew to bale out before it crashed and burst into flames with Manser still at the controls.

But experience with the Manchester would not be in vain. It continued to serve with RAF Heavy Conversion Units training pilots for its derived successor, the legendary **Avro Lancaster**.

The first of the RAF's four-engined heavy bombers, the Short Stirling, had been in service since August 1940. The second, the Handley Page Halifax, was based initially on the same specification as the Avro Manchester but its manufacturers wanted nothing to do with the Vulture engine and came up instead with an aircraft powered by four Merlins which entered service in November 1940.

At Avro, Roy Chadwick and Assistant Designer Stuart Davies, who became Head of the company's Experimental Flight Department at Ringway in April 1940, had also been considering a four-Merlin version of the Manchester before the outbreak of war. Designated the Avro Type 683, its development had been subordinated to getting the Vulture-powered Manchester into service at a time when the requirements of Fighter Command had placed the Merlin at a premium. None of the parties involved – Avro, Rolls-Royce, MAP or the RAF – was content with the Manchester situation and relationships were not helped by MAP suggestions that British aircraft designers should go to America to see how heavy bombers such as the Boeing B-17 Flying Fortress were being made. Moreover Dobson and Chadwick were incandescent at an MAP suggestion that Avro's production capacity should be used to build Halifaxes. Immediate and vigorous representations resulted in MAP agreeing to the construction of prototypes of the Type 683, then referred to as the Manchester Mk.III. Direct high-level contacts between Roy Dobson and Ernest (later Lord) Hives of Rolls-Royce, who was doubtless aware of the excellence of the Manchester airframe,

resulted in the supply of an initial number of Merlin engines.

A standard three-finned Manchester Mk.I was taken from the Newton Heath production line to the Experimental Department at Chadderton to be fitted with four Merlins. A larger wing centre-section and new outer wings were required, extending the Manchester's span – already up from 80 to 90 ft. – to 102 ft., together with a wider 33 ft. tailplane. Dismantled at Chaddderton it was re-erected at the Experimental Flight Department at Ringway in December 1940 for engine running tests during the first week of 1941. Sufficiently modified to justify a new name, that of Lancaster was chosen by its manufacturers and soon adopted by the Air Ministry. It was one that would become synonymous with bomber aircraft for all time.

The prototype Lancaster was first flown by Sam Brown and Bill Thorn at Ringway on 9 January 1941. This and a subsequent series of flights at the Aircraft and Armament Experimental Establishment (A & AEE) at Boscombe Down revealed excellent overall performance. A degree of directional instability was solved back at Avro by a redesign of the tail, dispensing with the centre fin and replacing the outers with larger, oval endplates. Major production orders were anticipated and the balance of the original contracts with Avro and Metrovicks for Manchesters were amended so that from late 1941 to early 1942 they were built as Lancasters. The first production Lancaster B.Mk.I was flown from Woodford on 31 October 1941. A month later the delayed third prototype, which MAP had insisted should be built as a B.Mk.II 'proving' aircraft with alternative Bristol Hercules engines, flew for the first time.

With Avro's headquarters transferred from Newton Heath to Chadderton, in 1939 discussions at the instigation of the Air Ministry focused on planning another

giant Avro factory this time to be built on the other side of the Pennines in Yorkshire, between Leeds and Bradford at Yeadon. Completed in February 1941 and covering 1.5 million sq.ft., Yeadon was twice the size of Chadderton and the largest factory in Europe under a single roof. It had unprecedented camouflage with earth mounding and a roof detailed with dummy farm buildings, country lanes, dry stone walls and even a 'herd' of animals. Initially all Anson production was transferred there, the first example rolling off the line in June 1941. 3,881 Ansons were to be built there up to 1945, production peaking at 135 per month in 1944. Work on the Lancaster started at Yeadon in January 1942, the first aircraft flying in November.

To relieve pressure on Hawker Siddeley factories busily engaged elsewhere on the Hurricane and Typhoon, even before the Yeadon factory was fully completed work on the production of five all-metal Vulture-powered **Hawker Tornado** fighters was transferred there late in 1940. Problems once again with the Vulture engine resulted in the cancellation of the project after only one Tornado had been completed and flown at Woodford in August 1941.

But it was production of the Lancaster that virtually fully engaged Avro for the duration of the war. It was their largest and most complex aircraft so far and the scale of orders for what turned out to be

one of the biggest armaments programmes of the war required remarkable organisation. The problem had already been anticipated with the Manchester, resulting in the establishment of a production group of companies comprising Avro, Metropolitan-Vickers, Sir W.G. Armstrong Whitworth and the Fairey Aviation Co. In the event, curtailment of the Manchester required it to be produced by only the first two of these companies. It was they who, in September 1941, formed the nucleus of the Lancaster Production Group established to co-ordinate manufacturing by five prime contractors and some 600 subcontractors and suppliers. They were joined by Armstrong Whitworth at Coventry, Vickers-Armstrongs at Castle Bromwich and, from 1943 by Vickers-Armstrongs at Chester and Austin Motors (Austin Aero) at Longbridge. The Lancaster inherited the Manchester's sectional construction, its fuselage and wing each made up of five distinct units facilitating both production and repair. In a famous initiative related by C.E. 'Teddy' Fielding, who chaired the Lancaster Production Group, in May 1941 Roy Chadwick took an army of a hundred draughtsmen to Woodford where together they went over every inch of the second prototype Lancaster before its first flight, designing out potential production snags, eliminating unnecessary equipment and

Yeadon-built Lancaster B.Mk.III RE172, photographed eastbound over the Fallowfield and Withington districts of Manchester.

improving the accessibility of components requiring servicing.

During late 1941 and early 1942 production gradually increased from two to four aircraft per week at both Newton Heath and Trafford Park, the first being delivered for service with No. 44 (Rhodesia) Squadron at RAF Waddington, Lincolnshire in December 1941. Thereafter, as one complete pattern aircraft and five sets of components were issued to each member company of the Production Group for familiarisation by a rapidly expanding labour force, output increased dramatically. The Avro plants alone were to employ 40,000 people of whom 18,000 were women. Chadderton and Yeadon each employed 11,000 and by 1943 extensions took the Chadderton plant to well over one million sq.ft., the Woodford assembly building to more than 750,000 sq.ft. and facilities at Ringway to 300,000 sq.ft. In total, with over 20 sites around Manchester, the factory at Yeadon and repair centres at Bracebridge Heath near Lincoln and Langar near Nottingham, Avro controlled over six million sq.ft. of factory floorspace.

In the North West, Avro manufactured 3,050 Lancasters at Chadderton and Newton Heath. Rather less than a third were Rolls-Royce Merlin-engined Mk.Is, the remainder Mk.IIIs powered by Packard-built Merlins which started to arrive from Detroit at the end of 1942. With another 623 – mostly Mk.IIIs – made at Yeadon, total Avro output was 3,673 representing at peak over 150 per month. Metrovicks made 1,080 at Trafford Park, 948 of which were Mk.Is, with peak production of 50 per month by a labour force which had reached 8,400 on bomber production in 1943. With Chadderton, Newton Heath and Trafford Park production all going to Woodford for final assembly and flight testing, by 1944 the Cheshire plant had four production lines turning out an average of 150 Lancasters per month and on occasions up to seven per day. A Lancaster could be erected in 3½ days at an average cost of £16,000 per airframe and £60,000 for the complete aircraft. Such output presented a huge workload for Sam Brown and the seven Avro air test crews and between 1942 and 1945 the test pilot Jimmy Orrell personally flight tested some 900 Lancasters prior to their

During 1943-44 the Woodford assembly hall was turning out up to seven Lancasters a day from components supplied by Avro and Metrovicks. Altogether Woodford completed 4,130 Lancasters between 1940 and 1945.

delivery to the RAF. Altogether over 4,100 Lancasters were assembled at Woodford. Elsewhere in the region another 235 Lancaster Mk.Is were assembled by Vickers-Armstrongs at Chester. By the time the last example was delivered by Armstrong Whitworth in February 1946 a breathtaking grand total of 7,377 Lancasters had been produced, 6,947 by the Lancaster Production Group at up to 300 per month, and 430 by Victory Aircraft of Toronto, Canada.

No. 44 Squadron was the first to operate the Lancaster with hostile intent, minelaying the Heligoland Bight on 3 March 1942. On 17 April, in Operation *Marlin*, Newton Heath and Chadderton-built Mk.I Lancasters of Nos. 44 and 97 Squadrons under the command of Squadron Leaders John Nettleton and John Sherwood undertook a hazardous long range unescorted daylight attack at low level on the Maschinenfabrik Augsburg-Nürnberg (MAN) U-boat diesel engine factory. The target sustained significant damage but the price was high with seven of the twelve Lancasters shot down. On the return, in the sole survivor of the six aircraft of No. 44 Squadron, Nettleton experienced navigational problems and with little more than fumes left in his fuel tanks was diverted to land at Squires Gate, Blackpool. He and his crew were 150 miles adrift from their Waddington base and had been airborne for ten hours. No other type of bomber then in service in Europe could have carried out such a mission. Nettleton was awarded the Victoria Cross.

The most famous Lancaster action of all took place on the night of 16 May 1943 when No. 617 Squadron led by Wing Commander Guy Gibson attacked the Ruhr dams. Controlling water supply for the heavily industrialised Ruhr Valley, regulating canal flow and generating hydo-electric power they had long been considered strategic targets but, in the absence of sufficiently powerful weapons

and means of delivery, had been consigned to the 'impregnable' category. That was not the view of Dr. Barnes Wallis. Following his work on airships at Barrow-in-Furness and in Yorkshire, he had applied himself to developing aircraft structures at Vickers (Aviation) Ltd. at Weybridge. A prolific generator of ideas, at the outbreak of war he turned his mind to shortening the proceedings by hitting the enemy hard in its centres of heavy industry. He reasoned that the explosive force of bombs could be magnified to create an 'earthquake' effect if exploded at depth in either earth or water in contact with the target. Shock waves of a seismic nature would be more likely to cause irreparable structural damage to deeply embedded and massively built installations than would surface explosions. By 1942 Wallis was aware that with the new Avro Lancaster the RAF had the means of delivery – what was now needed was the weapon. With the Ruhr dams specifically in mind he conducted an elaborate series of experiments including the ricochet characteristics of spheres across the surface of water. He was allowed access to the National Physical Laboratory's huge experimental water tank at Teddington. The 550 ft.-long, 30 ft.-wide, 13 ft.-deep structure, used primarily by naval architects, had been constructed and installed just prior to the First World War by the civil, mechanical and electrical engineers Messrs. Dick, Kerr and Co.

The resulting weapon, code-named *Upkeep*, progressed to a cylindrical mine – a forged steel drum some five feet in length and 50 inches in diameter. The metal casings were manufactured by Vickers at Barrow-in-Furness with additional work by Armstrongs' Elswick Ordnance Works near Newcastle. With a gross weight of 9,250lbs, 60 of the mines were each filled with 6,600lbs of *Torpex* high explosive at the Royal Ordnance Factory at Euxton near Chorley in Lancashire. Wallis' final calculations indicated that if given a 500rpm backward spin and released 400-450 yards from the dams by Lancasters flying at 232mph only 60 ft. above the water, the mines would decelerate sufficiently to run down and remain in contact with the dam walls. Detonation to devastating effect 30 ft. below the surface would be achieved by hydrostatic depth fuse.

On 8 March 1943 Avro were instructed to convert a special Lancaster to carry the weapon and a Mk.III built by the company was selected at random from the Woodford assembly line. This was flown to Ringway to be modified in great secrecy. A further 22 Mk.IIIs, comprising two 'provisioning' aircraft and 20 for delivery to No. 617 Squadron were chosen the same way, these to be converted at Woodford itself. Barnes Wallis liaised directly with Roy Chadwick on the initial modifications which included removal of the bomb doors and dorsal gun turret, installation of V-shaped arms to carry the weapon with a hydraulic mechanism to apply reverse spin, and fairing in the ends of the bomb bay. Two angled spotlights were fitted so that their beams would converge on the surface of the water from a height of 60 ft. The late Dougie Godfrey, a former Production Superintendent at Avro, once related to the author how, whilst working on bomb bay modifications, he was berated by an over-anxious superintendent who was evidently in no doubt of exactly how much a Lancaster cost to build. The latter was totally deflated when no less than the mild-mannered Barnes Wallis himself appeared from the aircraft's innards to say "Please don't worry – Mr Godfrey is cutting precisely where I have asked him to!"

Sam Brown played an important part not only in testing and delivering the aircraft but also in piloting some of them during the bombing trials conducted by Vickers' Chief Test Pilot 'Mutt' Summers and others off the North Kent coast at Reculver in April. When Operation *Chastise* was undertaken by 19 Lancasters from RAF

Scampton in Lincolnshire on the night of Sunday 16th and early hours of Monday 17 May 1943, only three days after the last aircraft had been delivered, it evoked memories of another raid involving a force of Avro aircraft from Manchester 29 years before when Avro 504s also flying low over water had attacked the Zeppelin sheds at Friedrichshafen. The infinitely more devastating 1943 dams operation by No. 617 Squadron – immortalised thereafter as the Dam Busters – was encapsulated by the inimitable tones of BBC announcer Frank Phillips in the hours following the attack:

"This is London. The Air Ministry have just issued the following communiqué:

'In the early hours of this morning a force of Lancasters of Bomber Command, led by Wing Commander G.P. Gibson, DSO, DFC, attacked with mines the dams of the Möhne and Sorpe reservoirs. These control two-thirds of the water storage capacity of the Ruhr Basin. Reconnaissance later established that the Möhne Dam had been breached over a length of one hundred yards and that the power station below had been swept away by the resulting floods. The Eder Dam, which controls the headwaters of the Weser and Fulder Valleys and operates several power stations was also attacked and was reported as breached. Photographs show the river below the dam in full flood. The attacks were pressed home from a very low level with great determination and coolness in the face of fierce resistance. Eight of the Lancasters are missing'."

Gibson was awarded the Victoria Cross, one of ten received for valour by Lancaster aircrew during the war. Both Barnes Wallis and Roy Chadwick were appointed CBE following the raid. Links would be maintained between Wallis and Avro for the remainder of the war with the Lancaster the only means of delivering his 12,000lb 'Tallboy' and 22,000lb 'Grand Slam' spin-stabilised deep earth penetration earthquake bombs. Lancasters dropped 854 of the 21 ft.-long 'Tallboys' on targets which included V1 and V2 launching sites, the Peenemunde rocket research establishment, U and E-boat pens. On 12 November 1944, using 'Tallboys' Lancasters finally sank the *Tirpitz* which had been moved to Tromsö after being incapacitated by Fairey Barracuda dive bombers in April. During late 1944 and early 1945, 32 Lancasters were converted at Newton Heath to carry the 25 ft.-long 'Grand Slam', the heaviest bomb to be dropped by any aircraft during the war, 41 of which were used in its closing stages most famously in demolishing the Bielefeld Viaduct in March 1945.

During the course of its career, technical developments which had little impact on the Lancaster's outward appearance had seen the power of its Merlin engines increase from 1145 to 1750hp with consequential improvement in its payload from an initial 4,000lb to 22,000lb. Operated by 59 squadrons of the RAF, Lancasters made 156,000 sorties in the course of which they dropped 608,612 tons of high explosive and over 51 million incendiary bombs. Marshal of the Royal Air Force Sir Arthur Harris described the Lancaster as a shining sword in the hands of Bomber Command, the finest bomber of the war and the greatest single factor in its winning. He paid full tribute to Roy Chadwick as its designer and Roy Dobson for overseeing its production. Over half of the grand total of 7,377 Lancasters produced were lost on operations or otherwise destroyed or damaged beyond repair whilst in service.

A Metropolitan-Vickers Lancaster Mk.I (R5868) is today preserved on static display at the RAF Museum, Hendon. As *S Sugar*, this remarkable aeroplane was a veteran of 137 wartime operations with Nos. 83 and 467 Squadrons. As well as building over 1,000 Lancasters at Trafford Park, Metropolitan-Vickers also carried out

highly secret development work on the gas turbine jet engine throughout the war. Whilst the Rover Company, Rolls-Royce and Joseph Lucas were engaged in the development and production of Frank Whittle's centrifugal gas turbine engine elsewhere in the region at Clitheroe and Barnoldswick, Metrovicks were pioneering axial flow turbine technology at Trafford Park. Avro Lancasters performed many different roles during their lifetime and the prototype, BT308, following extensive handling trials, service evaluation and development work during 1941-2, was made available to Metrovicks in 1943 as a flying test bed for their F2/1 axial turbojet under development at Trafford Park. Whilst retaining its four Merlin engines, with the turbojet installed in the rear fuselage it became the first axial-engined aircraft to fly outside Germany. A Lancaster Mk.II with Bristol Hercules radial engines was similarly used in further trials of the F2/1 and, in 1945, of Metrovicks' F2/4 Beryl turbojet. Metrovicks also undertook wartime production of Dowty and Messier aircraft landing gear, automatic pilots and radar equipment at Trafford Park.

An informal understanding between the US and Britain, ostensibly for strategic reasons and to avoid duplication of effort, allowed America to monopolise the wartime design and production of large new long-range transport aircraft whilst Britain concentrated on bombers. To a large degree inevitable, given that unlike in war-torn Europe internal air services in North America were able to proceed virtually without interruption, the arrangement gave the US a head start in a new era of post-war intercontinental civil aviation. Yet it did not preclude the British aircraft industry from carrying out a number of modifications, conversions, and even a development in tandem, of certain bomber designs as stop-gap transports and freighters.

The size and range of the Lancaster

offered clear potential for use as a transport. After a Newton Heath example was sent to Canada in 1942 as a demonstration and pattern aircraft for Canadian bomber production, it was subsequently de-militarised by Victory Aircraft of Toronto. With gun turrets removed and faired in, it was returned to Avro at Manchester for further work to be undertaken. As the prototype of the **Avro 691 Lancastrian** transport it was first flown by Sam Brown at Ringway in June 1943 before inaugurating the Trans-Canada Air Lines/Canadian Government Trans Atlantic Air Service the following month. TCA themselves carried out two conversions and Victory Aircraft another six during 1943-44. In Britain a Metrovicks' Lancaster was delivered to the BOAC Development Flight for conversion and evaluation as a wartime passenger transport. Convinced of the Lancastrian's interim potential pending availability of a proposed post-war purpose-designed Avro airliner, the Type 688 Tudor, Avro and MAP decided that its manufacture, as a more refined development of the Canadian conversions, should begin at Chadderton in 1944. The first production Lancastrian was flown by Jimmy Orrell at Woodford in January 1945. Altogether, 82 were built up to the end of 1946, entering service with the RAF, BOAC, QUANTAS, British South American Airways (BSAA) and other airlines. BSAA was operated by the former RAF Bomber Command Pathfinder chief, Air Vice-Marshal D.C.T. Bennett.

Operating range was all-important. In December 1944 a Lancaster specially prepared by Avro's service and repair establishment at Bracebridge Heath, Lincolnshire, became the first British service aircraft to circumnavigate the globe, completing a 41,454 mile flight staged between airfields throughout the Empire. Early in 1945 a Lancastrian set a new record of 3½ days from Britain to New Zealand. Another became the first aircraft to circumnavigate the world in under a

week in March 1946. With additional fuel tanks in its bomb bay giving a range in excess of 4,000 miles, in the Lancastrian Britain had its first commercial aeroplane capable of tackling the South Atlantic route to Buenos Aires. Seating limited to between seven and 13 passengers could never be profitable but it served the purpose of proving future airline routes. More significantly the Lancastrian would offer the soon-to-be victors the means of asserting a commercial presence around the world in the immediate post-war period.

Avro Lancastrian G-AGMD *Nairn* in BOAC Speedbird livery c.1946.

But as with many aspects of aviation over half a century ago, it came at a price. Navigational and other perils of long flights over both sea and land resulted in several being lost. In March 1946 a BOAC Lancastrian carrying Roy Dobson's eldest son Jack, travelling on company business to Australia, disappeared without trace over the Indian Ocean. A BSAA Lancastrian, *Star Dust*, en route to Santiago was lost in the High Andes in August 1947, possibly as a result of descending too soon when its positioning by dead reckoning was compromised by high altitude jetstream headwinds. Only now, nearly six decades later, has glacier melt started to reveal the grim remains of its wreckage.

Like its progenitor, the Lancastrian also served as a flying test bed for the new jet turbine engines. In 1946 Rolls-Royce at

Hucknall fitted an example with two 5,000lb-thrust Nene turbojets designed by the company at Barnoldswick. With its inboard Merlins feathered it became the world's first commercial aircraft to fly purely on jets. Appropriately carrying Roy Chadwick as a passenger, in September it flew from London to Le Bourget in 50 minutes at a speed of 263mph. In 1948 another was similarly engined with Rolls-Royce Avons also designed at Barnoldswick and in 1950 a Lancastrian was fitted with Armstrong Siddeley Sapphires initially designed and developed by Metrovicks at Trafford Park.

In parallel with the Lancaster, using its main and tail planes, engines and undercarriage, at Chadderton in 1941 Roy Chadwick started to design a larger-bodied transport and cargo aircraft with potential also to carry paratroops. It had an entirely new square-section fuselage, twice the internal capacity of the Lancaster, with uninterrupted floor area throughout, conveniently low-slung to facilitate admission of bulky loads through large double doors aft of a shoulder-mounted wing. The Chadderton-built prototype was assembled at Avro's Experimental Flight Department at Ringway only five months after completion of design, Sam Brown 'first-flighting' it on 5 July 1942. Designated the **Avro 685 York**, three further prototypes were ordered. The first prototype was completed as a through-hold freighter, the second had full passenger seating, the third prepared as a VIP carrier and the fourth evaluated for paratroops. Ringway was the location of the Airborne Forces Experimental Establishment (AFEE) and No.1 Parachute Training School with a dropping zone at Tatton Park, where over 60,000 paratroops trained, but investigations soon proved the York unsatisfactory in that role due to the degree of slipstream wash along the fuselage. Its aerodynamics further dictated the addition of a centreline third tail fin from the third prototype onwards.

With increased bomber production the greater priority, in March 1942 the MAP earmarked a site on the south side of Ringway for two assembly sheds and a flight shed to provide Metropolitan-Vickers with over 250,000 sq.ft. of additional capacity for assembly and flight testing of Lancasters. In the event Metrovicks retained their Trafford Park and Woodford arrangements and it was Avro who took over the new Ringway premises in March 1943 for assembly of the York. Even though 300 were ordered from the end of 1942, production remained a low priority with only another three being completed in 1943, before output gathered momentum early in 1944.

Named *Ascalon* after the legendary spear of St. George, the third prototype VIP York carried Winston Churchill to Algiers within days of entering service in May 1943. Fitted out with state room, dining room and galley it was used shortly afterwards by King George VI on his tour of British Forces in North Africa and the Middle East. A fleet of five VIP Yorks provided transport for other commanders including Lord Mountbatten, the Duke of Gloucester, General de Gaulle and Field Marshal Smuts to destinations such as the Tehran, Moscow and Yalta Conferences. Churchill referred to *Ascalon* as his 'aerial yacht' but, even with appointments verging on the luxurious for wartime, it remained an unpressurised aircraft. Long flights with Merlins of a combined 6,480hp vociferating for hours on end were inevitably wearying. Accordingly the RAE at Farnborough designed an egg-shaped pressurised capsule $7\frac{1}{2}$ ft. × $4\frac{1}{2}$ ft. capable of accommodating the PM for sleeping purposes. Although one was made at Avro's Experimental Department at Ringway other priorities prevented its installation and use.

The King and the Prime Minister having demonstrated their confidence in the York, in October 1943 it was the makers' turn. Roy Dobson, with Sir Frank Spriggs of

RAF Avro York C.Mk.I passenger freighter, the last of which and the final York of all to be produced, PE108, was delivered from Woodford on 29 April 1948.

Hawker Siddeley, Air Ministry officials and Sam Brown flew across the Atlantic in the first production York, which Brown had only just flight tested, for discussions with Victory Aircraft at Toronto. Routed via Prestwick, Iceland, Greenland, Goose Bay to Montreal and Toronto, they encountered periods of atrocious weather. Even on the last leg of the return they had to grope their way along the Manchester Ship Canal from Liverpool under dense cloud.

By October 1945 some 153 Yorks had been completed at Ringway as VIP, passenger, heavy cargo and combined passenger freighters. The latter, with freight stowed forward and 12 seats aft, was the final version to be introduced when rolled out in April 1945. V-J Day released considerable capacity at Avro's Yeadon factory and the York jigs were moved across from Ringway. Built from sub-assemblies brought across the Pennines from Manchester by road, a further 77 Yorks rolled off the Yeadon line, alongside that of the veteran Anson, until the decision was taken to close Yeadon in 1947. Another 27 Yorks were assembled at Woodford between 1945 and 1948 when the final aircraft, a passenger freighter, was

delivered to the RAF in April.

Of a total of 258 Yorks produced, including one by Victory Aircraft in Canada, 114 were built as freighters and 64 as combined passenger freighters. 12-passenger and 30-passenger versions served with BSAA and BOAC respectively. Post-war, Yorks gave sterling service throughout Europe and the Mediterranean, the Middle and Far East, North and South America. Unsuitable for dropping paratroops they nevertheless proved useful troop carriers and, until the arrival of newer aircraft such as the Handley Page Hastings, were the mainstay of RAF Transport Command. Perhaps they are best remembered for their contribution to the Berlin Airlift of 1948-49 when, in the course of 29,000 sorties with payloads averaging $7\frac{1}{2}$-9 tons, nine RAF York squadrons delivered 239,000 tons of supplies to the beleaguered city. This represented ten per cent of all inbound tonnage delivered to Berlin during the eleven-month Soviet blockade and the 15-month airlift. The figures do not include the additional contribution made by civil Yorks and other Avro aircraft such as Lancasters, Lancastrians, Lincolns and

Tudors operated by Airflight, BSAA, Flight Refuelling, the Lancashire Aircraft Corporation and Skyways. Avro Yorks had the distinction of delivering the one-hundred-thousandth ton of freight on 17 December 1948 and the one-millionth on 18 February 1949. Civil operators including Air Charter and Dan-Air later used Yorks for trooping contracts and passenger services in the 1950s and others as freighters up to 1964.

As well as generating the Lancastrian and York transport derivatives, Chadwick's superb Lancaster offered potential for even further development as a heavy bomber. By 1943 the war in the Pacific had already pointed to the need for a larger, heavier successor capable of operating faster and higher over even greater distances. An enlarged version, designated the Avro 694 and initially referred to as the Lancaster Mk.IV, took shape on the drawing boards at Chadderton. With a wingspan extended by 18 ft. to 120 ft., powered by four 1,750hp Merlin engines, of flush-riveted construction and armed with cannon as well as machine guns, it was later considered sufficiently different to merit a new name – the **Avro Lincoln**.

Sam Brown lifted the prototype off from Ringway on 9 June 1944, finding that in spite of its greater size it handled as well if not even better than the Lancaster. Trials progressed smoothly and orders for 800 were placed with the Lancaster Production Group with the prospect of demand going into thousands depending on the duration of the war. These were not rushed into however, it being decided to take no risks with the high output then being achieved with the Lancaster. The entry of production Lincolns into RAF service coincided with Japan's unconditional surrender in August 1945 and was followed by an immediate cut-back of orders. As a result, as part of a reduced 'Lancaster' Production Group, Avro made 165 Lincolns at Chadderton and Woodford between 1944-46 and another six at Yeadon, whilst Metropolitan-Vickers built 80 at Trafford Park before leaving the Group at the end of 1945. Sir W.G. Armstrong Whitworth Aircraft made 299 at Coventry, the last being delivered to the RAF in April 1951. Overseas, the Australian Government Aircraft Factory at Melbourne constructed 54 for the RAAF and in Canada just one was completed out of five initially laid down by Victory Aircraft at Toronto.

Too late to see operational service in WW2, the Lincoln served as the RAF's standard long-range heavy bomber for the next ten years. In the early stages of the Cold War, with the Berlin Airlift a recent

Avro Lincoln B.MkII RF570 was built by Sir W.G. Armstrong Whitworth Aircraft Ltd. at Coventry. It was one of five Lincolns that remained in RAF service, for radar and signals duties, until March 1963.

success, in 1950 a great show of strength was given when 15 of the 20 RAF Lincoln squadrons flew in mass formation at the Farnborough Air Show. The Lincoln's range enabled it to undertake a number of international public relations tours and geophysical research flights although not all of its overseas deployment was of a goodwill nature: between 1950 and 1956 it was used in anti-terrorist operations in Malaya and against the Mau Mau in Kenya.

Historically, the Lincoln was significant as the RAF's last piston-engined bomber. Like the Lancaster and Lancastrian it proved an ideal test-bed for the new generation of turbojet and turbo-prop engines. Progressively phased out of service in favour of the Canberra jet bomber and later the Valiant, some Lincolns remained in use for airborne radar development until 1963. But their architecture would live on in the Avro Shackleton, a further derivative for long-range anti-submarine and maritime reconnaissance duties which itself would see service for a remarkable four decades from 1951-91.

The English Electric Co. Ltd., Preston and Samlesbury

Following the discussions in June-July 1938 between Frederick Handley Page of Handley Page Ltd. and George Nelson of English Electric, it was agreed in August and formalised by contract in December that English Electric should initially produce 75 twin-engined **Handley Page Hampden** bombers at Preston. The verbal approval of the Air Ministry was considered adequate authority to begin major extensions of the Preston 'East' Works and convert them from peacetime assembly of electric locomotives to aircraft. With the Hampden now coming off the parent production line at Radlett, Hertfordshire, an example was delivered to Strand Road as a pattern aircraft. Handley Page staff including F.D. Crowe were transferred to Preston to ease the setting up of the

shadow operation. By the turn of the year the Strand Road labour force had increased from under 1,000 to 1,200 including 150 women.

In February 1939, with preliminary work on the Hampden well in hand, English Electric were also asked to consider making arrangements for producing 100 of the new **Handley Page Halifax** four-engined heavy bombers. Considering that the Halifax would not make its maiden flight at Handley Page's Bicester, Oxfordshire facility until October, the request represented remarkable forward planning by the Air Ministry. It was decided in August that, in the event of war, the whole of the Preston 'West' Works should be committed to the Halifax programme.

Meanwhile, the first indications of the coming end of centuries of rural idyll in the Ribble Valley was the start of construction in April of a flight shed on the northern fringe of the proposed aerodrome at Samlesbury. This was completed in October in good time to receive the major sub-assemblies for the first Hampden, delivered from Strand Road on specially made articulated tractor trolleys, on 31 December. Construction of tarmac runways which had started in August was completed in January 1940 and after final assembly and engine runs the first Hampden flew on test on 22 February, only 14 months after confirmation of the contract. During that time, the Strand Road factory had been extended and production activated, over 5,000 employees recruited and trained and a new aerodrome established – a remarkable achievement. The first 'English Electric' Hampden was delivered to the RAF at Boscombe Down in March and with production accelerating, work started on a second flight shed in May. The same month a number of Hampdens were flown to RAF Burtonwood. With the 50th Hampden ready for delivery by the middle of the year further orders came thick and fast. A contract for 200 Halifaxes in April was followed by more in July for another 550 Hampdens, swelled also by orders for salvage and repair of battle-damaged examples. The original December 1938 contract was discharged upon completion of the 75th Hampden on 30 July 1940.

Bellman hangars were erected on the south side of the aerodrome near Samlesbury Hall for use by another company, Burnley Aircraft Products. Little documented, it is possible that they acted as subcontract repairers to aircraft factories elsewhere in the region such as Rootes Securities at Speke, Fairey at Stockport, Vickers-Armstrongs at Chester and Short Brothers. There are references to wartime Bristol Beaufighter repair work undertaken by the Samlesbury company. Two more flight sheds were authorised for English Electric as were runway extensions in anticipation of forthcoming flight testing of the heavier, four-engined Halifax. In October 1940, with the site now a hive of activity, the Air Ministry considered it prudent to exercise greater control by requisitioning the aerodrome. A total of 260 Hampdens had been delivered by the end of the year, with English Electric's employment in the Preston area having increased further to 7,200 men and 2,500 women. The Aircraft Design and Experimental Building at the Strand Road 'West' Works was engaged on Halifax-related development and large new airframe erecting shops were about to begin producing the heavy bomber. Considerable extensions had been made to the Wellfield Machine Shop and a large Detail Parts Shop completed. The MAP also requisitioned various premises throughout the district as satellite factories for dispersal of component, detail parts and small assemblies production. Part of the giant Courtaulds synthetic fibre plant was used for manufacturing self-sealing fuel and oil tanks and sheet metal work for Halifax nose fairings and engine nacelles. Austin

House, the Deepdale Omnibus Sheds, Victoria Warehouse and even Preston Prison were used for storage purposes and Stevensons' Canal Foundry for drop stampings.

Hampden production reached 50 per month in March 1941. Powered by two Bristol Pegasus radial engines it was a mainstay of Bomber Command in the early years of the war. It was the first Handley Page design with stressed-skin structure, retractable undercarriage and variable-pitch propellers. Build on the line was facilitated by its assembly from wing centre and outer sections, separate front and centre fuselage units with the rear fuselage – in effect a pencil-slim boom – split lengthwise to enable controls and wiring to be fitted before final assembly. For a design dating back to a specification issued in 1931 it was quite fast – 255mph – and could carry a useful bomb load of 4,000lb over long distances. It handled well, leading edge slots enabling it to land at little more than 70mph with the pilot having an excellent view from his position high up on the deep but exceedingly narrow-section fuselage. Only three feet wide, the fuselage interior was so cramped as to make it extremely difficult for the crew to change positions in an emergency. That apart, the aircraft was regarded with some affection by its crews who dubbed it 'the flying suitcase'. Pilots liked to fly with the cockpit cover open whenever possible. But, as with its contemporaries the Avro Anson, Bristol Blenheim and Fairey Battle, the Hampden's vulnerability was its lack of effective defensive armament. As a daylight bomber, early in the war it sustained unacceptable losses at the hands of German fighters off the enemy coast and in the Norwegian campaign. Reassigned to night operations, Hampdens participated in the RAF's first raid on Berlin on 25-26 August 1940. They joined Coastal Command as torpedo bombers and were also sent on detachment to Russia in the convoy

Assembly of Handley Page Hampden front fuselages by the English Electric Co., Strand Road, Preston, November 1941.

Hampdens returned for modifications and repairs in 3A Shed, Samlesbury. In the foreground is the dis-assembled P1202, built initially by Handley Page at Radlett.

Preston and Samlesbury-built (November 1941) Hampden Mk.I AT137 of No. 455 (Australia) Sqn., May 1942. Whenever practicable, pilots liked to fly the cramped aircraft with cockpit open.

protection role. In March 1941, when English Electric had completed 400 Hampdens out of 900 on order, MAP cut the orders to 770 'due to altered requirements for this type of bomber'.

When English Electric completed the last of their 770 Hampdens in March 1942 they had built 268 more than Handley Page themselves. It represented average output and delivery of over one aircraft per day for two years.

Samlesbury's first runway extensions were completed in April 1941 and in June the main assemblies for the first Rolls-Royce

Merlin-powered Halifax Mk.II were delivered for final assembly at the Flight Sheds. The aircraft flew on 15 August and was delivered in September, followed by another six by the end of the year. 'English Electric' Halifax Mk.II (W1048), delivered in March 1942, was shot down on its first mission on 27/28 April when No. 35 Squadron flew from Kinloss to attack the *Tirpitz* in Foettenfjord, near Trondheim in Norway. The aircraft crash-landed on the frozen Lake Hoklingen but melted the ice and sank to a depth of 90 feet. All the crew survived. W1048 remained on the

Rolls-Royce Merlin-powered Halifax B.Mk.II Series I DT585 at Samlesbury, October 1942.

Merlin-powered Halifax B.Mk.IIs at Samlesbury in 1943, showing drag-reducing design changes including fairing in the original front gun turret (Series I Special) and a smoother profile dorsal turret on the distant (Series IA) aircraft. The middle aircraft, bearing a maple leaf, belongs to No. 405 (Vancouver) Sqn. That in the foreground appears to have undertaken five operations over enemy territory.

lake bed for 31 years until it was recovered in 1973. It is now displayed at the RAF Museum, Hendon. 1942 brought further orders, including some for Bristol Hercules-powered Halifax IIIs. By July the monthly output of 36 Halifax IIs had exceed even that of the previous Hampden and no less than 212 had been delivered by the end by August. A fourth flight shed would soon materialise and work started on the laying of concrete runways, completed in summer 1943.

In a separate venture, in November 1942 George Nelson was appointed to advise the firm of D. Napier & Son Ltd. of Acton, London, on the production of the company's Sabre engine at a large new shadow factory built at Walton, Liverpool. All manner of technical and manufacturing problems were delaying the efficient production of this complex and powerful engine and the resulting entry into service of improved versions of the Hawker Typhoon and Tempest fighters. The outcome in December was that English Electric, supported by MAP, took over Napiers, so joining the ranks of Bristol, de Havilland and Hawker Siddeley as members of a select group of manufacturers of both aero-engines and airframes.

At Preston and Samlesbury, the English Electric workforce which in 1943 totalled 7,900 men and 5,500 women, was exceeding all its production targets. By the summer, monthly Halifax output had reached 64 compared with the programme for 60, with total Halifax completions standing at 769 as against the 764 projected. At the end of the year 1,006 had been delivered and in February monthly production peaked at 80. Orders for more continued to flow in, including Halifax Mks. VI and VII with uprated Hercules engines, together with eight Mk.AVIIs for transport of airborne forces and glider towing. In the run-up to 'D' Day, Samlesbury was an assembly point for Halifaxes and troop-carrying gliders forming part of the 'Air Armada'. A suggestion that English Electric should install Bristol Mercury engines in giant General Aircraft Hamilcar gliders for projected use in the Pacific was deemed impracticable due to the intensity of existing commitments and the relatively small size of Samlesbury Aerodrome. In another 1944 proposal the MAP sought to involve English Electric in the manufacture of the Folland Fo.117A fighter, a potential replacement for the Tempest. Having progressed the matter to the extent of enlarging their design team, which had been

Halifax B.Mk.III front and rear fuselage assembly at Strand Road, Preston, 1943.

working on Halifax development, English Electric withdrew from the Folland project when it became apparent that another, of much greater significance for the longer term, was in the offing.

Progress elsewhere with the turbojet engine, in Germany by von Ohain and Heinkel and, in Britain, by Frank Whittle at Power Jets in the Midlands; Rover, Lucas and Rolls-Royce at Clitheroe and Barnoldswick; Metropolitan-Vickers at Trafford Park and de Havilland at Hatfield, had demonstrated its practicability for aircraft propulsion. The Gloster/Whittle E28/39 had flown in 1941, the Gloster F.9/40 Meteor and **de Havilland D.H.100 Vampire** in 1943. The Air Ministry decided to put both the Meteor and Vampire into production although only the former would see action before the end of hostilities, entering service with the RAF in July 1944 as did the Messerschmitt Me.262 with the Luftwaffe. But de Havilland factories were already full to capacity with work on piston-engined aircraft such as the Mosquito and Hornet. Impressed by English Electric's exemplary record with the Hampden and Halifax, on 13 May 1944 the MAP notified the company of its intention to assign them production contracts for the Vampire. The first, for 120 aircraft, was placed in June. For the company to be given the opportunity to take Britain into the jet age only five years after re-entering aircraft manufacturing was a remarkable achievement. It was excellent news for English Electric, whose Chairman and Managing Director Sir George Nelson – knighted in 1943 – and Board of Directors had only recently taken the decision to remain in the aircraft industry after the war. As realists they were acutely aware of the risks of remaining purely as subcontractors relying on business from the traditional British 'family' of aircraft manufacturers. The summary termination of their flying boat contracts after the First World War served

as a warning of what could happen after the Second and they reasoned that the best prospects for future continuity lay with the establishment of a full design team of their own, capable of conceptualising and detailing a new generation of specifically English Electric aircraft. Although the company's status in the Vampire programme would be as subcontractors, experience in series production of such advanced aircraft would prove invaluable in developing their own designs in the future.

In April 1944 English Electric took over the former Barton Motors garage and showroom in Corporation Street, Preston, which the MAP had requisitioned as a Training Centre. The two-storey premises, with interesting art deco façade, offered space for a drawing office and workshop for small scale development and production of prototype components. As an Experimental Department separate from the Strand Road Works it became known as 'TC' and enabled preliminary work to begin on the Vampire in May without disrupting production of the Halifax. The same month, 35-year-old W.E.W. Petter, previously of Westland Aircraft Ltd. of Yeovil, was appointed Chief Engineer of English Electric's aircraft division. As well as assuming responsibility for the company's new design team Petter brought with him ideas for a new jet fighter-bomber, shortly to be amended in response to official requirements for a high altitude jet bomber. As English Electric's first in-house design of a new aircraft since the Wren, Ayr and Kingston of the 1920s, the English Electric A1 as it was initially known would prove to be of the greatest significance for the company's future in aviation.

But at the end of 1944 and into 1945 the immediate tasks were to complete orders for the wartime Halifax and start production of the new Vampire. With the end of the war in prospect, the Halifax was progressively phased out although production did not finally end until November 1945 with the completion of the 2,145th off the Preston and Samlesbury lines. As with the preceding 770 Hampdens, all had been flight tested from Samlesbury, where J.D. Rose was the Chief Test Pilot, without the loss of a single aircraft. For what had started as a shadow factory operation, English Electric had succeeded in combining quantity and quality without sacrificing either. The aircraft they turned out were regarded by many as superior to those of any of the 'family' of established manufacturers including Handley Page themselves, better than those from shadow factories run by the motor industry and others produced by the London Aircraft Production Group sometimes unflatteringly referred to as 'London Buses'.

As to the respective merits of the RAF's wartime triumvirate of British-built four-engined 'heavies' – the Short Stirling, Handley Page Halifax and Avro Lancaster – the debate has rumbled on since the war. Flt. Lt. G.R. Woodward, a pilot of No. 7 and No. 15 Squadrons and family friend of the author, who flew Wellingtons, Stirlings, Lancasters and Liberators, whilst full of praise for the superb Lancaster's overall performance, handling and seemingly unlimited payload, nevertheless held the Stirling in high regard. Albeit slow, heavy, condemned to a lower ceiling by its restricted wingspan, it was rugged, refined and outstandingly manoeuvrable for its size – "a gentleman's aeroplane". The Halifax, more akin to the Lancaster, had great assets of reliability and versatility for other roles as well as a bomber, partly offset by poorer handling until markedly improved as the Halifax III. Others more knowledgeable than the author will continue the discourse.

One of the prototype Vampire jet fighters, hand-built by de Havilland, was sent to English Electric, enabling production to gather pace in 1944 under the control of R.N. Hollock. The Vampire was all metal

apart from the front fuselage and cockpit which, reviving a link with English Electric's traditional use of timber in tramcars and flying boats, was of plywood and balsa sandwich construction similar to the Mosquito. Powered by a 3,100lb-thrust de Havilland Goblin turbojet set in a short fuselage immediately aft of the cockpit, it employed a twin-boom tail layout permitting maximum thrust from the shortest possible jet pipe. The first flight of an English Electric production Vampire was made at Samlesbury on 20 April 1945 by the designers' Chief Test Pilot, Geoffrey de Havilland Jnr. The aircraft was delivered to the RAF for evaluation three days later. With orders standing at 300, another five had flown by the end of the war in Europe less than a month later. At that time 'English Electric' D.H.100 Vampires, with a top speed of 540mph and a service ceiling in excess of 40,000 ft., were the first fighters in the world capable of exceeding 500mph in level flight.

Even English Electric's record of wartime achievement would not in itself have guaranteed the company a position in the post-war British aircraft industry. But against that background, it was in the enterprising decision to continue making aircraft taken by the Board of Directors in 1944, announced publicly by Sir George Nelson at a celebration lunch in Preston in April 1945, that much of the credit rests for the large scale presence of the industry in Lancashire today.

Vickers-Armstrongs Ltd., Broughton/Hawarden, near Chester (with Cranage, near Holmes Chapel)

Squires Gate, Blackpool (with Stanley Park Aerodrome)

Vickers built aircraft in the former Itala car factory at the centre of the Brooklands race circuit, near Weybridge in Surrey, from 1915. Seven years earlier, Alliott Verdon

Roe had exasperated the Brooklands management with his flying experiments on the same site. When the Luftwaffe seriously disrupted production of the **Vickers Wellington** bomber in an air raid on Weybridge on 4 September 1940, it showed the wisdom of the company and MAP's decision to strategically disperse the Wellington programme to two large new shadow factories which had then just been completed in North Wales and the North West of England.

The first of these, at Broughton near Chester, was opened in September 1939 and provided over a million square feet of production space. Having rejected possible sites for the second factory at Doncaster, Exeter – and Samlesbury, which was deemed more appropriate for English Electric – the various parties concerned opted for Squires Gate, an extensive open area on the Lancashire Coast between Blackpool and Lytham St. Annes. With a long history of aviation use it offered excellent approaches from both land and sea. The Blackpool plant, operational from mid-1940 was larger even than Chester, both being owned by the Government but leased and managed by Vickers-Armstrongs. Initially, Trevor Westbrook was General Manager responsible for all three factories. Progress on the Chester factory was accompanied by the establishment of a small team of key personnel headed by Gordon Montgomery as Assembly and Works Manager, despatched from Weybridge to supervise the new production line. Whereas Chester was primarily a centre for assembly of Wellingtons from parts supplied by a chain of 500 subcontractors throughout the North West and Midlands, Blackpool was more akin to Weybridge as a full manufacturing plant with its own extensive machine shops. For production test flying both shared adjoining airfield facilities with the RAF – Chester with RAF Hawarden and Blackpool with RAF Squires Gate.

Hawarden, a former relief landing ground for RAF Sealand, a short distance away near Queensferry, also saw use as RAF No. 48 Maintenance Unit, No. 57 Operational Training Unit and No. 3 Ferry Pool, Air Transport Auxiliary (ATA). RAF Squires Gate was requisitioned as a Coastal Command training unit in 1938 and, after construction of three tarmac runways in the standard 60 degree pattern with four Bellman hangars, became operational in December 1940. As well as Ansons of the School of Air Sea Rescue, Squires Gate operated Battles, Wellingtons, Bothas, Hurricanes, Defiants and Henleys on various duties including the air defence of Lancashire and Merseyside.

Both the Chester and Blackpool factories were large enough to justify having their own satellite 'shadow' assembly plants, opened in 1941. That for Chester lay 25 miles to the east at Byley, adjoining the aerodrome at RAF Cranage between Northwich and Holmes Chapel. A number of smaller facilities were dispersed throughout Cheshire and Flintshire. At one point Hurricanes of No. 96 Squadron stationed at Cranage were detached to serve at Squires Gate. The Vickers-Armstrongs' Blackpool factory satellite was at the pre-war former Stanley Park municipal aerodrome two miles to the north of Squires Gate. It was requisitioned by the RAF at the start of hostilities, initially as a technical and training centre. In 1940 Vickers-Armstrongs selected it for a satellite factory for their main Blackpool plant and five new Bellman hangars were built. Stanley Park became fully operational on 26 October 1941 when the first Wellington bomber to be assembled there took off for the short flight to Squires Gate where all subsequent pre-delivery production test flying took place. Stanley Park's short grass strips had to be reinforced by surface laying of steel mesh and could only be safely used for take-off, not landing, by such relatively large and

heavy aircraft, and then only lightly loaded. After the war Stanley Park became a centre for scrapping surplus aircraft such as Hurricanes, a gliding school, was later the site of the Royal Lancashire Show and from 1971 the home of Blackpool Zoo. Today, still bearing faint but recognisable hangar numbers, the former airfield buildings are used as the Zoo's animal houses.

The Wellington was the second aeroplane to employ the geodetic structure developed by Barnes Wallis initially for use in the *R.100* airship. Having left Vickers at Barrow-in-Furness soon after the First World War, following a further period working with airships which culminated in the brilliant *R.100* in 1930, Wallis had been appointed to Vickers (Aviation) at Weybridge as Chief Structural Designer under Rex Pierson. There he applied the principles of the geodesic – the shortest distance between two points on a curved surface, exemplified in global navigation by the 'great circle' route – to the design of the Vickers Wellesley bomber of 1933. But

it was with Wallis and Pierson's subsequent design of the Vickers Wellington that the geodetic structure would become synonymous.

In utilising the geodesic for airframe construction, Wallis ran two opposing helices or spirals of alloy strip mounted on longitudinal stringers to create a diagonal lattice structure. By incorporating the primary structure in the surface, equalising and absorbing all loadings and stresses, it obviated the need for conventional secondary structures usually manifested by internal bulkheads. Notwithstanding the somewhat portly profile of the Wellington, the result lent itself to improved aerodynamics, proved immensely strong yet flexible and was easy to repair after battle damage. Moreover, it did not require stressed-skinning for structural integrity but could revert to traditional weight-saving fabric. In itself the latter would only prove of short term advantage due to the incompatibility between fabric-covered surfaces and ever increasing aircraft speeds.

Considering that the Vickers Wellington and Handley Page Hampden had both been designed to the same Air Ministry specification of 1932, they were markedly different in appearance. The corpulent, roomy Wellington, first flown at Brooklands in June 1936, contrasted with the pencil-slim, narrow-bodied 'flying suitcase' and soon acquired the nickname 'Wimpey' after the cartoon character Popeye's tubby sidekick J. Wellington Wimpey. For many though, the Wimpey would forever be known as the 'basketweave bomber'.

Wellingtons participated in the first bombing raid of the war, a daylight attack on the German fleet near Wilhelmshaven on 4 September 1939. At this point in the hostilities the RAF still adhered to the theory of collective formation defence in daylight operations. This was invalidated on 18 December when, in another raid on Wilhelmshaven and in the subsequent Battle of the Heligoland Bight, out of a force of 24 Wellingtons of Nos. 6, 37 and 149 Squadrons, ten were lost to German fighters and three extensively damaged. Once the formation had been split up in the heat of battle, the Wellingtons proved acutely vulnerable to fighter attacks from the beam. Moreover, at that time they were deficient in armour plate and self-sealing fuel tanks. Like the Hampden, the Wellington was assigned to night operations, in which it became the mainstay of Bomber Command until the new four-engined 'heavies' – the Stirling, Halifax and

Lancaster – started to enter service from 1941. Wellingtons flew on the first attack on Berlin on 25 August 1940 and formed over half the total force engaged on the RAF's first thousand-bomber raid on Cologne on 30-31 May 1942.

Gordon Montgomery brought formidable experience to the new Chester plant. Having prepared the Vickers Vimy in which Alcock and Brown had crossed the Atlantic in 1919, later he had been closely involved with development of the Wellesley and Wellington and was totally familiar with the manufacture and assembly of their complex geodetic structures. The first Chester-assembled Wellington Mk.I, on which work started in a temporary hangar in advance of the commissioning of the main factory in October, was flown from Hawarden to Brooklands on 2 August 1939 for testing. Thereafter all pre-delivery flight testing was at Hawarden. Chester's labour force of 700 in 1940 increased to 7,000 in 1943, of whom more than two-thirds were women. Female labour was considered vital for the skilled sewing and fitting of linen fabric as cladding for the airframes. Over the same period Chester's annual output of Wellingtons increased from some 485 to 1,356. The first Cranage aircraft was completed in September 1941 and, together, the Chester factory and its satellite assembled a total of 5,540 Wellingtons before production, having peaked at 130 aircraft per month, ceased in September 1945. In 1944 Vickers-

Armstrongs set a world record at Chester by fully assembling a Wellington from scratch and rolling it out in just under 24 hours, prior to the aircraft taking off from Hawarden three-quarters of an hour later.

Such levels of output placed great demands on production test flying at Hawarden under the control of the Chief Production Test Pilot Maurice Hare who was credited personally with clearing over 3,000 Chester-built aircraft. A contingent of the Air Transport Auxiliary Ferry Pilots Pool was on hand to deliver 'signed off' aircraft to RAF units. Chester produced Wellington Mks.I, IA, IC, III, IV, X, XII and XIV, the most numerous of which were 1,583 Mk.ICs, 737 Mk.IIIs and 2,434 Mk.Xs. The great majority were powered by Bristol Pegasus or Hercules engines, different versions of which largely determined the aircraft mark number. 220 Mk.IVs produced exclusively at Chester were, however, powered by American Pratt & Whitney Twin Wasp engines. The Mk.IV, with Air to Surface Vessel (ASV) radar and Leigh Lights, was used by RAF Coastal Command for anti-submarine and shipping operations.

In an outstanding act of bravery, returning from Munster on the night of 7 July 1941, Sgt. J.A. Ward of No. 75 (New Zealand) Squadron, second pilot of a Chester-built Wellington Mk.IC, won the Victoria Cross for extinguishing an engine fire after being attacked by a night fighter over the Zuider Zee. Tearing hand and foot-holds in the fabric cladding he crawled out along the wing to stem leaking petrol and smother the flames. Subsequently promoted to first pilot, this brave man perished on another operation two months later when he stayed too long at the controls of his stricken aircraft to give his crew time to escape.

Wellington production at Chester started to decline from 1943 as requirements shifted in favour of four-engined bombers. MAP included the Vickers-Armstrongs

plant in the Lancaster Production Group and in 1944 Chester had orders for 680 **Avro Lancasters** and 840 **Avro Lincolns**. These were severely cut back in the final year of the war to the extent that 235 Lancasters were assembled between June 1944 and August 1945, production peaking at 36 per month. Wing centre sections were built at Chester with other sub-assemblies supplied by Avro from Chadderton and Yeadon. 23 of the 235 were completed from sub-assemblies received from Metropolitan-Vickers at Trafford Park, who also supplied those for eleven Lincolns assembled at Chester between June and August 1945. Lancaster Mk.I PA474, today part of the Battle of Britain Memorial Flight and a popular attraction on the UK air show circuit, was assembled at Chester in 1945. It is one of only two remaining airworthy Lancasters, the other being in Canada.

At Vickers-Armstrongs' Blackpool factory, an initial shortage of skilled labour in the locality had to be overcome by transferring workers from the Vickers shipyard at Barrow-in-Furness. Preparatory work began in one of the Squires Gate Bellman hangars. Operational from mid-1940, the new factory rolled out its first Wellington in July but suffered an immediate setback in August when part of the main roof structure collapsed killing six employees and injuring 13. Thereafter, unlike the Chester assembly operation, Blackpool developed as a fully independent manufacturing facility with a vast machine shop accommodating rows of machinery extending to a distant, hazy vanishing point, producing components for the Wellington's geodetic structures. The operation was sustained by a wide range of subcontractors with ancillary production taking place throughout Blackpool in various garages, bus and tram depots and even a market hall. The satellite assembly line at Stanley Park Aerodrome, where there was also a technical training school,

came into operation in October 1941. In addition to its manufacturing role, Blackpool also became Vickers-Armstrongs' principal centre for experimental and development test flying after Weybridge was bombed in 1940.

Blackpool manufactured a total of 3,406 Wellingtons up to October 1945, 430 of which were completed at Stanley Park. Production of Mks.IC, III, X, XI, XIII, XIV and XVIII, the bulk of which comprising 780 Mk.IIIs, 1,369 Mk.Xs and 802 Mk.XIIIs, peaked at 102 per month. Mks.XI, XIII and XIV were general reconnaissance variants and Mk.XVIIIs, trainers. The Weybridge parent factory, which had not been established on such mass production lines nevertheless manufactured 2,515, peaking at 70 per month. The last of the grand total of 11,461 Wellingtons produced at Chester, Blackpool and Weybridge was a Mk.X (T.Mk.X trainer conversion) built at Blackpool in October 1945. The Wellington was manufactured in greater numbers than any other British aircraft with the exception of the Spitfire and Hurricane. A contract which had been placed with the Blackpool factory for 300 Vickers Warwick aircraft, developments of the Wellington, was cancelled.

Today, the only surviving totally complete Wellington, a Blackpool-built Mk.X (MF 628) which first flew on 9 May 1944 and was converted to a T.Mk.X trainer by Messrs. Boulton Paul in 1948, is preserved on static display as part of the Bomber Command Collection at the RAF Museum, Hendon. The only other survivor is a Weybridge-built Mk.IA (N 2980) which participated in the disastrous raid on Wilhelmshaven on 18 December 1939. Of six No. 37 Squadron Wellingtons involved, it was the only one to return. Subsequently on the strength of No. 20 OTU, it was ditched in the waters of Loch Ness a year later. Raised from the bed in 1985 it has since been restored for display at the Brooklands Museum, parts of the

airframe left uncovered to show its geodetic structure.

F. Hills & Sons Ltd., Ringway and Barton

Following the requisition of Barton Aerodrome by MAP in September 1939, F.W. Hills & Sons relocated to Ringway, receiving around that time a contract to manufacture under licence 50 single-engined **Percival Proctor** navigational and radio trainers and light communications aircraft. Primarily of wooden construction, the three/four-seaters were built at Hills' Trafford Park factory and taken by road for assembly in a hangar initially shared with Avro at Ringway, where the first flew in December 1940.

The Ringway facilities were not ideal for Hills and after more than 70 aircraft had been assembled there, in 1941 the company returned to Barton where MAP had requisitioned further land and built two more hangars. Hills occupied one and David Rosenfield Ltd. the other. The latter, a subsidiary of the national firm of motor dealers, Henlys Ltd., was extensively involved in the Manchester area with subcontract work, modification, repair and refurbishment of over 300 aircraft including Battles, Fulmars, Hurricanes and Corsairs. 500 Avro Ansons were also overhauled at Barton by Air Taxis Ltd. Additional orders for the Proctor flowed in to Hills from the RAF and Fleet Air Arm. When they ceased production in September 1945, Hills had built 740 Proctors at Barton out of their total output of 812. After the war, production was reinstated at Luton by Percival Aircraft and the Proctor served

Opposite: Blackpool-built Wellington T.Mk.X trainer RP590 was the last of all the 11,461 Wellington bombers made at Weybridge, Chester and Blackpool. Here it overflies the camouflaged Squires Gate factory before being delivered to the RAF on 25 October 1945. Another Wellington is on the apron. The marquee and knot of spectators outside the nearer hangar suggest that the occasion was marked by some form of reception. *Photo: RAF Museum, Hendon, Charles Brown Collection.*

A civil Percival Proctor, generally similar to the military trainers built by F.W. Hills & Sons at Trafford Park, Ringway and Barton.

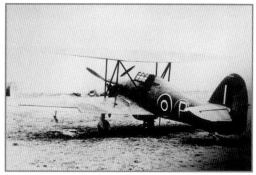

with the RAF until 1955.

In 1940, with work on the Proctor underway, Hills' Managing Director, W.R. Chown, developed an interest in fitting a monoplane with a jettisonable upper or 'slip' wing. The idea had been around since the 1920s, offering the potential to harness the additional lift of two wings at take-off, and in the climb, to an increased payload of armament and fuel. On reaching optimum altitude the upper wing would be released, the aircraft continuing its mission and returning to land as a monoplane. Moreover, it held out the prospect of application to small 'emergency' fighter aircraft capable of operating from a small field, airstrip or even a road. Hills designed an experimental 'demonstrator' aircraft known as the **Hillson Bi-mono** which they built at Trafford Park late in 1940 to be flight tested in both monoplane and biplane configuration from Barton early the following year. Using Squires Gate as its base, the first mechanically-released test of the upper wing of the 20 ft.-span aircraft was successfully made over the Irish Sea five miles off Blackpool on 16 July 1941.

The tests were sufficiently successful to justify the issue of an elderly Hawker Hurricane Mk.I fighter to Hills who, having modified it at Trafford Park and Barton by adding a 'slip' wing successfully air-tested it from RAF Sealand on 26 May 1943 as the **Hillson FH.40**. After further testing by the A&AEE at Boscombe Down it was deemed insufficiently practicable and too expensive for service.

Hills had carried out a most competent research and trials project with the 'slip' wing but their greater contribution to the war effort remained the volume production of Percival Proctors. When this ceased at the end of the war the company closed its Trafford Park factory. Several Proctors remain on the UK civil register and a Hills-built Barton example is today preserved on display at the Imperial War Museum, Duxford.

Rootes Securities Ltd., Speke

Having supplanted Hooton Park as Liverpool's official airport in 1933, Speke became one of the busiest centres of aviation in the North West during WW2. Used by the RAF from 1936, it was requisitioned as an operational airfield at the outbreak of hostilities. Service aircraft to be seen there over the next five years included Hampdens, Hudsons, Lysanders, Hurricanes and Sea Hurricanes, Spitfires and Seafires, Rocs, Skuas and Blenheims variously engaged on air defence of the Port of Liverpool, coastal reconnaissance and convoy protection in the approaches to Liverpool Bay. As a 'Scatter Scheme' station for aircraft dispersal and for general operational purposes, Speke was one of a group of North West RAF stations which included Hooton Park, Squires Gate, Cranage, Ringway and others. Speke also played a major role in the manufacture and assembly of British bomber aircraft and the assembly of many types of American aircraft from components imported via Liverpool.

After a site at White Waltham, Berkshire, had been ruled out, Rootes and the Air Ministry selected land on the periphery of Speke Airport, close to Merseyside's large centres of population and labour, for a large shadow factory of more than half a million sq.ft. for the manufacture initially of **Bristol Blenheim** bombers. Fully funded by the Government, site works and construction began in February 1937 and the factory was sufficiently advanced to begin production 13 months later. With the exception of Bristol Mercury engines which were brought from the Rootes-managed Bristol aero-engine shadow factory at Ryton-on-Dunsmore, Speke had full manufacturing facilities including milling and forming capacity and a foundry. Final assembly operations were underway by mid-1938 and the first Blenheim lifted off the grass airfield in October. Ambitious production targets required early extensions to the factory and additional premises in Speke were also requisitioned for airframe build, including a factory at Edwards Lane previously used as a training centre for the workforce. Four Bellman hangars were built on the airfield and work on the Blenheim Mk.V, initially known as the Bisley, was undertaken there, at RAF

Burtonwood and elsewhere. On 8 October 1940 three Hurricanes of No. 312 Squadron based at Speke were scrambled to intercept a Ju88 which was making a bombing run on the airfield's production facilities. Shot down, the German aircraft crash-landed at Bromborough. A total of 2,555 Blenheim Mks.I, IV and V, averaging 51 per month, was produced up to 1942. Various other factories in Liverpool contributed sub-assemblies. Dobson & Barlow Ltd., textile machinists of Bolton, Lancashire, reputedly built and supplied 6,065 pairs of Blenheim wings for use in final assembly by Bristol, Rootes and Avro. Rootes also established an associated plant producing Blenheims and Beaufighters at Blythe Bridge, some 50 miles away near Stoke-on-Trent.

A possibility that Rootes might also manufacture the Short Stirling bomber was overtaken by the advent of newer types of four-engined heavy bombers such as the Halifax and Lancaster. Just before cessation of work on the Blenheim, in September 1941 they received a Radlett-built Handley Page Halifax B.I as a pattern aircraft for large scale production. The first Speke-built Halifax flew from the airfield on 15 March 1942, the subsequent programme, together

Bristol Blenheim IV (V6083) built by Rootes Securities at Speke, Liverpool, in service here with No. 13 Operational Training Unit in the early summer of 1943.
Photo: Aeroplane.

with intensification of activity at the neighbouring No. 1 AAU (see below), requiring construction from mid-1942 of three hard surface runways to supersede the previous grass strips. Altogether 1,070 Halifaxes were made up to July 1945, comprising Mks.B.II, III and V bomber and meteorological aircraft with A.III and VII transport versions for use by airborne forces including glider towing. The factory also converted many bombers for reconnaissance and other uses.

Lockheed Overseas Corporation – British Reassembly Division – No. 1 Aircraft Assembly Unit, Speke

In 1938 the British Purchasing Committee placed an order for up to 250 Hudson maritime reconnaissance and patrol bombers with the Lockheed Corporation of America. Shipments started to arrive at the Port of Liverpool in February 1939 by when it had been decided that, given the unfamiliar tooling and American threading, reassembly would be more efficiently undertaken by the manufacturers themselves. Accordingly the Lockheed Overseas Corporation took over an existing large hangar at Speke Airport, supplemented by two further Bellman hangars later in 1939, the total facility becoming known as the British Reassembly Division. The Hudson became the first American aircraft to be operated by the RAF in WW2. Logic determined that Lockheed's assembly arrangements at Speke should also cater for aircraft supplied by other US manufacturers, beginning in 1940 with the Douglas Boston. Following the establishment of MAP in 1940 the entire operation was re-designated as No. 1 Aircraft Assembly Unit (AAU). Other types assembled included Lockheed P-38 Lightnings and Venturas, Republic P-47 Thunderbolts, North American P-51 Mustangs, Harvards and, in 1944, Northrop P-61 Black Widows. Among the thousands of aircraft, precise numbers of which are

not documented, that passed through Speke were also many less well-known types. The aircraft unloaded at Liverpool were towed along the public highway, either on their own wheels or on trailers, for final assembly at Speke, Hooton Park or Burtonwood. An essential part of the process was the de-greasing of aero-engines and removal of the coats of rubberised *Para-al-tone* applied to airframes in the USA to protect them from seawater corrosion, particularly when carried as deck cargo. Thousands of aircraft for the RAF, FAA and USAAF were processed, those assembled at Speke and Hooton Park usually to be flown to USAAF (BAD 1) at Burtonwood or BAD 2 at Warton for final checks and modifications (see below). W.H. Moss, founder of the Mosscraft light aircraft company at Chorley and his brother Geoffrey were both Chief Test Pilots for Lockheed at Speke during the war. In addition the Rootes factory at Speke also overhauled 2,690 fighters for the USAAF under contracts with Lockheed who themselves continued operations into 1946 with the conversion of B-24 Liberator bombers into stop-gap transports for the RAF. The original Speke Airport of 1933, with art deco terminal buildings and control tower, made additionally famous to many as the backdrop for return journeys to Liverpool by the Beatles and the Liverpool football team during the 1960s-'80s, closed on 29 August 2000. Today, the adjacent Liverpool John Lennon Airport to the south east continues to provide the city with an expanding regional and international passenger and freight air facility.

Martin Hearn Ltd. – No. 7 Aircraft Assembly Unit, Hooton Park

Hooton Park Aerodrome, home to the pre-war aircraft engineering and general aviation business of the Martin Hearn Company, also became an RAF station at the beginning of the war. Operations included the use of Ansons on anti-submarine patrol over the Irish Sea and Bothas for radio training, whilst No. 48 MU was established there later for storage of Halifaxes and Mosquitoes. Hearn's company secured contracts for maintenance, overhaul and repair of Ansons, Spitfires and Mosquitoes and after contracting to assemble 80 Hampden bombers made in Canada, Hooton Park was designated No. 7 Aircraft Assembly Unit (AAU). The redoubtable Major James Cordes, from 1933 Handley Page's Chief Test Pilot, had vast experience of the Hampden and in 1941 took charge of assembly at No. 7 AAU. His reputation amongst the staff as the 'Mad Major' was reinforced by his 'looping' of a Hampden at Hooton Park. The story is told that when he asked visiting representatives of the Douglas Aircraft Corporation of the USA whether they had looped their A-20 Boston bomber, also later to be assembled at Hooton Park, they turned rather pale. No. 7 AAU went on to assemble a large and varied range of American aircraft unloaded at Hooton from the Manchester Ship Canal or towed there by road from the Port of Liverpool. These included Bostons, Thunderbolts, Harvards and in 1944 a number of early Sikorsky R-4B Hoverfly two-seater helicopters. Major Cordes was issued with Helicopter Certificate No. 2 to enable him to test fly the first of these, reputedly the UK's first helicopter flight. Wartime assembly and repair at Hooton Park has been estimated as totalling some 10,000 aircraft. After the war Hearn built over 70 Slingsby wooden sailplanes including Kirby Kites, Cadets, Tutors, Motor Tutors and Sedberghs. His successor company at Hooton Park, Aero & Engineering (Merseyside) Ltd., also later supplied de Havilland at Chester with components for Chipmunk and Comet production. Together with Airwork General Trading at Speke and Ringway, in the mid-1950s A&E (M) Ltd. provided

aviation maintenance, overhaul and repair services for aircraft including large numbers of Canadair Sabre jet fighters and some Lockheed T-33 Shooting and Silver Stars. Hooton Park Aerodrome closed in 1957 and in 1962 much of the land was acquired by Vauxhall Motors.

Martin Hearn Ltd. – No. 1 Packed Aircraft Transit Pool, Hesketh Park

In conjunction with No. 7 AAU at Hooton Park, Hearn's activities also extended to Hesketh Park Aerodrome, adjoining Southport Sands, where a large new hangar was built next to two dating from the 1914-18 war. Between the wars and post-1945 until the mid '60s, the Hesketh Park facilities were used by the Royal Flying Corps veteran pilot Norman Giroux, who in 1920 established the Giro Aviation Company providing air services and pleasure flights along the coast. Much of Hearn's wartime maintenance and repair work was carried out there by over 200 people, including assembly and flight testing of aircraft repaired at Speke. Nearly 1,000 Ansons, Spitfires, Mosquitoes, Albacores, Martinets and Waco gliders passed through their hands before work ceased in May 1946. Hearn operated these services as the No. 1 Packed Aircraft Transit Pool at Hesketh Park with a depot at Birkdale. RAF Woodvale, established between Southport and Formby in 1941 as an all-weather fighter station to bolster the air defences of Liverpool and the North West, was also used for nearby storage of crated aircraft repaired at Speke awaiting transit to Hesketh Park for reassembly.

USAAF Base Air Depot (BAD) 1, RAF Burtonwood

Burtonwood Airfield, on the north west side of Warrington, was opened in April 1940 to serve an Aircraft Storage Unit, Aircraft and Aero-engine Repair Depot, and No. 37 Maintenance Unit (MU) of the RAF, build-up of which had commenced on site during 1939. In broad terms these facilities were responsible for the final preparation and storage of aircraft received from the manufacturers prior to their delivery to RAF squadrons for operational use. In 1940 the Burtonwood Repair Depot (BRD) employing 4,000 people was civilian-managed by the Fairey Aviation Co., with the later involvement also of the Rolls-Royce, Rootes, Bristol and Rover companies, dealing initially with the supply of both American and British-built aircraft. Among these, in 1940 No. 37 MU processed some of the Spitfires – aircraft constructed outside the North West – which fought in the Battle of Britain. Even before America's entry into the war, in the spring of 1941 a search was instigated in the strategically safer North to identify sites for air depots to facilitate the assembly of US aircraft being imported into Britain. Burtonwood, together with land at Warton between Preston and Lytham St. Anne's, then recently brought into use as a satellite airfield for RAF Squires Gate and where runways were under construction, were selected for further development.

Despite its remaining officially RAF Burtonwood, an agreement of May 1942 paved the way for relinquishing control of the entire site to the US 8th Air Force following a period of joint Anglo-American operation which ended in October 1943. Initially designated Base Air Depot (BAD) 1 as the central maintenance establishment for the US 8th Air Force in Britain, from 1943 it was the HQ of Base Air Depot Area (BADA), controlling all maintenance and support throughout the UK, including BAD 2 at Warton and BAD 3 at Langford Lodge, Northern Ireland. Ultimately, Burtonwood's responsibility extended to maintenance of all the aircraft of the US 8th, 9th, 12th and 15th Air Forces operational throughout the UK, Europe, the Mediterranean and the Middle East. In the North West of England BADA controlled satellite bases at Liverpool Docks, Knowsley

Park, Kirkby, Aintree, Haydock Park, Bruche Hall and Poynton.

Burtonwood was the largest military establishment in Europe during WW2. It had a foundry capable of casting engine blocks, a fabrication department able to manufacture any part or component, with milling machines, shapers, planers, cutting machinery, welding, brazing and electrical facilities. With over four million square feet of covered floorspace at their disposal, up to 18,500 American personnel assembled, modified or repaired over 20 types of US military aircraft between 1943 and 1945. The total of 11,575 aircraft included 4,243 B-17 Flying Fortresses flown in from America sometimes at up to 50 per day, 4,381 P-47 Thunderbolts, 1,004 P-38 Lightnings and 694 B-24 Liberators. Burtonwood also overhauled more than 30,000 aero-engines, mostly Wright Double-Wasp radials, peaking in 1944 at over 2,000 units a month involving 30 engine testing bays running continuously round-the-clock.

Many aircraft unloaded at Liverpool were towed through the city, single-engined examples on tractor-drawn trailers, larger twin-engined on their own wheels as wingless centre-sections and fuselages, for assembly at Speke or Burtonwood. P-47s and P-38s assembled at Speke were flown to Burtonwood for final pre-delivery checks and adjustments. P-51s were flown from Speke to BAD 2 at Warton. After the war, Burtonwood's tremendous capacity guaranteed it a major role in the Berlin Airlift of 1948-49, including carrying out 200-hour-interval servicing on all 309 USAF C-54 Skymasters involved. The build up of American strength in Europe during the early years of the Cold War demanded further expansion of the Burtonwood Air Base as the principal US transit, storage, overhaul and repair facility. During 1951 work began on almost doubling the length of its main east-west runway to 9,000 ft., enabling it to cope with some of the largest and heaviest bombers and transports, and fastest fighters, of the day. On occasions these included the nuclear bomber colossus of USAF Strategic Air Command, the 200-ton ten-engined piston and turbojet 'six turnin', four burnin' ' Convair B-36. RAF 'V'-bombers also used Burtonwood as a dispersal location. But by the late 1950s, as other US air bases in Britain became increasingly self-sufficient, it was apparent that Burtonwood's days were numbered. The progressive withdrawal of the USAF from the site was completed in 1965. Proposals to develop it as a new international civil airport for the North West were not taken forward, major investment taking place instead at Manchester and Liverpool airports. In fact, much of Burtonwood's 1.7-mile runway had started to show the effects of subsidence due to previous eras of coal mining in the area. When, between 1971 and 1973, the M62 South Lancashire Motorway was built, it was decided to incorporate the greater part of the then disused runway beneath the carriageway. It is a salutary thought that some six feet beneath the wheels of today's motorway traffic lies another surface along which, during the Second World War, the Berlin Airlift and the Cold War, ran the wheels of thousands of the most awe-inspiring aircraft in the world.

USAAF Base Air Depot (BAD) 2, RAF Warton

Progress with the air depots gained further impetus following America's entry into the war on 7 December 1941. Work on extending Warton's runways and reinforcing them for use by heavy aircraft began in mid-1942 and the first US personnel arrived in July. They and the thousands that followed were particularly impressed with the attractions of nearby Blackpool, if not always the weather. Short of returning home, it was the nearest they would get to Coney Island or Atlantic City.

RAF Warton was officially handed over to the USAAF in July 1943 to be designated Base Air Depot (BAD) 2 and became the largest American maintenance base in Europe after Burtonwood. Further strengthening of runways and rebuilding of perimeter tracks took place together with construction of engine test beds alongside the River Ribble. At peak nearly 15,000 personnel were on site. Between 1943 and 1945 BAD 2 assembled, repaired or modified 10,068 aircraft including 4,372 P-51 Mustangs, 2,894 B-24 Liberators and 711 A-26 Invaders. Paratroop-carrying Waco CG4A 'Hadrian' gliders were also assembled on the airfield to be 'snatch-lifted' into the air by overflying cable-equipped C-47 transports. As with Burtonwood, these figures do not include a further 4,000 aircraft handled purely for inspection purposes. With Burtonwood responsible for radial engines, Warton specialised in water-cooled in-line units, repairing and overhauling 3,578 Packard Merlin and 2,586 Allison aero-engines. Unlike Burtonwood, Warton closed as a USAAF base at the end of the war, reverting to the RAF who used it as a storage facility for No. 90 MU.

Short Bros. Ltd., Windermere

When English Electric closed down aircraft work at Preston and Lytham in 1926, apart from Blackburn Aircraft Ltd. at Brough on Humberside flying boat manufacturing became increasingly concentrated in the South of England. The Lancashire factories had built 70 Felixstowes and Kingstons but afterwards flying boat production was largely the preserve of Short Brothers at Rochester on the Medway, Supermarine and Saunders-Roe on the Solent. The Supermarine Southampton, Stranraer and Short Singapore became the RAF's standard large, long-range biplane flying boats of the inter-war years.

In 1933, hard on the heels of an Air

Ministry specification for a new, four-engined long-range flying boat came an urgent request from Imperial Airways for a civil version for use on Empire air routes. Short Brothers took both forward together, but giving greater priority to the Empire boat. After seeing the new American DC-2 airliner in 1934, Oswald Short, designer Arthur Gouge and test pilot John Lankester Parker decided to adopt a monoplane design. The resulting all-metal Short S.23 of 1936, with single mainplane spanning 114 ft., commodious fuselage and 200 mph performance revolutionised the large flying boat. Imperial Airways immediately ordered 28 for use on Empire mail routes and for passenger services to the Middle and Far East, Australia, Africa, the West Indies and New York.

For the military requirement Short Brothers drew up the S.25 to be named the **Short Sunderland**, based closely on the Empire boat with which it shared a marked family resemblance. Significantly different was the incorporation of gun turrets, power-operated for the first time in a flying boat of British design. The Sunderland prototype was flown from the Medway by J.L. Parker on 16 October 1937. One of the world's most experienced flying boat and seaplane pilots, in 1915 Parker had joined the Northern Flying Company at Lake Windermere as a newly qualified aviator keen to learn the art of flying off water. After serving as an instructor, in 1916 he left to join Short Brothers as a test pilot under Ronald Kemp, himself a former Windermere flyer. Oscar Gnosspelius, the pioneer of water-borne flight at Windermere, also worked in Short's experimental department at Rochester between 1919 and 1925 and remained connected with the company thereafter. Shorts had some close links with Windermere.

The tight confines of Short Brothers' Rochester factory and its potential vulnerability to air attack meant that additional production capacity had to be located elsewhere. In 1936 the Government constructed a large new factory for Shorts adjacent to the Harland & Wolff shipyard at Belfast, together with an airfield which today is Belfast City Airport. Several types of aircraft were built there, including the Sunderland's heavy bomber sibling, the Short Stirling. Actual production of the Sunderland did not start at Belfast until April 1942. When both the Rochester and Belfast factories were bombed in 1940, with the U-boat threat also demanding urgent expansion of Sunderland production, Blackburn Aircraft Ltd. were contracted to establish a Sunderland line at a factory they operated with Denny Brothers of the Dumbarton shipyard on Clydeside. It was also decided in 1940 that yet another factory would be required to further augment production. The MAP indicated that following a thorough search of sites, including Lytham where there were problems of mud flats, the need for access to deep water had dictated the choice of a location near Troutbeck Bridge on the east side of Lake Windermere between the towns of Windermere and Ambleside.

The decision faced immediate opposition from the Friends of the Lake District who, describing it as 'an abomination in such a beautiful area', exacted an agreement from the Government that the factory would be closed, taken down and the site restored to its original uses at the end of the war. From an operational point of view the location was secluded, well away from the main centres of German bombing and alongside the deep waters of Windermere, England's largest and, at 21 miles, longest lake. Moreover, it lay little more than 100 miles across the Irish Sea from Shorts' Belfast factory, in surroundings familiar to J.L. Parker, with the local knowledge of Oscar Gnosspelius also available for the setting up stages.

Opposite:
Prototype Short Sunderland Mk.III flying boat T9042, converted from a Rochester-built Mk.I, makes its first flight from the River Medway on 28 June 1941 in the hands of J.L. Parker. 35 similar Mk.IIIs were built at Windermere 1942-44. In 1942 *Coastal Command* made by the Crown Film Unit captured superbly an Atlantic operation involving Sunderlands, most notably Mk.I P9606 built at Rochester.

Site works and construction proceeded among 28 acres of farmland and woods adjacent to Calgarth Park, involving laying 15 ft. concrete base foundations in the marshy ground by the lakeside, together with a concrete slipway to the waters of White Cross Bay. The two principal buildings comprised a Detail Shop and Assembly Building, the latter 70 feet high to the apex with 40 ft. doors. It was reputed to be the largest single span building in the country. 243 pre-fabricated bungalows and hostels were erected at Troutbeck Bridge to accommodate a labour force of over 1,500, many of whom were drafted in from aircraft and other factories including Shorts at Rochester, Faireys at Manchester, Vickers

at Barrow-in-Furness and Austin Motors in the Midlands. The factory was under the overall direction of Oswald Short's son, Francis.

Operational within a year of the start of construction, manufacturing of small parts and aircraft assembly all took place initially in the Detail Shop before the jigs were transferred to the Assembly Building. The latter could accommodate Sunderlands alongside each other under the massive roof span. Significant manufacturing in the Detail Shop involved cutting and milling machinery for production of wing spars and other wing components. These were taken to Rochester to be jigged into complete wings which were then returned

Top left:
The first Sunderland Mk.III completed at Windermere, DP176, awaiting launch at White Cross Bay before being flown to Pembroke Dock by J.L. Parker, September 1942.
Photo: via A. King.

Top right:
Production of Sunderlands in their later white and grey camouflage inside the giant Shorts factory at White Cross Bay. Just visible is the Slingsby Falcon 2 glider converted into a flying boat at the factory.
Photo: via A. King.

Bottom:
Another view showing the vast scale of a Sunderland flying boat erecting shop, this one probably at Shorts' factory at Belfast.

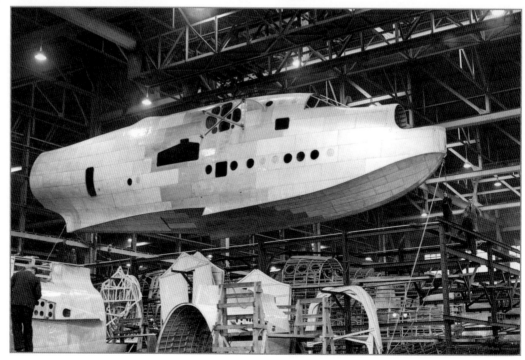

to Windermere for final assembly of the aircraft. Other parts, including floats, were contracted out. The Sunderland's aluminium keel was laid on large girder jigs and the complete aircraft built up to receive wing and tail, the latter erected on a separate jig nearby. All processes generated a massive cacophony of riveting. Following installation of the four Bristol Pegasus radial engines, fuel-flow and engine running tests, the complete aircraft were rolled down the slipway on their beaching gear to the lake.

The first aircraft to be completed, Sunderland III DP176, was flown from Windermere to Pembroke Dock by J.L. Parker in September 1942. Comfortably exceeding the initial target to complete three aircraft every two months, a total of 35 new Sunderland IIIs was assembled between then and May 1944, some to be flown to the somewhat bleaker surroundings of No. 57 MU at Wig Bay, Loch Ryan, near Stranraer for fitting out with navigational radio, radar and all manner of military stores and equipment prior to delivery to their units. Wig Bay was little more than 30 miles across the North Channel of the Irish Sea from Shorts' Belfast factory. The Sunderland III was distinguished by an improved planing surface to its hull which, as on all flying boats, had to achieve a compromise between aerodynamic and hydrodynamic efficiency in the air and on water. It was a formidable aircraft, carrying 2,000lb of bombs, depth charges and mines with numerous dorsal and under-wing ASV radar protuberances. Despite the size and bulk of the 30-ton, ten-crew flying boat, eight or more trainable machine guns in various positions around the aircraft made it a risky target for Luftwaffe fighters to engage. That was provided the Sunderland descended to wave-top height when under attack to avoid presenting its vulnerable hull and underside. After shooting down two out of six Ju 88s on one occasion and

three out of eight on another, the Sunderland's armament earned it the German nickname 'Fliegende Stachelswein' or 'Flying Porcupine'.

When in 1944 the Windermere factory was visited by Sir Stafford Cripps, Minister of Aircraft Production, he announced the cessation of new aircraft production, the plant being redesignated as a repair facility. Sunderlands were then flown in for heavy repairs and overhaul, still bearing the grim evidence of both external and internal battle damage sustained by aircraft and crew alike. Ten Sunderland IIIs were converted to Mk.Vs with more powerful Pratt & Whitney Twin Wasp engines, radar and armament. Seven Mk.IIIs still awaiting conversion at the end of the war were flown away to Belfast and elsewhere and an estimated five declared uneconomic to repair were broken up at Windermere in 1944.

One of the last events to take place at the Windermere works was a visit by one of two prototype Short Shetland flying boats, flown from Rochester by test pilot Geoffrey Tyson on 13 January 1945. The 150 ft.-wingspan 60-ton leviathan, a collaborative venture between Shorts and Saunders-Roe, was the largest aircraft ever to alight and take off from Windermere. Of all the facilities around the country, Shorts' Assembly Building was the only one capable of accommodating it under cover for purposes of accurate weighing. The Shetland never entered full production.

One other aircraft was turned out from the Windermere works. A privately-owned Slingsby Falcon 2 glider was modified by fitting a hull, enabling it to take off from the Lake under tow. It is today preserved at the Windermere Steamboat Museum.

Sunderlands made at Windermere saw action in the Battle of the Atlantic and one, EJ150 of No. 201 Squadron based at Castle Archdale in Northern Ireland, sank a German U-boat in the Bay of Biscay in

Sunderland
Mk.III EJ164, built
by Shorts at
Belfast, shows
the white and
grey colour
scheme also
applied to later
production
Mk.IIIs made at
Windermere.

Sunderland Mk.III EJ164, built by Shorts at Belfast, shows the white and grey colour scheme also applied to later production Mk.IIIs made at Windermere.

August 1944. After the war, in 1948 RAF Sunderlands played an important role in the Berlin Airlift, their anti-corrosion treatment enabling them to be used, amongst other duties, for bulk transport of salt to the Havel Lake on the outskirts of the city. In the Far East, in April 1949, when the frigate HMS *Amethyst* became trapped after running aground on the Yangtze River under the guns of the Chinese Communists, Rochester-built Sunderland ML772 of No. 88 Squadron at Kai Tak, Hong Kong, made a number of landings under fire to deliver personnel and supplies. As a result, in July the frigate made good its escape under cover of darkness. On regaining the East China Sea, its Captain, Lt.-Cmdr. John Kerans, was able to issue the order for his classic signal: 'Make from *Amethyst* to Admiralty: "Have rejoined the Fleet south of Woo Sung. No damage or casualties. God Save The King."' Windermere Sunderland DP199, also of No. 88 Sqn., supported evacuation flights out of Shanghai. Her sister ship, DP198 of No. 205/209 Sqn., on RAF charge from 1944 to 1959, was the longest serving of all 749 Sunderlands built. Based at Seletar,

Singapore, DP198 flew the last operational flight of an RAF Sunderland in May 1959.

After the war, around 1949, when the Windermere factory was removed, the concrete foundations and slipway were found to be so massively embedded that they were allowed to remain and today provide hardstanding for a caravan park and boat launching. The Detail Shop was dismantled and re-erected at Newcastle-upon-Tyne where it remains currently in use as a Stagecoach bus depot. The Assembly Building was re-erected for use as a chemical factory on Merseyside but later demolished. Ever since the closure of the Windermere works rumours have persisted of one or more Sunderlands having been scuttled to the lake bed as redundant or beyond economic repair. No categorical evidence exists although, at 200 feet, Windermere is at its deepest off White Cross Bay...

Evoking the events of 1942-45 was the alighting, after an absence of 45 years, of a Sunderland on Windermere in June 1990. The visit to White Cross Bay, as part of the Windermere Festival, was by an aircraft

Edward Hulton's civilianised Sunderland Mk.V G-BJHS *Islander* (ex-ML814) rides at her moorings at White Cross Bay during the Windermere Festival, June 1990.

Sunderland Mk.V G-BJHS *Islander.* *Photo: J. Loader.*

Sunderland
Mk.V *Islander*
thunders down
Windermere on
her departure,
June 1990.
Photo: J. Loader.

then owned by the publisher Edward
Hulton. Built as a Mk.III at Belfast in 1944,
subsequently converted to a Mk.V and
civilianised for post-war passenger use in

various parts of the world, it attracted
considerable attention. Today it resides at
Kermit Weekes' 'Fantasy of Flight' museum
in Florida, USA.

The Second World War had seen
unprecedented production of munitions,
particularly aircraft. The precise numbers
made are notoriously difficult to
determine for purposes of standard
comparison. But available information
indicates that the North West
manufactured some 30,000 during the
war, including its immediate prelude and
aftermath. At least as many again, maybe
another 40,000, were also assembled at
centres such as Speke, Hooton Park,
Burtonwood and Warton from sets
imported under Lend-Lease from the
USA, or otherwise modified or repaired.
The figure of 30,000 represents some 23
per cent of the sometimes-quoted
wartime grand total of 133,000 aircraft
reputedly built from scratch throughout

the UK as a whole, of which the RAF
and Fleet Air Arm retained nearly 40,000
on charge at the war's end including
some 10,500 front line fighters and
bombers. It is remarkable testimony to
the capacity of the indigenous aircraft
industry in the North West in 1939,
subsequent expansion schemes and the
phenomenal success of the shadow
factory programme in the region. Nor
must the strategic importance of the
Port of Liverpool to the air war in
Europe and elsewhere be forgotten:
well over 70,000 aircraft of all types are
reputed to have entered Britain from
across the Atlantic via the Mersey Docks,
to be assembled in other parts of the
country as well as the North West.

Chapter 6
Post-war – 1945 to the present day

Ushering in the Jet Age and Intercontinental Civil Aviation

Of the 30,000 aircraft made in Lancashire and the North West in response to the demands of the Second World War, just six were jet-propelled. They were the D.H.100 Vampire fighters built by English Electric at Preston and Samlesbury between late 1944 and the end of the war in Europe in May 1945. The six Vampires were the advance guard of a technological revolution set to transform the industry. But, whilst the military requirements of the Cold War would continue to drive a large sector of the region's aircraft industry beyond 1950, so also would the potential for growth in civil air transport as the UK sought to regain ground lost to the USA in the development and production of large transport aircraft.

With the advent of the jet engine WW2 saw the speed of fighter aircraft virtually double from 300 to nearly 600mph. Only aerodynamics, notably wing design, stood in the way of further advances. Well before the swept-back wing became the standard means of reducing compressibility drag, only German designers had given it serious attention. Thanks largely to technology acquired during the overrun of Germany, both the USA and USSR had swept-wing fighters – the F-86 Sabre and MiG-15 – in service from 1949. Astonishingly it would be a full five years later, in 1954, before the RAF got its own first British-built[1] swept-wing jet fighter, albeit the disappointing Vickers-Supermarine Swift. Fortunately the Swift was followed within months by the supremely successful Hawker Hunter.

Back in October 1941 the British Government had obligingly sent a Whittle centrifugal jet engine to the General Electric Company in the USA, facilitating the establishment of the American turbojet industry. Another gift followed in 1943 in the shape of a Halford H.1 engine (later to become the de Havilland Goblin) for installation in Lockheed's YP-80A Shooting Star fighter. Better resourced and organised than that of Britain, America's jet engine industry pulled ahead and by mid-1944 GE had engines of 4,000lb thrust under test. In return America sent Britain a pair of GE-powered YP-80As which were assembled at Burtonwood in December. At Rolls-Royce, Chief Engineer Stanley Hooker was determined that Britain should regain its lead and had run his superb 5,000lb-thrust Nene engine at Barnoldswick in October. When fitted experimentally in one of the YP-80As in the summer of 1945, the combination proved so successful that Pratt & Whitney entered into licensed production of the Nene in the USA in 1946.

That year, in the face of American opposition, in Britain the Attlee Government agreed to sell 25 Nene and 30 Derwent turbojets to the USSR. Although nowadays often reviled as a strategically crass decision, in 1946 the Berlin and Korean crises were not foreseen, Britain was virtually bankrupt and starved of cash, food, raw materials and

---

[1] Between 1953 and 1956, to redress the air superiority of the MiG-15 in Europe, with financial aid from the US and Canada the RAF had the use of 425 Canadian-built CL-13 (F-86E) Sabres which were flown across the Atlantic.

trading opportunities with a need for massive investment in social infrastructure. Unfortunately for the Western Powers however, one of the Nenes was used to power the prototype MiG-15 and, unlicensed, the engines were subsequently produced in large numbers by Klimov, establishing the USSR's jet engine industry. The Russians even had the nerve to license production of their Nene copies to China. Any hopes in Britain for reciprocal access to Russo-German technology were soon dashed. Technology exchange remained distinctly one-sided and, if one of the purposes had been to engender good relations with the Soviets, at the time it did little for those with America.

On the outbreak of the Korean War across the 38th Parallel in June 1950, Britain and Australia had to pitch the piston-engined Sea Fury and straight-wing Meteor jet, both essentially WW2 aircraft, against the excellent swept-wing MiG-15. Little wonder that a seasonal drinking song popular amongst Commonwealth pilots that year was "All I want for Christmas is my wings swept back!". Although the older aircraft acquitted themselves remarkably well, it remained for the F-86 Sabre to redress the balance. At least it rang the necessary alarm bells and in 1951 a new British Government with Churchill once again at the helm undertook an urgent assessment of the country's military forces. Much of Britain's aircraft manufacturing capacity had been reduced and its wartime labour force dispersed, although the 27 separate companies that still comprised the industry remained beavering away in the background generating a multiplicity of competing designs. A proliferation of short-lived research, prototype and one-off aircraft characterised the annual Farnborough Air Shows from 1948. The urgent need to rationalise, restructure and increase the efficiency of Britain's aircraft industry was swept under the carpet as something to be dealt with in the future.

Fairey Aviation Company Ltd., Heaton Chapel and Ringway

Fairey ended the war having produced nearly 4,000 Battle, Fulmar, Barracuda, Beaufighter and Halifax aircraft at Heaton Chapel, Errwood Park and Ringway. They had overhauled and repaired some 2,000 others, having also managed the Burtonwood Repair Depot from 1940-43. In the inevitable post-war contraction, the 500,000 sq.ft. Errwood Park plant reverted to the Board of Trade, subsequently to be reoccupied by Crossley Motors for manufacture of buses in a restructuring which included the closure of Crossleys' old-established Gorton, Manchester works in 1946.

Production and development work on the Fairey Barracuda at the Heaton Chapel factory continued well into 1947. Four years earlier, a two-seat dive and torpedo bomber replacement had been called for, to which Fairey had responded with designs for the **Spearfish**. With wingspan and length of 60 ft. and 44 ft. respectively, an all-up weight of nearly 22,000lb and powered by a 2,470hp Bristol Centaurus 58 radial engine turning a 14 ft.-diameter five-bladed propeller, the Spearfish was one of the largest and heaviest single-engined aircraft ever made. The first of five prototypes took to the air on 5 July 1945 and was a handful to fly. Soon deemed unnecessary, proposals to manufacture 152 at Heaton Chapel were abandoned.

Fairey's next Heaton Chapel product, which could not have been in greater contrast, was an experimental aircraft which emerged from a research exercise into German wartime ideas for the use of delta configurations in rocket-boosted VTOL aircraft and guided missiles. Known as the **Fairey Delta FD1**, powered by a Rolls-Royce Derwent 8 turbojet, it was the company's first venture into jet propulsion. The FD1 was distinguished by the use of delta planforms for all its flying surfaces, including a wing spanning only 19½ ft., a delta fin and fixed tailplane with marked rear overhang. With a short, rotund fuselage it was a veritable 'flying barrel'. Work began on three airframes at Heaton Chapel in 1948, but only one was completed, in spring 1950. At around that time, reflecting post-war downturn in aircraft work, Fairey's employment in the North West had slumped from 16,000 to 2,700.

Taxiing trials were carried out in May 1950 at Ringway by test pilots Gordon Slade and Peter Twiss, who had joined the company after war service. Early in 1951 the FD1 was dismantled for transport to the A&AEE at Boscombe Down where it was first flown by Slade in March. The aerodynamics of this curiously dumpy, diminutive aircraft required large control surfaces which made it sensitive to handle, leading to its description by Twiss as "a dicey little box". Initial problems of oscillation at low speed delayed its further use but, after modifications, the FD1 made a useful contribution to research into delta wingform. Demonstrated at Farnborough in 1954 it was rendered unusable after a landing accident in 1956.

The FD1 is probably best remembered as the research aircraft that preceded the contrastingly elegant **Fairey Delta FD2**. The FD2 was built at Fairey's Hayes plant, incorporating sub-assemblies made at Heaton Chapel. In the hands of Peter Twiss it became the first aircraft to set a world speed record of over 1,000mph when it attained 1,132mph off the Sussex coast on 10 March 1956. Converted as the BAC 221 it later pioneered the combination of 'droop snoot' articulating nose and delta wing technology used in Concorde.

Fairey's retention of extensive hangar and assembly sheds at Ringway proved a useful asset after the war. When production of the **D.H.100 Vampire** jet fighter by English Electric at Preston and Samlesbury ceased in 1952, continuing demand for later versions gave Fairey the opportunity to build 67 FB.Mk.9 versions during 1952-53. These were followed by 30 D.H.115 two-seat Vampire Trainers in 1954-55. De Havilland had introduced a more powerful development in 1949, the Ghost-powered **D.H.112 Venom**. Similar in overall configuration, the Venom had recognisably different wings fitted with 75-gallon combat-jettisonable fuel tanks at the tips. At Ringway between 1953-56 Fairey built 37 Venom FB.Mk.1 fighter bombers and NF.Mk.51 night fighters, the latter for the Royal Swedish Air Force by whom they were designated J.33s. Fairey's Heaton Chapel works also supplied de Havilland's own production line at Chester, acquired from Vickers-Armstrongs in 1948, with many Vampire fuselages. Both Vampire and Venom saw service in the Suez Crisis of 1958.

In 1952 Fairey transferred new build of the **Fairey Firefly Mk.7** from Hayes to Heaton Chapel and between then and 1956, concurrently with work on the Ringway jets, the company produced 75 Firefly T.Mk.7 ASW two-seat advanced trainers and U.Mk.8/9 pilotless target drones. The Firefly was no stranger to Fairey's northern factories. After the war large numbers of Hayes-built examples had been overhauled and modified from combat aircraft to trainers and target tugs. The first Firefly T.1 trainer, converted from a Mk.1, flew at Ringway in 1946. The Firefly was originally designed as a carrier-borne reconnaissance fighter developed from the Fulmar. Powered by the 1,750-2,000+ hp Rolls-Royce Griffon engine, developing twice the output of the Fulmar's Merlin, it first flew in 1941 and entered service in 1943. It was very ruggedly built, of tubular steel alloy-clad structure with folding wings fitted with Fairey-Youngman flaps for excellent slow-flying performance essential for deck landing. Nine variants gave 13 years' service as fighters, night fighters, anti-submarine and strike aircraft, trainers, target tugs and pilotless radio-controlled target drones used in the development of Firestreak and Seaslug missile systems. They saw active service against the *Tirpitz* in Norway, Japanese oil refineries in Sumatra, in Korea and Malaya. A total of 1,702 of all types were built, the great majority at Hayes.

Fairey secured important contracts for service, overhaul and modification of a variety of aircraft made by themselves and others including Avro Yorks used in the Berlin Airlift and D.H. Mosquitoes for export markets. Between 1955-57 they carried out IRAN (Inspect, Repair as Necessary) contracts for 96 USAF Douglas B-26 Invaders. On their withdrawal from Europe where they were replaced by American licence-built Martin B-57 Canberras, the Invaders were inspected at Ringway for serviceability prior to their return flight across the North Atlantic.

A 1945 specification for a carrier-borne anti-submarine attack aircraft attracted proposals from Fairey, Blackburn and Shorts. Fairey achieved success with a design using an Armstrong Siddeley Double Mamba coupled turboprop engine turning two contra-rotating propellers in tandem. The engine configuration offered the power of two engines whilst eliminating asymmetric torque, with the economy of one when the other was disengaged for cruising. The resulting Fairey 17, later named the **Gannet**, was a large 54 ft.-span attractively fully-figured aircraft which first flew at Aldermaston in 1949. The prototype became the first turboprop to land on an aircraft carrier when trials commenced with HMS *Illustrious*.

In production at Hayes from 1953, Gannet AS.Mk.1s entered Fleet Air Arm service the following year, replacing Firefly and Grumman Avenger aircraft. The Mk.1 was superseded by the AS.Mk.4 with a more powerful version of the Double Mamba and other modifications. Trainer versions were built of both. In 1957 the

need to replace the Fleet Air Arm's ageing Douglas Skyraider early warning aircraft was met by the Gannet AEW.Mk.3 featuring a redesigned fuselage with large front radome 'chin'. Serving from 1960 to 1978, the withdrawal of the last of these created a gap in naval defences shockingly demonstrated by the vulnerability of surface ships to air attack during the Falklands Conflict in 1982. Out of a total build of some 356 Gannets of all types, Fairey built 102 AS.Mks.1/4 at Heaton Chapel between 1954-58.

The 1950s saw Fairey diversifying into non-aircraft work notably nuclear engineering. In 1957, jointly with Ferranti, Fairey produced the world's first CNC 3D milling machine. A major reorganisation of 1959 created the Fairey Company Ltd. as a holding company of subsidiaries including Fairey Aviation, Fairey Engineering and Fairey Hydraulics. Much of the work on production of the Fairey Fireflash air-to-air missile took place at Heaton Chapel. Ringway manufactured modification parts and undertook final assembly of 29 out of 34 **Jindivik Mk.102B** jet-propelled target drones made by the Australian Government Aircraft Factory at Melbourne, including installation of the Bristol Siddeley Viper 8 turbojets, autopilot and electronic controls. Power control systems were made for Trident, Harrier, Jaguar and Tornado aircraft.

Following work on the Fairey Gyrodyne and Rotodyne rotating wing aircraft at Hayes, with Heaton Chapel supplying sub-assemblies for the Rotodyne, Fairey Aviation (together with Bristol and Saunders-Roe helicopter activities) was taken over by Westland in 1960. Aircraft work experienced a revival in 1972 when the Fairey Company acquired Britten-Norman Ltd. of the Isle of Wight. As Fairey Britten-Norman, the company made Islander and Trislander two and three-engined passenger aircraft in overseas factories including Fairey's Gosselies plant in

Heaton Chapel, Stockport-built Fairey FD1 approaches the photographer's aircraft with wing trailing edge air brakes deployed, c.1954.

Hayes, Middlesex-built Fairey FD2, which incorporated components from Heaton Chapel, c.1956.

Belgium, some being pre-delivery serviced at Ringway. After the Fairey Group went into liquidation in 1977, Britten-Norman were acquired by Pilatus of Switzerland, becoming Pilatus Britten-Norman Ltd. with production in factories in Romania and Bembridge, I.O.W. In 1998 Pilatus sold the company which reverted to trading under its original name of Britten-Norman Ltd., continuing to manufacture and support Islander, Trislander and Defender aircraft worldwide.

Between 1936 and 1958, from the Hendon to the Gannet, Fairey at Heaton Chapel, Errwood Park and Ringway turned out 13 different types of aircraft of their own and other makers' designs, totalling 4,418 new-build machines. Of these, all but 19 aircraft were production flight tested from Ringway. In addition more than 2,000 others were modified, repaired, serviced or inspected for further use. The complex of former Fairey factories at Heaton Chapel is today in multiple uses as the Crossley Park Industrial Estate and Sir Richard Fairey Road commemorates its historic past.

Hawker Aircraft (Blackpool) Ltd., Squires Gate

After Vickers-Armstrongs completed their last Wellington bomber at Blackpool in October 1945, their final Lancaster and Lincoln having been completed at Chester in August, they were left with the two largest, most modern aircraft factories in Europe standing idle. Discussions between MAP, the Blackpool Corporation and the Fairey Aviation Company concerning the possible post-war use of the Squires Gate factory came to nothing. Years of German bombing had left the cores of many British towns and cities devastated, with building materials of necessity re-directed from housing to war infrastructure not least the building of aircraft factories. The need for renewal, together with demobilisation of large numbers of service personnel, created an urgent requirement for housing

which the building industry was unable to satisfy with conventional building methods and materials. With Government and MAP support, the Vickers-Armstrongs, Bristol and Blackburn aircraft companies formed a consortium to build sectionalised, easy to erect aluminium and concrete pre-fabricated houses, known as 'prefabs.' Between 1945 and 1948 the Blackpool and Chester factories were given over to the manufacture of these units, each turning out 11,250 'prefabs' as a contribution to more than 150,000 produced throughout the country. In fulfilling a vital social need the work also helped safeguard jobs until military and civil aviation requirements came to the fore once again at Chester in 1948. The Blackpool factory was mothballed for over three years after completion of the housing contracts until, after the review of the armed forces in 1951, aircraft work started to resume there also.

One of the results of the review was to super-prioritise certain key aircraft programmes, notably for the **Hawker Hunter** and Sea Hawk land and marine fighter and attack aircraft, the Fairey Gannet carrier-borne anti-submarine aircraft and the Canberra twin-jet bomber. As a classic but, as it turned out, ironic 'insurance' stratagem against failure of the Hunter, production of the Vickers-Supermarine Swift fighter was also expedited. Such fail-safe measures remained central to Britain's military aircraft procurement policies, most graphically demonstrated later in the 1950s when the Valiant, Vulcan and Victor bombers all entered service as the V-force but with few more than 100 built of each.

Vickers-Supermarine and Hawker were long-standing competitors with the Spitfire, Hurricane and their predecessors. Responding to a 1946 specification for a jet fighter to replace the Meteor, they came up with the Type 535 Swift and P.1067 Hunter, prototypes of which flying in August 1950 and July 1951 respectively. Designed by Sir

Sydney Camm of Hurricane fame, three Hunter prototypes were built at Kingston-upon-Thames, two powered by Rolls-Royce Avon axial turbojets and the third by an Armstrong Siddeley Sapphire. Chief Test Pilot Neville Duke flew the first at 700mph at the 1951 SBAC Farnborough Air Show. With a maximum speed of Mach 0.93-0.95 the Hunter, formally named in time for the 1952 show, was marginally subsonic in level flight but supersonic in a shallow dive. Both Supermarine and de Havilland had still to go supersonic with their Swift and D.H.110 aircraft and Hawker took great delight in subjecting their rivals' factories in the South of England to the occasional sonic boom courtesy of the Hunter. Duke and the Hunter took the world air speed record to 727.6mph on 7 September 1953. Both the Hunter and Swift entered RAF service but the latter, conceived as a transonic aircraft, experienced aerodynamic problems which confined it to subsonic speeds and seriously curtailed its service career.

The Korean War brought officialdom to a state of near panic in terms of getting the Hunter into production. Complex arrangements were hurriedly made to increase Hawker's production capacity and to expand and train up the depleted workforce. Manufacture of the Rolls-Royce Avon-powered Hunter F.Mk.1 started at Kingston, with assembly and flight testing at Hawker facilities at Langley in Buckinghamshire and Dunsfold in Surrey. A production line for Sapphire-powered Hunter F.Mk.2s was also established at Hawker Siddeley's Sir W. G. Armstrong Whitworth factory at Baginton, Coventry.

In 1951 Hawker entered discussions with the Ministry of Supply concerning the use of the then still vacant one million sq.ft. Squires Gate, Blackpool factory as a production, assembly and flight test centre for the Avon-powered Hunter F.Mk.1. Such was the importance of the matter that no-

one flinched at the need to construct a new 6,000 ft. east-west runway to accommodate take-offs and landings of the high performance jets. Additional land to the east of the existing airport had to be acquired from the Clifton Estate and the new runway required the closure of Division Lane running from St. Anne's to Blackpool and construction of a new road, Queensway, swinging around the runway's eastern extremity. The first Blackpool-built Hunter, one of a batch of 26, flew from Squires Gate on 26 May 1954 and the first Hunters, Kingston-built examples, entered RAF service in July. The RAF's first swept-wing aircraft, the Swift, had been in service since February but within a month problems had required its withdrawal from use as an interceptor fighter, although later versions served for some years in a tactical reconnaissance role in Germany.

The Offshore Procurement Bill passed by the United States Congress in 1952 was instrumental in funding the production of a number of key aircraft in Europe to bolster the strength of NATO. Hunter production qualified, surging ahead in Britain and under licence in Holland and Belgium. At Squires Gate, output switched from the F.Mk.1 to the Mk.4 with an up-rated Avon engine and additional fuel for extended range. The Mk.4 was required to replace the RAF's Canadian-built F-86 Sabres supplied as a stop-gap measure in December 1952 for service in Germany. The first of a batch of 20 Mk.4s flew from Blackpool on 20 January 1955 with the rest delivered during the year. Another batch of 100 was turned out during 1955/56 followed by a third, of 57 aircraft, also supplied in 1956. In 1954 negotiations between Hawker and the Swedish Government resulted in a £25 million order for 120 F.Mk4s for the Royal Swedish Air Force, for whom they were designated the Hunter Mk.50. Production was shared between Blackpool (96) and Kingston (24). The first 'Swedish' Hunter flew from Squires Gate on 24 June 1955 and the contract kept the factory busy until 1958. During this period it is believed that a number of piston-engined Hawker Sea Furies were refurbished at Blackpool.

The Hunter design was an aesthetic delight from the start. A true thoroughbred, its heritage dated back to the Sopwith Aviation Co. established in 1912. Sir Sydney Camm, who had designed some 52 different aircraft types since becoming Hawker's Chief Designer in 1925, described it as "my most beautiful aeroplane". Pilots and operators worldwide enthused about its handling, general performance and multi-role versatility as an interceptor fighter, ground and naval attack, tactical reconnaissance and training aircraft. But various problems had to be sorted out during its development, some of which required the addition of appendages that cluttered somewhat the purity of the original design. One was a drop-down barn door-type ventral panel rigged beneath the rear fuselage to replace the Hunter's originally unsatisfactory air brakes, clumsy but essential to slow down such an aerodynamically 'slippery' aircraft in flight. More seriously, RAF pilots of early

Hunter F.Mk.1s were dismayed to find that firing the aircraft's guns could provoke surging of the Avon engine risking flame-out. Engine surging was a known problem with the early Avons, eventually rectified by fitting them with the superior Sapphire compressor in the greatly improved Avon Series 200. Firing the guns had caused gases to be ingested into the engine, exacerbating the problem. Because initial gunnery trials had been undertaken with the surge-free Sapphire-engined third prototype, the matter had lurked undiscovered in Avon-powered Hunters until they entered service. Moreover, jettisoning spent shell cases and links was found to damage the aircraft exterior. This was solved by the addition of collection bins beneath the front fuselage in two bulged fairings, nicknamed 'Sabrinas' after a buxom young starlet of that time.

The Hunter became a major export earner, serving with the air forces of nearly 20 countries in Europe, the Middle and Far East, Africa and South America. It saw action in the 1967 Six Day War in the Middle East, in border clashes between India, Pakistan and China, in Chile and in

Hawker Hunter F.Mk.6, cancellation of an order for 50 of which precipitated the closure of Hawker's Squires Gate, Blackpool factory in 1958. The plant made 299 F.Mk.1, 4 and Mk.50 Hunters 1953-58. The Hunter entered the record books when, at the 1958 Farnborough Air Show, 16 black-painted F.6s of No.111 (Treble One) Sqn., the RAF's aerobatic team the *Black Arrows*, with six F.6s from other squadrons, performed two world record 22-aircraft loops.

anti-insurgency operations in Rhodesia and Aden. RAF Hunters despatched the stricken *Torrey Canyon* oil tanker by multiple rocket attacks off the Scilly Isles in 1967.

In 1957 Defence Secretary Duncan Sandys' notorious Defence White Paper indicated that the English Electric P.1B (Lightning) would be the RAF's last manned fighter and that no manned successors would be required for the V-bombers. Future defence would hinge on nuclear deterrence by ballistic missiles and UK air defence by surface-to-air missiles. Nearly 50 years on, the policy statement is now regarded as one of the most risible of all time. Then however it sent a shock wave through the British aircraft industry resulting in the termination of a number of new projects on the drawing board together with cancellation of certain orders already placed. One such was for 50 Hunter F.Mk.6s placed with Hawker at Blackpool in 1955 but revoked by the Government in 1957. Within little more than five years the Government's desperation to get the Hunter into service had been replaced by a doctrine of abandonment of the manned fighter. It spelt the end of large scale aircraft production at Blackpool after completion of the Swedish order in 1958. Hindsight suggests that subsequent closure of the plant, which had employed 5,000 people, could well have been premature given renewed overseas demand for Hunters, much of which had to be met by refurbishment. Advertised as the largest vacant factory in the world it lay empty on the property market until piecemeal occupation by other concerns began in the 1960s.

Altogether, Blackpool produced 299[2] Hunters out of a total of 1,975 made in Britain, Holland and Belgium. By contrast, Supermarine made a total of only 197 of its competitor the Swift. As the saga of volume aircraft production at Blackpool ended, fortunately for the future of the industry and jobs in Lancashire the baton of large scale profitable manufacturing had been firmly grasped by English Electric just a few miles away at Warton, Preston and Samlesbury.

The de Havilland Aircraft Company Ltd., Hawarden Aerodrome, Broughton, near Chester

During the immediate post-war years, somewhat exceptionally the de Havilland Aircraft Company of Hatfield, Hertfordshire, found itself with more orders than it had production capacity. Contracts remained operative for **Mosquito, Hornet** and **Vampire** military aircraft together with the company's new Dove transport for both civil and military use. But their most exciting project in the late 1940s involved a giant leap into the future of civil aviation with the **Comet** jetliner. With home and overseas demand for all these aircraft secured or anticipated and a Government keen to promote an export-led recovery spearheaded by the aircraft and motor industries, the future looked bright for de Havilland. In 1948, redundant as far as Vickers-Armstrongs were concerned, the giant Chester factory remained one of the most modern in the world and was judged ideal for de Havilland's needs. Early in the year an advance party moved in to reclaim the plant from the relative mess of two years of 'prefab' construction, with a view to establishing facilities for the discharge of final orders for Mosquito and Hornet aircraft.

Work began on the **Mosquito** at Chester in May 1948. Conceived by de Havilland ten years earlier as a lightweight twin-engined bomber of high power to weight ratio, fast enough to operate at speeds and altitudes which obviated the need for defensive armament, the Mosquito had been in production at Hatfield, Leavesden and in shadow factories in the Midlands and South for much of the war. Hitherto,

[2]*See Production Appendix 1 notes.*

factories in the North West, including the Waring & Gillow furniture works at Lancaster, had contributed sub-assemblies and Rolls-Royce Merlin engines to the Mosquito programme, but not complete aircraft. Dubbed the 'Wooden Wonder', it represented de Havilland's revolutionary approach to designing the lightest possible airframe strong enough to take two Merlins. They boldly chose to make the airframe entirely of wood with laminates of cedar ply and balsa. The fuselage comprised two half shells, facilitating installation of controls, wiring and pipelines. A wooden stressed-skin mainplane contained ten fuel tanks totalling 540 gallons capacity and carried two almost disproportionately large and powerful-looking 1,250hp engines. At first the Ministry of Aviation looked askance at the apparently retrograde idea of an unarmed wooden aeroplane. Resulting delays, coupled with an air raid on Hatfield in October 1940 which miraculously left the prototype unscathed, might well have resulted in it being stillborn. But after a first flight in November when its performance astonished even the test pilot,

Geoffrey de Havilland Jnr., the authorities' doubts were swept aside. Moreover, the Mosquito placed fewer demands on scarce 'strategic' supplies of metal alloy than other aircraft and, as a 400mph bomber with all the agility of a fighter, priority production was authorised. Not merely competent as a bomber, intruder, day and night fighter and photo-reconnaissance aircraft, the Mosquito excelled in all those roles, proving to be the most versatile aircraft of the war. Up to 1944 it had the highest performance of any aircraft available to the combatant powers. As the Sea Mosquito it was the first British twin-engined aircraft to operate from an aircraft carrier. It was the world's first true multi-role combat aircraft.

The Mosquito was associated with many notable wartime operations including a daylight raid on Cologne in May 1942 on the day following the RAF's first one-thousand-bomber raid on the city. Mosquitoes made low-level attacks on Gestapo headquarters in Oslo and Copenhagen in 1943 and 1945 respectively and in 1944 famously carried out a raid to free resistance fighters imprisoned in Amiens. Such was Goering's fury after a

Two wartime de Havilland Mosquito B.Mk.IVs, DZ353 and DZ367, of No. 105 Sqn., Marham, December 1942. De Havilland made 65 later versions of the Mosquito and Sea Mosquito at Chester, 1948-50.
Photo: Aeroplane

parade he was addressing in Berlin in January 1943 was intentionally disrupted by Mosquitoes that the Reichsmarschall established a special Luftwaffe unit to counter their activities. It was unsuccessful and ground fire presented the only serious threat to Mosquitoes as they ranged over enemy territory almost at will. Mosquitoes were an integral part of the Pathfinder Force and it was on returning from a raid as Master Bomber in 1944 that Wing Commander Guy Gibson, VC, DSO, DFC and his navigator, Squadron Leader J.B. Warwick, lost their lives when their Mosquito was shot down by ground fire over the Netherlands.

A total of 65 late-version Mosquitoes was manufactured at Chester between 1948-50 comprising 51 NF.Mk.38 Night Fighters and 14 TR.Mk.37 Sea Mosquitoes. The final example, an NF.Mk.38 which flew from Hawarden on 15 November 1950 was the very last of a grand total of 7,781 built in Britain, Canada and Australia. Fairey Aviation reconditioned others at Ringway between 1950-53 for use in Belgium and Sweden. The last airworthy Mosquito, a Leavesden-built T.Mk.III, was preserved for many years at Hawarden and was a familiar

aircraft on the air display circuit until tragically lost in an air show accident at Barton Aerodrome in July 1996. Astonishingly, the original prototype designed and built at Salisbury Hall, London Colney, St. Albans and first flown by Geoffrey de Havilland Jnr. at Hatfield on 25 November 1940 was found stored in a shed at the Chester factory after the war. Restored, it is now on display at the de Havilland Heritage Centre at Salisbury Hall.

Out of the Mosquito's success emerged a 1942/43 design for a smaller, single-seat long range fighter version conceived specifically for use against the Japanese in the South Pacific. Bearing a strong family resemblance the resulting **D.H. Hornet** was even more streamlined and slim, with specially designed 2,030hp Merlin engines of low frontal area, both with inward-rotating de Havilland Hydromatic four-bladed propellers to eliminate swinging forces on take-off and landing. Retaining the Mosquito's ply and balsa sandwich build for its fuselage, the Hornet had a composite wood and metal stressed-skin laminar flow wing of double-ply birch for the upper surfaces with 'Alclad' alloy for the underside. Composite wing spars were

Hatfield, Hertfordshire-built de Havilland Hornet F.Mk.1 PX244 joined No. 64 Sqn., Horsham St. Faith, in May 1946. De Havilland's Chester factory made 149 Hornets and Sea Hornets. *Photo: Aeroplane*

cemented together, wood to metal, using the advanced new 'Redux' adhesive bonding process for the first time. The prototype first flew at Hatfield on 28 July 1944 with Geoffrey de Havilland Jnr. at the controls. Subsequently attaining 485mph the Hornet was possibly the fastest-ever propeller-driven aircraft. It was too late to see service in WW2 but in 1951 was used in successful anti-terrorist rocket and bombing operations in Malaya. Up to 149 Hornets and Sea Hornets were made at Chester between 1948-52 out of a total of 409 produced by de Havilland.

De Havilland Aircraft of Canada Ltd. had been established in 1928 to provide service and repair facilities for the company's products used in that country. Licensed manufacture of Tiger Moth and Mosquito aircraft took place at the Downsview, Toronto works during WW2. In 1946 W.J. Jakimiuk designed the **D.H.C.1 Chipmunk** basic trainer as a successor to the Tiger Moth biplane. The Chipmunk, a sturdy all-metal stressed-skin monoplane powered by a 145hp D.H. Gypsy Major engine, proved immediately successful as an *ab initio* trainer

with aerobatic capability. No fewer than 735 were ordered for RAF Training Command, the RAF (VR) and University Air Squadrons. 218 were built in Canada. In Britain de Havilland made 111 at Hatfield and an amazing 889 at Chester between 1950-56. Chester Chipmunks were mostly T.Mk.10s for the RAF, T.Mk.20s supplied to other air forces worldwide and a small number of Mk.21s for civilian customers including Air Service Training of Hamble. Some work was subcontracted to Aero & Engineering (Merseyside) Ltd. of Hooton Park. Like the Tiger Moth before it, the Chipmunk provided initial flight experience for generations of new pilots. Both HRH Prince Philip and HRH Prince Charles learned to fly on Chester-built Chipmunks. A Chipmunk T.Mk.10 (WP962) built by de Havilland at Chester is today on display at the RAF Museum, Hendon.

Within a year of reopening under de Havilland, Chester entered the jet age by turning out the first of 1,244 **D.H.100 Vampire** single-seat fighter bombers, two-seat night fighters and trainers to be produced there between 1949 and 1963.

De Havilland
Venom
NF.Mk.3s,
powered by
4,950lb-thrust
Ghost engines,
pictured at the
1953 SBAC
Farnborough Air
Show. *Photo:
Aeroplane*

In 1949 de Havilland's Vampire subcontracts with English Electric at Preston and Samlesbury had already been running for five years, English Electric delivering 1,369 between 1944 and 1952. Additionally, Fairey Aviation completed 97 at Ringway between 1952 and 1955, their factory at Heaton Chapel also supplying a large number of Vampire fuselages to de Havilland at Chester. Production from Chester for export included 297 FB.50s (J.28Bs) for Sweden and 164 T.55 trainers for some 20 overseas air forces.

From 1952 to 1958 Chester also built 834 **D.H.112 Venom** single-seat fighter bombers, two-seat night fighters with airborne interception (AI) radar (including 62 for Sweden, designated J.33s) and two-seat Sea Venom all-weather naval fighters. Engined by the more powerful D.H. Ghost turbojet, these were developments of the Vampire retaining the twin-boom configuration but with a wing of new design. The Venom's maximum speed of

640mph was an advance of 100mph on the Vampire. The Swedish contract for NF.Mk.51s (J.33s) was shared with Fairey Aviation at Ringway and involved the installation of Ghost engines built under licence by the Svenska Flygmotor Company in Sweden and shipped to Britain. Substantial numbers of Vampires and Venoms were also overhauled and refurbished at Chester during the 1950s and '60s, busy years for the de Havilland factory with work proceeding concurrently on five or six overlapping aircraft programmes with several different production lines in close proximity.

During the 1930s, hundreds of de Havilland's ubiquitous D.H.84 Dragon and D.H.89 Dragon Rapide twin-engined and D.H. 86 four-engined 6-10 passenger biplanes enhanced the firm's reputation worldwide as a constructor of superb medium-sized transport aircraft. They would prove hard acts for post-war successors to follow but, just a few weeks

Chester-built de Havilland D.H.104 Dove 8 G-ARUM, powered by two 400hp D.H. Gypsy Queen 70 Mk.3 engines, was used as an executive aircraft by the National Coal Board.

after V-J Day, the **D.H.104 Dove** 8-11 seater twin-engined light transport monoplane made its first flight at Hatfield. The Dove was noteworthy as the first British transport to have reversible pitch, as well as fully feathering, constant speed propellers fitted to its Gypsy Queen engines, permitting reverse thrust airscrew-braked short landings. The pretty-looking Dove proved attractive to airline operators all over the world and was also operated as a corporate transport by 'blue-chip' companies at home and abroad. As the D.H. Devon and Sea Devon the aircraft were fondly regarded by the RAF and the Royal Navy in the communications role and also served with many overseas air forces. With demand high and Hatfield increasingly busy with the Comet jetliner and other work, the Dove production line was transferred from Hatfield to Chester in 1951 where 244 were built up to 1967. Altogether de Havilland made 542 Doves over a 22-year production span.

In 1949 de Havilland decided to proceed with designs for a larger four-engined version of the Dove, designated the **D.H.114 Heron**. With wingspan extended from 57 to 71 ft. and fuselage lengthened from 39 to 48 ft. the Heron accommodated up to 17 passengers and proved rugged and economical in operating from small, substandard airstrips worldwide. The Heron found much favour as a VIP transport operated by the Queen's Flight, other Heads of State, airlines, company executives and armed forces including the RAF and Royal Navy, the latter naming it the Sea Heron. Of a total of 150 made by de Havilland, 143 were produced at Chester between 1953 and 1967.

In 1944 the Brabazon Committee outlined a specification for a post-war jet airliner viewed as a flagship project to wrest back ground lost to the Americans in the development of large transport aircraft. Initially with accommodation for 36 passengers and four crew, the stressed-skin pressurised cabin **D.H.106 Comet** first took to the air in July 1949 at Hatfield with test pilot and former wartime nightfighter ace John 'Cats Eyes' Cunningham at the controls. Powered by four de Havilland Ghost turbojets each of 4,450lb thrust buried in the roots of a moderately swept wing, the revolutionary and exciting 500mph Comet undertook extensive proving flights in Europe, Africa, the Middle and Far East over the next twelve months without significant incident. Production of ten Comet 1s for BOAC started at Hatfield. Deliveries commenced in April 1952, BOAC introducing the world's first pure jet fare-paying passenger service on 2 May, to Johannesburg. Orders followed from Canadian Pacific Airlines and Air France for the longer range 44-seat Comet 1A with more powerful Ghost engines and additional fuel capacity.

Investigation of two take-off accidents, at Karachi in 1952 and Rome in 1953, revealed that the Comet would not attain flying speed if the nose was held too high off the runway. The matter was solved by redesigning the wing leading edges. Much more perplexing was a series of tragic accidents involving the complete loss of three BOAC Comet 1s, their passengers and crews, near Calcutta, Rome and Stromboli in 1953-54. Comets were grounded pending the results of one of the most intensive series of investigations ever undertaken of an aircraft. Metallurgical analysis, pressurised testing under water and fatigue testing to destruction revealed the cause to be structural failure of the Comet's pressurised cabin, emanating from one corner of the rectangular Automatic Direction Finding (ADF) 'window' in the rear fuselage.

Demand had been riding high for the Comet until the accidents. An extended 44-seat Comet 2 with additional fuel capacity and Rolls-Royce Avon engines had been developed for potential transatlantic operations. Though its range remained inadequate for single stage North Atlantic

crossings, BOAC ordered 12 for South American services. De Havilland announced their intention to establish two further production lines, one in conjunction with Short Brothers & Harland at Belfast and the other at Chester. But suspension of all Comet production in 1954 resulted in the early abandonment of the Belfast line, Shorts' Comet 2 fuselages, sub-assemblies, components and tooling being shipped to Chester via Liverpool Docks. It was 1955 before Comet work resumed at Chester, beginning with re-working the existing Comet 1As of the Royal Canadian Air Force and Air France, together with all Comet 2 fuselages built hitherto. Modifications included use of heavier gauge metal, rounded window openings and the angling of engine jet pipes and efflux away from the rear fuselage. Chester converted 15 Hatfield-built BOAC Comet 2s for transport and training use by the RAF. In 1957 the first Comet produced completely at Chester, albeit using a re-worked Shorts' fuselage, became the final C.Mk.2 for the RAF. Four Comet 2s remained unfinished at Chester.

With Comet problems overcome and the North Atlantic route still beckoning, in 1955 Hatfield put forward proposals for the Comet 4 with more powerful Avon engines and seating for 78 passengers. BOAC placed orders in 1957 and two of their Hatfield-built examples simultaneously inaugurated east and westbound London-New York flights on 4 October 1958, passing each other in mid-Atlantic. It was the world's first transatlantic jet service for fare-paying passengers, starting just 22 days before Pan American commenced Boeing 707 services on the same route. Comet 4 build was shared between Hatfield and Chester. Two further variants were developed, both flying for the first time in 1959 with lengthened fuselages capable of accommodating up to 101 passengers. The 4B had a wingspan clipped to 108 ft. and was used by BEA and Olympic Airways for

short hauls between European capitals.
The 4C, with full-span 115 ft. wing, was the
ultimate 'stretched' long range version
operated by various South American and
Middle East airlines and, from 1961, by RAF
Transport Command as the C.Mk.4. The
4B and 4C entered production at Hatfield
and Chester around the time the de
Havilland Aircraft Co. became part of the
Hawker Siddeley Group, in January 1960, as
one of the elements of the Government-
inspired restructuring of the British aircraft
industry. The D.H. name would live on for
another five years in the Hawker Siddeley
Group de Havilland Division.

Altogether Chester built some 40 Comets
between 1957 and 1964 including a single
C.Mk.2 for the RAF, 16 Comet 4s of which
12 were for BOAC, two Comet 4Bs for
BEA and nine 4Cs for operators including
Misrair-United Arab Airlines, Middle East
Airlines and Kuwait Airways. Five C.Mk.4s
built at Chester for the RAF from 1961
were sold in 1975 to Dan-Air of London,
then the major remaining operator of the
Comet. Chester also produced a number
of large Comet sub-assemblies for
completion at Hatfield.

During a production term spanning some

14 years the Comet had been enlarged
from 36 seats to 101, the thrust of each
engine increased from 4,450 to 10,500lb
and its range extended from 1,750 to
3,000 miles. In its early life it had paid the
price of trail-blazing new technologies that
had unleashed unforeseen forces,
investigations into which benefited all
succeeding large jet transport aircraft.
The Comet 4 evolved to be a superb
airliner, not only inaugurating transatlantic
passenger jet services but offering excellent
field performance especially in the thinner
atmosphere of high altitude airports. But
even the ultimate, stretched 4C was limited
by its basic design and unable to compete
with the Boeing 707 which could carry
twice as many passengers 100mph faster
more than 2,000 miles further. Over 1,000
Boeing 707 airframes were completed
compared with under 120 Comets.

One of the best known of Chester's
Comets is 4C X5235 *Canopus*, the
third from last built, which first flew on
26 September 1963. On her withdrawal
in 1997 after 34 years spent entirely as a
research aircraft with Government agencies
at Bedford, Boscombe Down and
Farnborough, *Canopus* was the last

airworthy Comet and is today cared for by the British Aviation Heritage Collection at Bruntingthorpe, Leicestershire.

In 1965 Chester had its last two Comet 4Cs still on site with no obvious customers. Between 1960-62 the factory had overhauled and modified 24 Shackleton maritime reconnaissance and anti-submarine aircraft, piston-engined derivatives of the wartime Lancaster built by Avro at Manchester and Woodford. The decision was taken to use the surplus Comets as development prototypes of a new jet-powered aircraft to replace the venerable 'Shacks'. One was flown to HSA Woodford where, retaining the original Avon engines, it was modified as one of two prototype **HS 801 Nimrod** maritime patrol aircraft. The second was fully converted at Chester, including fitting with Rolls-Royce Spey engines which were to become standard in production Nimrods. The Chester prototype flew from Hawarden on 23 May 1967 and the other from Woodford on 31 July, followed by extensive aerodynamic, navigation and attack avionics systems and engine/airframe integration testing. Several other Chester-made pre-owned Comet 4s contributed to the development of the Nimrod which, recognisably Comet-based, had a shorter, deeper 'double bubble' fuselage to accommodate weapons systems and an extended tail with Magnetic Anomaly Detector (MAD) 'stinger'. Later, a variety of external finlets, in-flight refuelling, avionics and weapons system excrescences would be acquired. Production Nimrods would all be assembled at Woodford but HSA Chester remained integral to the programme, from 1966-1970 manufacturing 41 sets of major airframe structures including fuselages and wings. These were transported to Woodford for final assembly and addition of the weapons bay. All the aircraft were flight tested and delivered from Woodford as Nimrod MR.Mk.1s. Further details are given later.

Between 1974 and 1976, with HSA Woodford building the HS 748 airliner and busy also with the Nimrod programme and converting Victor bombers to in-flight refuelling tankers, two 748s were diverted to Chester for final assembly. Additionally, a pre-owned 748 airliner was converted at Chester into a prototype maritime patrol aircraft, the 'Coastguarder', but with no orders forthcoming was restored to use as an airliner.

In complete contrast to the Comet and Nimrod, amongst the amazing diversity of overlapping projects at Chester during the 1960s was the assembly of **D.H.C.2 Beaver** aircraft from kits received from de Havilland Canada. Designed there as a bush transport for six people or half-a-ton of freight, this all-metal high wing STOL aeroplane was powered by a single 450hp Pratt & Whitney Wasp Junior. Between 1960 and 1967 Chester turned out 46 Beavers for use by the British Army Air Corps for reconnaissance, liaison and casualty evacuation.

Different again was the **D.H.110 Sea Vixen**, the ultimate development of de Havilland's trio of twin-boom jet fighters which began with the Vampire, followed by its derivative the Venom. Conceived back in 1946 as an all-weather fighter for both the RAF (later to get the Gloster Javelin instead) and the Royal Navy, the D.H.110 had a fully swept wing which owed much to the tailless D.H.108 'Swallow' research aircraft. Three D.H.108s were built at Hatfield in 1946-7 using fuselages 'lifted' from English Electric's early post-war Vampire production line at Preston in 1945. They were also used as flying 'scale models' for development of the Comet and investigating flight at low and high Mach numbers. Geoffrey de Havilland Jnr. lost his life in the second of them in 1946. Two years later the third aircraft, piloted by John Derry, became the first to exceed the speed of sound in Britain. Derry himself was killed when the D.H.110 prototype broke up in the air at Farnborough in 1952.

When it entered service in 1959 the twin-jet Sea Vixen, with 51ft. wingspan and all-up weight of 40,000lb, was the Royal Navy's heaviest deck-lander to date. As well as its twin-boom design it was distinguished by a cockpit canopy offset to port, with a radar operator below and aft of the pilot on the starboard. It was the first British interceptor to dispense with guns in favour of D.H. Firestreak infra-red homing missiles and two-inch air-to-air rockets. The final stages of production were transferred from Christchurch near Bournemouth to Chester in 1962 where the first aircraft off the line was the last FAW.Mk.1 version. It was followed by 29 Mk.2s produced up to 1966, with booms extended forward of the wing holding additional fuel allowing some to serve as flying tankers. Red Top AAMs were fitted. Between 1965 and 1968 Chester also modified 37 Christchurch-built Mk.1s to Mk.2 status. A Chester-built Mk.2 based at Hurn near Bournemouth is today the sole surviving airworthy example, frequently seen at air displays.

In 1961 de Havilland, as members of the Hawker Siddeley Group, announced a jet-powered successor to the piston-engined Dove then still under construction at Chester. The **D.H.125**, with two rear fuselage-mounted Bristol Siddeley Viper turbojets, was a swept-wing fully pressurised two-crew aircraft able to carry 6-8 passengers over 1,500 miles in outstanding comfort at 450-500mph. Two prototypes built at the Hatfield experimental shop flew in August and December 1962. With Hatfield floorspace required for the Trident airliner, series production of the D.H.125 began at Chester in 1962-3. The 125 proved one of Chester's most successful revenue earners with volume production extending over a period of 35 years. Key to that success was the enthusiastic reception given by the North American business market. Many D.H.125s were flown across the Atlantic to have interiors individually fitted out to the luxurious specifications of corporate clients. 100 had been delivered by 1966, Hawker Siddeley exploiting de Havilland's reputation by using the D.H. prefix for

De Havilland/ Hawker Siddeley D.H./HS.125 G-AYOJ, one of 871 of the series built at Chester.

several years before redesignating it as the HS.125.

The 125 was the subject of continuous development, beginning with Series 2 aircraft in the 1960s, 20 of which were supplied to the RAF as Dominie T.Mk.1 navigation trainers to replace ageing Meteors and Varsities. Series 300 and 400 aircraft had longer range, Series 600 an extended fuselage with more powerful Viper turbojets. These were changed to more economical Garrett turbofans in Series 700 whilst the 800 had aerodynamic improvements including a new wing giving intercontinental range of 3,400 miles and a maximum cruise of 525mph.

After the formation of British Aerospace (BAe) as a nationalised concern by the merging of the British Aircraft Corporation (BAC), Hawker Siddeley Aviation (HSA), Hawker Siddeley Dynamics and Scottish Aviation in 1977, the following year the plant became part of the BAe Aircraft Group Hatfield-Chester Division. From 1989 manufacture and sale of the then BAe 125 was undertaken by BAe Corporate Aircraft Division and the 125 Series 1000 was introduced in 1990. Further restructuring created British Aerospace Corporate Jets Ltd. in 1992 but the following year, with BAe focusing on its core Airbus interests at Broughton, the then Corporate Jets Ltd. was sold to the Raytheon Company of the USA. Production and assembly of completed 125s at Broughton ended in 1996 after a total of 871 had been built. Raytheon transferred the assembly line of the aircraft, now named the Raytheon Hawker 800 XP Corporate Business Jet, to Wichita, Kansas. BAe, which became BAE Systems after amalgamating with Marconi Electronic Systems in 1999, maintained involvement with the Hawker 800 by making fuselage and wingbox assemblies under contract for export to Raytheon in the USA, with Airbus UK subsequently doing likewise. Raytheon took over the former BAe 125

servicing facility at Broughton which they continue to operate today as the Raytheon Aircraft Services Ltd. international aircraft service centre, also with production facilities for their US factory.

Over the six decades from 1939 to 1996 Chester built, flight tested and delivered nearly 9,500 aircraft of some 15 major types and over 40 variants, ranging from the Vickers Wellington to the BAe 125 1000. Many of these and aircraft of other manufacturers including Avro Shackletons, Blackburn Beverleys and Hawker Hunters were also serviced and overhauled. Such scale of operation is maintained today on an international level by BAE Systems/ Airbus UK with an investment programme of hundreds of millions of pounds ploughed into the Broughton plant which for the last 30 years has been responsible for manufacturing all of the wings for every member of the **Airbus** family of aircraft.

Hawker Siddeley Aviation, British Aerospace, BAE Systems and Airbus UK Ltd. – Airbus operations from 1970, Broughton (Hawarden), near Chester

By the mid-1960s, after 20 years of US domination of the civil airliner market it was apparent that the development costs of a proposed new generation of large capacity European airliners powered by turbofan engines would require the resources of an international consortium. Working relationships between aircraft manufacturers in Britain and France were established and West Germany was also invited to join a programme to design, develop and build a **European 'Airbus'**.

A Memorandum of Understanding was signed by the three Governments in 1967 for the development of a widebody, twin-aisle twin-engined airliner. The company partners would be Hawker Siddeley Aviation of Britain by virtue of its unique experience in advanced design and manufacture of the Comet 4 and Trident airliner wings; Sud-Aviation of France who were early collaborators on the Anglo-French supersonic transport later to become Concorde; and Deutsche Airbus GmbH of Germany. Alarmed at the possibility of poor sales, the UK Government subsequently withdrew but in May 1969 France and West Germany launched the programme for the A300 European Airbus. To its immense credit, Hawker Siddeley Aviation elected to remain involved as a private subcontractor, risking its own resources by assuming responsibility for the advanced technology design and manufacture of the entire wing structure. It was doubtless a calculated decision, for several earlier HSA programmes were in their final stages of production and about to release considerable capacity at the huge Chester factory. Matters were formalised by the establishment of Airbus Industrie in 1970, with Deutsche Airbus at Bremen to provide most of the fuselage and tail, Aérospatiale (formerly Sud) at Toulouse to contribute other fuselage structures and taking responsibility for final assembly of the complete aircraft. Fokker of the Netherlands and CASA of Spain were to supply wing moving surfaces and tailplane respectively.

The all-new, advanced Hawker Siddeley-designed wing would be key to the future success of the Airbus. With a quarter chord sweep of 28 degrees it benefited from superior aerodynamic and structural technology giving a greatly improved lift/drag ratio. Of advanced design, the all-speed ailerons descended on activation of Fowler flaps which themselves increased wing chord by a quarter. Distinctively different was its variable camber profile which, with automatic load alleviation was able to react continuously to changes in the aircraft's weight, speed and altitude, maximising structural and operating efficiency. The thicker section 'wet' wing provided enhanced fuel-carrying capacity.

From the outset the size of wing components required investment at Chester in some of the largest machine tools and production jigs anywhere in the world for machining skin panels and assembling wing torsion box structures. Initially wings built at Chester were taken by road to Manchester Airport or Liverpool Airport, the first set being loaded into an Aéromaritime/Airbus Industrie Super Guppy Freighter at Manchester on 23 November 1971. Flown first to Bremen for equipping they were then forwarded to Aérospatiale at Toulouse for final assembly of the prototype demonstrator **Airbus A300B** which flew for the first time on 28 October 1972. It was the world's first widebody twin-aisle twin-jet airliner.

When British Aerospace (BAe) was formed in 1977, Hawker Siddeley Aviation had produced 45 A300 wing sets at Chester. In 1978 the HSA Hatfield-Chester Division became the BAe Hatfield-Chester Division, BAe accordingly gaining the Airbus wing operation. By the following year BAe was a full decision-making partner in Airbus Industrie with a 20 per cent shareholding and, in June, Chester delivered the 100th wing set to Bremen. In 1981 British Aerospace became a public limited company, acquiring the assets and business of the former nationalised corporation. Under its aegis the 1980s saw spectacular increases in production of wing sets for a proliferating Airbus range. Technological developments continued apace including CAD, three-dimensional wing-skin forming, superplastic forming and diffusion bonding. Composite materials were already used in secondary structures but in 1985 Airbus was the first to certificate a composite primary structure in a transport aircraft with the A310-300 vertical tail unit fin box. That year, Chester completed the first wing set for the **A320** single-aisle regional twin-jet, delivering it to a new wing equipping centre at Filton, Bristol, under arrangements which continued until 1993, and then on to

Opposite: North Wales advanced wing technology by Airbus at Broughton and North West wide-chord fan blade expertise of Rolls-Royce at Barnoldswick have contributed immensely to the success of the Airbus range. Shown here is a Rolls-Royce Trent-powered A330.

Toulouse. The A320, first flown in 1987 and certificated in 1988, was the world's first commercial aircraft to employ an electronically managed flight control system or 'fly-by-wire' with a side-stick controller replacing the conventional central control column and mechanical system of cables and pulleys. The new system, first tested in an Airbus Industrie A300 development aircraft, further enhanced the cockpit and constructional commonality already a strong feature of the Airbus range. Use of composites was extended to the A320's tailplane.

In 1989 the Chester and Filton plants became the Airbus Division of British Aerospace (Commercial Aircraft) Ltd., operating as British Aerospace Airbus Ltd. from 1992. The 2,000th Airbus wing set was delivered in February 1999. On the amalgamation of BAe and Marconi Electronic Systems in November to form BAE Systems, BAe had delivered in excess of 2,200 sets for seven variants of single

and twin-aisle, medium and large capacity, short, medium and long haul, two and four-engined Airbuses comprising the **A300/310/320/340/330/321** and **319**. During the 30-year Airbus programme to date, other BAe/BAE Systems plants have contributed to wing production, notably Samlesbury with manufacture and assembly of leading and trailing edges, other wing components and advanced control surfaces for the A300/310/320 and 321, and Chadderton with long-bed machining of stringers by numerically controlled machines.

Airbus UK Ltd. was established by BAE Systems in 2000 as part of a proposed Airbus Integrated Company (AIC). Known simply as Airbus, the AIC became operational in 2001 as a creation of BAE Systems and EADS, the European Aeronautic Defence and Space Company, who hold 20 per cent and 80 per cent partnership shares respectively in Airbus. EADS is itself the product of the merger of

Rolls-Royce Trent-powered Airbus A330 over the Pyrenees..

Aérospace-Matra of France, DaimlerChrysler Aerospace of Germany and CASA of Spain. In general terms Airbus France manufacture the nose, flight deck and flying control systems, Airbus Deutschland the fuselage sections and Airbus España the tailplane. There are two final assembly lines, at Toulouse and Hamburg.

Today, Broughton is the preferred name for the wing-manufacturing centre of Airbus UK Ltd., the wholly owned subsidiary of BAE Systems, operating integrally with Airbus UK Ltd. headquarters, management, design and engineering facilities at Filton. Broughton manufactures wings for all four families of Airbus: **A320 (A318/319/320/ 321)** single-aisle 107-185 seaters, **A300/310** widebody twin-aisle 220-266 seaters, **A330/340** widebody twin-aisle long-range 253-380 seaters and the latest **A380** double-deck 555-seater superjumbo. The range now offers 14 variants including short, medium, long and very long-range (up to 9,000nm) two and four-engined airliners and freighters. Broughton delivered its 3,000th wing set in 2002. By May 2004 Airbus had sold almost 5,000 aircraft to 250 customers/operators and had delivered over 3,500 since first entering the market in 1974, Broughton having supplied wings for all of them. Airbus surpassed Boeing in the number of aircraft delivered in 2003. Total Airbus sales up to May 2005 exceeded 5,370.

Since 1996 runway improvements at Broughton have permitted daily transport of wings to the assembly lines by **Airbus A300-600 ST Super Transporter 'Beluga'** aircraft. Itself fitted with Broughton-built wings, the 'Beluga' first flew in 1994 and is the world's most voluminous aircraft. Individual wingboxes ranging from 55 ft. to 100 ft. in length and 2.75 t to 12.1t in weight can be accommodated in pairs, apart from those for the **A340-600** which require transporting individually. Wing sets for the short to medium haul

A318/319/320/321 are completed at Broughton with hydraulic, air and electrical systems and flying control surfaces before being flown to the aircraft final assembly lines – Toulouse for the **A320** and Hamburg for the **A318/319/321**. Those for the medium to long-haul widebody **A300/310/330/340** go first to Bremen for equipping by Airbus Deutschland, then on to Toulouse.

Some £500-700 million has either been invested at Broughton in recent years or is proposed, particularly in wing production lines for the **A340-500/600** and **A380**, encompassing long-bed machinery, wing skin milling, stringer manufacturing, wingbox assembly and equipping. A new £345 million, 900,000 sq.ft. production building known as the 'West Factory', started in August 2001 was opened in July 2003. Wing build for the new 79.75m (261 ft.)- span, double-deck, 560-tonne, 8,000-mile range **A380 Superjumbo** began in December 2002. Wing panels are made on a long-bed milling machine, Europe's largest computer-controlled machine tool, which removes over 70 per cent of the metal from solid 35m, 4.5t billets of aluminium alloy imported from France and the USA. This is followed by shot peening, anti-corrosion surface treatment and painting. Skin panels, stringers, ribs and spars are assembled into the complete wingbox in jigs, each wing set requiring 100,000 rivet and bolt fasteners. Such is Airbus factory manufacturing precision that, during the setting up of Low Voltage Electromagnetic Riveting (LVER) machines on a piled, two metre-thick concrete bed, theoretical calculations took account of the curvature of the earth. Leading and trailing edges, anti-icing, fuel and hydraulic systems are added in the equipping area. Each 36.3m wing (45m along its leading edge) weighs 35t and is designed to flex vertically through 7m at its tip. Due to their size, special arrangements have been made for the transport of A380 wings from

A380 wing equipping, Broughton. The factory has produced the wings for every Airbus flying throughout the world, currently well over 3,700 wing sets since 1971. Maximum internal headroom of the 'West Factory' is 35 metres.

Transhipment of the first wing for the A380 'Superjumbo' from barge to the *Ville de Bordeaux* at Mostyn on the Dee Estuary, North Wales, March 2004, in transit to Toulouse.

Broughton to Toulouse. The first was completed in March 2004 and by summer two sets had been delivered with another four in production. The wings were taken by river barge for transhipment to a specially-built roll-on-roll-off seagoing cargo vessel, the *Ville de Bordeaux*, at Mostyn on the River Dee, thence to Pauillac near Bordeaux and up river by barge to the

Garonne port of Langon, completing the final stage to Toulouse by road trailer.

Other Airbus sites contributing to the A380 include: in France, Nantes (carbon fibre centre wing box), Saint Nazaire (forward and centre fuselage and belly fairing), including elements from Nantes, Méaulte, Hamburg and Puerto Real with suppliers including Alenia in Italy, SABCA in

Opposite:
The Airbus plant at Broughton in Flintshire, North Wales. The new 'West Factory' lies in the distance, to the left of the main runway.

147

The first A380 MSN001, having just emerged from its assembly jigs at Toulouse, 2004. © AIRBUS S.A.A. 2004 e'm company/ P. MASCLE

Below and opposite: The A380 prototype, appropriately registered F-WWOW, immediately before and during its first flight made from Toulouse on 27 April 2005. Its four-hour maiden flight is to be followed by an intensive programme of flight testing in all climatic conditions around the world, before the first production aircraft enters service with the first customer, Singapore Airlines, in 2006. The tailplane of the 555-seater A380 is larger than the wing of the smallest Airbus, the 100-seater A318. For all its size and power, the A380 generates only half the noise of its nearest competitor at take-off.

Belgium, Latécoère, Socata and Sogerma in France; in Germany, Hamburg and Stade (forward and aft fuselage sections, rudder and fin assembly) and in Spain, Getafe, Puerto Real and Illescas (forward and rear belly fairings, tailplane, rudder and carbon fibre fuselage sections). In the UK, at Filton, the largest ever landing gear test rig for a commercial aircraft was completed in 2002. Final assembly of the A380, 40 per cent of

whose structures and components are manufactured from the latest generation of carbon composite and advanced metals, is in a new 1.3 million sq.ft., 150 ft.-high assembly hall at Toulouse. Nearby facilities also provide pylons for the aircraft's Rolls-Royce Trent 900 engines.

Broughton's 6,500-strong workforce is drawn from Flintshire and North East Wales, Chester and Merseyside including the Wirral. Airbus wing work currently helps sustain 150 supply companies and 10,000 jobs in Wales, generating over 80,000 jobs throughout the UK. Airbus UK is now one of Britain's largest manufacturing companies with Broughton a contender for the largest single industrial production centre in the country. The company contributes in excess of £1 billion to the UK's balance of payments, a sum due to increase further with 154 firm orders in hand, including 32 for freighter versions, for the £156 million A380 which made its maiden flight at Toulouse on 27 April 2005 and is due to enter airline service in 2006. The next major Airbus programmes concern the A400M four-turboprop, high speed 37t-payload military transport aircraft, to be assembled at Seville and due to fly in 2008 with first deliveries in 2009, and the new carbon fibre composite-winged long-range A350 airliner due to enter service in 2010.

A.V. Roe & Company Ltd. (Hawker Siddeley Group), Avro-Whitworth Division of Hawker Siddeley Aviation, British Aerospace (Commercial Aircraft) Ltd., British Aerospace Regional Aircraft, Avro International Aerospace, BAE Systems, Chadderton and Woodford

After the ending of hostilities in 1945, inevitable contraction and disposal of surplus manufacturing capacity saw Avro concentrating at its Chadderton headquarters factory and Woodford assembly and flight test centre. Facilities at Yeadon and Ringway were retained until the end of 1946 after when their activities were transferred to Woodford. Yeadon would later be developed as Leeds Bradford Airport. On the south side of Manchester (Ringway) Airport, Avro's two vacated assembly sheds and flight shed (Hangar Nos. 521/522/523), built in 1942-43 for Metrovicks but retained instead by Avro for production of the York, were subsequently used for a variety of purposes. After providing storage for BEA Ju52/3m and Avro Tudor 4 transports, from 1954 the premises were used by Airwork Ltd. to overhaul over 200 Canadian-built Sabre jet fighters of the RCAF and RAF which NATO were supplying to Greece and Turkey. Airwork shared the contract with their facilities at Speke. The wartime sheds would later be cleared as part of Manchester's Second Runway Project.

Following the company's magnificent war record and Roy Dobson's deserved knighthood in the New Year's Honours List for 1945 (he remained 'Dobbie' to many) it astonished many in the industry that Roy Chadwick was not similarly honoured, both having previously been appointed CBE. Production of the Avro Lancaster ceased when the last of them flew from Yeadon in October 1945. Work on the Lincoln and York continued until Yeadon closed, after when York production was moved to Woodford where it ended in 1948. Manufacture of Avro's pre-war design, the Anson, returned to Woodford from Yeadon in 1946 and continued until 1952, concluding a 17-year production run.

The final Anson T.Mk.21 WJ561 is put through its paces by Jimmy Orrell at Woodford on 15 May 1952.

Anson WJ561 is handed over to Wg.Cdr. H. Budden, RAF, at Woodford on 27 May 1952, with Sir Roy Dobson (left) presiding.

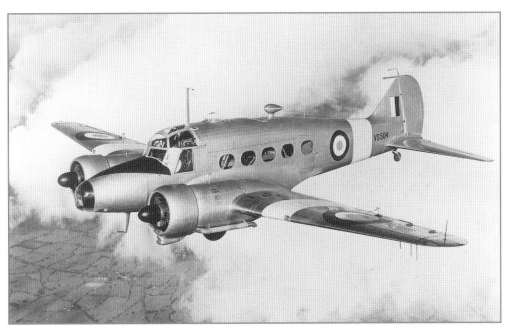

Close-up study of Anson T.Mk.20 VS504 flown by Jimmy Orrell on 5 February 1948.

Preserved Avro
Anson T.Mk.21,
ex-WD413, now
appropriately
G-VROE of
Air Atlantique,
photographed at
RAF Fairford,
2003.

Back in 1943 the Brabazon Committee had started to consider the future of civil aviation in the post-war era and were to report *inter alia* on the need for a large, new aircraft to ply between London and New York and on Empire air routes, and for a jet-powered airliner for the North Atlantic. In the middle of 1944, with Lancaster output at its height, Avro began design of a large four-engined transport aircraft designated the **Avro Type 688**, later named the **Tudor**. From the outset the Merlin-engined Tudor was one of several projects conceived by the industry as interim aircraft pending the availability of the proposed Bristol Brabazon eight-engined airliner and the four-engined de Havilland Comet jetliner. Roy Chadwick, like Alliott Verdon Roe, was by nature an evolutionary rather than revolutionary designer whose projects represented progressive advancement by careful introduction of innovations in design, technology and production one at a time. It was a conservative approach that not only facilitated the production transition between succeeding types but also minimised risk of commercial failure. Moreover, when the Ministry of Supply dictated both to BOAC as the client and

Avro as designer and manufacturer that the Tudor should incorporate as many Lincoln components as possible, the various parties had to comply. With hindsight it should have been obvious that in the Lockheed Constellation and Douglas DC4 the Americans had long since invested in purpose-designed airliners rather than bomber derivatives. Despite its conventional constraints however, the Tudor would be the first British airliner to have a pressurised cabin beneath which the wing spars passed via rubber seals. An initial order for 14 aircraft was increased later to 20.

Powered by four Rolls-Royce Merlin engines, the first of two Tudor 1 prototypes flew at Ringway on 14 June 1945 in the hands of Bill Thorn and Jimmy Orrell. A most elegant aircraft, it was found to have problems of directional and longitudinal stability which were resolved by fitting it with a wider tailplane and considerably enlarged tail fin. Large and brutish in appearance the latter detracted totally from the pleasing lines of the initial design. Much more comfortable to travel in than the Lancaster bomber conversions, the Lancastrian and the utility York that had

Avro Tudor 1
G-AGRF
*Elizabeth of
England* in
BOAC
Speedbird livery
in 1946/47.

preceded it, the Tudor 1 in its initial format had seating for just 12 passengers – only two more than the Lancastrian. The full rationale of building a 120 ft.-wingspan 30-ton aircraft to carry 12 people, even as an interim airliner, when the earliest versions of the Constellation and DC4 seated 44, has eluded aviation historians for many years. Moreover the Americans stood eagerly on the apron or at the end of the runway on modern nosewheel tricycle undercarriages, unlike the Tudor which continued to squat with apparent reluctance on a tailwheel.

In March 1946 BOAC demanded – unreasonably some thought – no less than 343 modifications, many concerning interior design and furnishings. With the prospect of a new Elizabethan Age, the fourth production aircraft, intended as the flagship of BOAC's Tudor fleet, was named *Elizabeth of England* by HRH Princess Elizabeth in a ceremony at London Airport on 21 January 1947. It was a premature celebration. Less than three months later BOAC rejected the Tudors which they considered incapable of transatlantic operation.

Two Tudors off the Woodford production line 'freed' by the cancellation were converted by Sir W.G. Armstrong Whitworth Aircraft at Baginton, Coventry, to Tudor 3 nine-seater transports for use by Government Ministers. Four others were completed with six-foot extensions let into the front fuselage as 32-passenger Tudor 4s for the British South American Airways Corporation (BSAA) operated by the former leader of the wartime Pathfinder Force, Air Vice-Marshal D.C.T. Bennett. The remainder were converted to 28-passenger 4Bs. BSAA commenced services between London and Bermuda late in 1947 but, after the loss of *Star Tiger* and *Star Ariel* in mysterious circumstances in the Bermuda Triangle in January 1948 and January 1949 respectively, the fleet was temporarily grounded. With no clear cause established but pressurisation problems suspected, the Tudors were recommissioned as unpressurised freighters. Bennett, considering sabotage more likely than design or manufacturing defects, never lost faith in the Tudor as a rugged long-range aircraft.

In an entirely separate exercise, the second Tudor 1 prototype, having been

rebuilt as a Tudor 4, was later fitted with four 5,000lb-thrust Rolls-Royce Nene turbojets paired in underwing nacelles. As the Tudor 8, it first flew in this form in September 1948 nearly a year before the maiden flight of the world's first true jet airliner, the de Havilland Comet. Accordingly the Tudor 8 became Britain's first four-jet transport. Although it never entered service as such the Tudor 8 provided much useful data for the later Avro 706 Ashton research aircraft.

Aware of the Tudor 1's seating capacity limitations, from 1944 and again with BOAC in mind, Avro had been looking into a 'stretched' version capable of carrying 60 passengers. Their redesign, resulting in the Avro 689 Tudor 2, involved widening the fuselage by twelve inches to a diameter of 11 ft. and lengthening it by 25 ft. to 105 ft. With its wingspan of 120 ft. it was the largest aircraft built in Britain up to that date – but still it sat on a tailwheel. BOAC and its associate airlines ordered 79 while it was still on the design board. The prototype, G-AGSU, was first flown at Woodford on 10 March 1946 by Messrs. Thorn and Orrell, revealing similar problems requiring modifications akin to

those made to the Tudor 1. The resulting weight increase so reduced the Tudor 2's tropical performance that the airlines cut their orders and began looking to America for new aircraft.

But these problems seemed as nothing when, on 23 August 1947, Avro and the whole Tudor programme suffered a grievous blow. G-AGSU crashed on take-off at Woodford. Killed were Chief Test Pilot Bill Thorn, his co-pilot David Wilson who had survived a large number of wartime flying operations, radio operator John Webster, together with Avro's Chief Designer of some 28 years, then Technical Director – Roy Chadwick. There were two survivors – Stuart Davies who had joined the company in 1938 as Chadwick's assistant designer, had been head of Avro's Experimental Department, local Head Designer at the Yeadon factory during the war and recently succeeded Chadwick as Chief Designer, and engineer Eddie Talbot. The tragedy might have been even worse. Avro's Managing Director Sir Roy Dobson had also been on board until minutes before take-off when he was called back to his office to take an urgent telephone call which it was decided should not delay the

test flight. Investigations revealed the cause to have been the inadvertent reversal of the Tudor's aileron control rigging during overnight adjustments. On take-off the starboard wing had dropped slightly, the pilot's reflex correction serving only to make matters worse, causing the wingtip to hit a tree, the giant aircraft then cartwheeling along the ground. If the aircraft had gained only a little more height the vastly experienced Thorn would in all probability have had enough time to appraise the situation and compensate sufficiently to bring it round and land. It was an accident that had nothing to do with pilot error, design or manufacturing.

Roy Chadwick was only 54 years of age. He had designed more than 200 aeroplanes since joining Avro in 1911, over 35 of which entered production. He was the true successor of Alliott Verdon Roe and would be best remembered for his design of the Avro Lancaster. At the time of his death he had further projects in mind and on the drawing board. He had been appointed CBE, awarded an Honorary MSc by Manchester University, an Associateship of Manchester College of Technology and an Honorary Freeman of the City of London. It remained one of the imponderables of the British honours

system why he had not been accorded the knighthood that so many in the industry believed he richly deserved.

After the teething troubles and problems with the airlines the tragedy must have seemed the final straw for Sir Roy Dobson who, on inspecting the Tudor assembly line, exclaimed "Burn the bloody lot!". Nevertheless, a number were completed in late 1947 and 1948, three as Tudor 2s and six with up-rated engines as 44-seater Tudor 5s for BSAA. None of the latter were used on scheduled services, all being converted into tankers for use on the Berlin Airlift. Altogether, a Tudor 1, Tudor 4 and five Tudor 5s of BSAA flew 2,562 sorties and delivered over 2,300 tons of freight and 19,800 tons of fuel. A BSAA Tudor 5 tanker, G-AKCA, flew 529 sorties – more than any other British or American aircraft involved in the Airlift. The total tonnage it delivered – 4,480 – was exceeded only by an Avro York of Skyways. The second largest number of sorties was made by a Lancastrian of Flight Refuelling. Air Vice-Marshal Bennett, his faith in the Tudor unshaken, had left BSAA to set up his own independent company, Airflight Ltd., buying a Tudor 2 from the Government and a Tudor 5 from BSAA, both for use on the Airlift. It was the

Anson Mk.18s for the Afghan Air Force, with T.Mk.21s for the RAF, on the Woodford production line in July 1948. In the background are several Tudor airliners including Tudor 4 G-AHNH construction of which was abandoned.

The second prototype Avro 688 Tudor 1 G-AGST was rebuilt as a Tudor 4 and later as a Tudor 8 with two pairs of Rolls-Royce Nene 5 turbojets replacing the aircraft's original Merlin piston engines. In 1948 it was Britain's first four-jet transport aircraft, was displayed at Farnborough in military insignia as VX195 and paved the way for the Avro Ashton.

Tudor's finest hour, the record showing the vital contribution made to this life-saving operation by Avro aircraft generally.

At the end of the Airlift, BSAA withdrew its Tudor fleet from service. A number of these and other Tudors were later acquired by Aviation Traders Ltd. of Southend and Stansted, who variously re-engined, lengthened and converted some back to passenger use and fitted others with large freight doors. In the latter form they were known as Traders and Super Traders. Operators included Bennett's new company Fairflight, together with Air Charter established by airline entrepreneur Freddie Laker in 1947. A number of unsold Tudors still in Avro's hands were

scrapped in 1949 but those in service continued flying up to 1959. Ill-fated but far from universally condemned, as an interim concept Britain's first post-war airliner had shown no evidence of any fundamental design shortcomings but experienced more than its fair share of bad luck. After trials with the Tudor 8, powered experimentally by two pairs of Rolls-Royce Nene turbojets, the Ministry of Supply ordered six similarly-engined research aircraft utilising Tudor 2 fuselages shortened to Tudor 1 length. Designated as the **Avro 706 Ashton** they were strongly built with thicker skinning, a redesigned tail fin and – at last – a nosewheel tricycle undercarriage to prevent the Nenes from excavating and

Avro Ashton Mk.3 WB492 first flew on 6 July 1951. Fitted with bomb containers beneath the wings and a ventral radome, it was used by the Radar Research Establishment for radar-assisted bombing research.

Ashton WB492 over the Port
of Liverpool.

blowing too much debris about Woodford. Built at Chadderton, assembled at Woodford and flown there for the first time in September 1950, the Ashton Mk.1 was demonstrated shortly afterwards at the Farnborough Air Show by Jimmy Orrell. The total of six Mks.1, 2, 3 and 4 Ashtons were used for wide-ranging investigations into high altitude turbojet performance, pressurisation, air conditioning, instrumentation and bombing research, yielding much useful information at the dawn of the age of the large, long-range jet aeroplane. They served as flying test beds for Rolls-Royce Avon and Conway, Bristol Olympus and Orpheus, and Armstrong Siddeley Sapphire engines and for engine icing tests. An Ashton powered by Olympus and Orpheus engines in underwing pods outboard of its paired Nenes had the distinction of being the only British six-jet aircraft to fly.

In 1945 the Air Ministry issued a specification for an advanced aircraft powered by a turboprop engine to replace the RAF's Percival Prentice standard trainer. Norwich-based Boulton & Paul Ltd. responded with the Armstrong Siddeley Mamba-powered Balliol, the world's first single turboprop aircraft, which flew in spring 1948. At Avro, Stuart Davies

produced the **T.Mk.1 Athena** of which three prototypes were built. The first, flown at Woodford by Jimmy Orrell in June 1948 and third were Mamba-powered, the second had a Rolls-Royce Dart. Shortage of turboprop engines resulted in a revised specification requiring the fitting of Merlin piston engines of which large stocks were available. The Merlin-engined Athena T.Mk.2 flew in August 1948, 15 being taken by the RAF to replace Harvards. Including prototypes Avro built a total of 22 Athenas before abandoning production when Boulton & Paul and the Balliol secured the RAF's principal order for some 175 aircraft.

In 1946, RAF Coastal Command stated its requirement for a land-based long-range maritime reconnaissance aircraft to replace American Fortresses and Liberators due to be returned to the USA on expiry of lend-lease arrangements. Roy Chadwick and the Avro design team came forward with an extensive adaptation of the Lincoln bomber. Initially styled Lincoln Mk.III, it employed the Lincoln mainplane and undercarriage together with many Tudor assemblies. The tailplane was redesigned with two larger fins, reset higher on a new stressed-skin fuselage shorter but more commodious than the Lincoln's. Four 2,450hp Rolls-Royce Griffon engines would

each drive six-bladed contra-rotating propellers. Architecturally, there was no mistaking its Lincoln, Lancaster and even Manchester heritage, but the aircraft was sufficiently advanced to merit separate identity. Chadwick designated it the **Avro 696 Shackleton** in honour of his wife's relative Sir Ernest Shackleton, whom he had met when providing an Avro 554 floatplane as back-up for the explorer's 1921 South Polar expedition.

When Jimmy Orrell lifted the Shackleton GR.1/MR.1 prototype off the Woodford runway on 9 March 1949 it was a particularly poignant moment – the first major design initiated by Chadwick that the great man did not live to see in flight. Production aircraft started to fly from October 1950, entering service at RAF Kinloss in February 1951 replacing the stop-gap Lancaster MR.3. The 40-ton Shackleton carried a ten-man crew and was equipped with a 'chin' radome, cannon either side of its nose with two also in a dorsal turret, two machine guns in the tail with bombs and depth charges in the weapons bay. Operational experience dictated a number of modifications and

after 77 MR.1s had been completed, work began at Chadderton and Woodford on 69 MR.2s with longer noses and revised armament, the 'chin' replaced by a semi-retractable 'dustbin' radome capable of scanning 360 degrees, located behind the weapons bay. The rear armament was dispensed with and a transparent Perspex tail cone fitted. The MR.2 entered service in 1952, was based in the UK and Malta, undertook extensive overseas 'goodwill' tours and operated in the Pacific during the Christmas Island atomic tests. The MR.2 is particularly remembered for a display at the 1953 Farnborough Air Show when, carrying a lifeboat beneath the fuselage in Air-Sea Rescue configuration, it performed a fly-past with only the starboard outer engine running, the other propellers feathered.

Work started in 1954 on another up-grade, the MR.3. Major modifications included a reshaped wing with auxiliary wingtip fuel tanks for extended range patrol, deletion of the dorsal turret and a new nosewheel tricycle undercarriage. 34 were built, entering service in 1957 and gaining a reputation for extended range

In its element – Shackleton MR.3 'B' of No. 120 Sqn. with 360 degree ventral radome descended, pictured during the 1960s.

Shackleton MR.3 production at Woodford in the latter part of the 1950s.

and endurance. They regularly stayed aloft for 18 hours and, in 1959, one established a record of 24 hours 21 minutes. It was demonstrated at Farnborough when an MR.3 took off, arriving back at the same time the following day. Impressed by the RAF's MR.2s on a joint exercise in 1955, the South African Air Force ordered eight MR.3s which they collected from Woodford in 1957. They served with the SAAF until 1984. Between 1965 and 1968 most of the RAF's MR.3s had Bristol Viper turbojets installed behind both outboard Griffon engines to improve take-off and climb when heavily loaded. The work was carried out at HSA Langar, Woodford and Bitteswell near Lutterworth, Leicestershire. In the 1960s both Chadderton and

Woodford gained additional work when given responsibility for manufacture and stress testing of wings for the HS650 Argosy four-turboprop twin-boom transport aircraft, sometimes unflatteringly referred to as the 'Whistling Wheelbarrow'. The Argosy's mainplane was based on that of the Shackleton MR.3 and given the type number Avro 733.

In the late 1960s an urgent requirement for improved detection of low-flying hostile aircraft precipitated work on an airborne early warning version of the Shackleton. 12 serving MR.2s were converted to that role, one 'prototype' at Woodford during 1970-71 and the rest at HSA Bitteswell between 1971-73. Some earlier MR.1s had already been withdrawn and the MR.2 proved to have a longer fatigue life than the MR.3 whose wings had been subject to additional strain by its Viper turbojets and heavy wingtip tanks. The resulting AEW.Mk.2, sprouting a large ventral radome forward of the weapons bay and housing radar equipment taken from Fairey Gannet AEW.3s, first flew in September 1971 and entered service early in 1972.

The introduction of the Hawker Siddeley Nimrod in 1969 indicated the ending of the Shackleton's maritime reconnaissance role and the MR.3, with shortened wing life, was withdrawn in 1972. But in the hands of No. 8 Squadron at RAF Lossiemouth AEW.Mk.2s, each named after a character in *The Magic Roundabout*, enjoyed a spectacular lease of life remaining in service until replaced by the Boeing Sentry AEW.Mk.1 in 1991. Old-fashioned valve technology in an aircraft conceived in the 1940s served Britain's air defences for nearly half of the Shackleton's overall 40-year service life.

New crew members were often amazed at the 'wartime' feel of the Shackleton's interior, the noise level, smell of fuel and oil and temperature ambience ranging from freezing cold in some areas to almost unbearably hot in others. Yet the aircraft,

variously referred to as the 'old growler', 'grey lady', 'ten thousand rivets flying in close formation' or even 'as ugly as a box of frogs' (surely not!), like many other Avro products generated great affection amongst crews and the public generally. Six AEW.Mk.2s overflew British Aerospace plants at Woodford and elsewhere on 9 March 1989 to commemorate the 40th Anniversary of the Shackleton's first flight. Shackleton AEW.Mk.2 WR960 *Dougal* which flew with No. 8 Squadron between 1972-82 is today displayed in the Aviation Hall of the Museum of Science and Industry in Manchester.

In 1947, with design of the world's first jet bomber – the A1 (Canberra) high altitude light bomber – well advanced at English Electric in Preston, Government issued Specification B.35/46 for a high altitude heavy bomber capable of carrying a nuclear weapon at speeds close to that of sound. The task was to carry a 10,000lb nuclear device for 1,750 miles at up to 50,000 ft. in an aircraft of 100,000lb (later 115,000lb) all-up weight. Seven companies responded in a scramble to harness such wartime German advanced high speed flight research data as had been left unappropriated by the USA and USSR: Armstrong Whitworth, Avro, Bristol, English Electric, Handley Page, Shorts and Vickers. In complete contrast to today when multi-national consortia are necessary to finance even single aircraft programmes, late in 1947 the Government gave the go-ahead to no fewer than three separate British submissions: Vickers, Avro and Handley Page. Moreover, the advanced Avro and Handley Page designs also required the financing and construction of no less than six small scale (one third) flying research versions to prove the technology. It was typical of the fail-safe Government procurement policy of the times, the relatively conventional Vickers proposal seemingly offering insurance against any failure of the more radical designs of Avro and Handley Page. Even more remarkably by today's standards, in the outcome all three entered production and service with the RAF as the V-bomber trio – the Valiant (1955), Vulcan (1956) and Victor (1957).

Roy Chadwick departed completely from Avro's traditional axiom of development through evolution when, in January 1947, he began to consider a truly revolutionary design taking account of as much German data on swept-wing, all-wing tailless and delta-form aerofoils as was available. As his original schematic became detailed into the **Avro 698** he could not have foreseen that it would be his final project. Due to the seemingly conflicting performance, size and weight specifications of B.35/46 it was not a very auspicious start. Initial calculations indicated that the wingspan necessary for a swept-wing configuration would result in an aircraft that grossly exceeded the weight limit, itself determined by the strength of RAF airfield runways at the time. In an inspired solution Avro reduced the span but maintained the wing area by filling in the space between the trailing edge and fuselage, creating a triangular or delta planform. Control would be by a combination of trailing edge elevons and wingtip fins. Such a wing, landing at a high angle of attack, would generate a huge air cushion eliminating the need for flaps or slots which in conventional designs induced pitching forces requiring compensating tailplane elevator control. Accordingly Chadwick was able to effect further weight reduction by dispensing with a conventional tail unit.

Preliminary designs were submitted to the Ministry of Supply in April 1947. On 17 July Hawker Siddeley Chairman Sir Thomas Sopwith informed Chadwick that they had been accepted and that a contract for detailed design and construction of prototypes would follow. Little more than five weeks later, before the contract was issued, Roy Chadwick died in the crash of the prototype Tudor 2 airliner at

Woodford. His deputy, Stuart Davies, survived and was subsequently able to take the Avro 698 project forward. Chadwick was succeeded as Technical Director by Bill (later Sir William) Farren, previously Director of Technical Development at the Ministry of Supply.

As design proceeded, in 1948 the Ministry ordered two one-third scale research aircraft from Avro to explore the virtually unknown low and high speed handling characteristics of delta wing aircraft. Handley Page built an equivalent research vehicle for their own crescent wing HP80 project, only Vickers' proposals being considered sufficiently conventional not to require a scaled-down trials version.

Woodford made rapid progress on the construction of the prototype research aircraft, designated the **Avro 707**. Built with components from various existing aircraft and powered by a single 3,500lb-thrust Rolls-Royce Derwent turbojet, it was completed in August 1949 and taken by road to the A & AEE at Boscombe Down where it first flew early in September. Tragedy struck Avro once more when later that month it crashed, killing test pilot Eric 'Red' Esler. A second version, the 707B, was completed the following year specifically for low speed research and again taken to Boscombe Down where it was flown in September by Wg. Cdr. R.J. 'Roly' Falk, Avro's Superintendent of Flying. It was displayed in the static park at the Farnborough Air Show. Three more were built over the next three years, two 707As for high speed research and a 707C for two-seat familiarisation. The latter was completed at Avro's Bracebridge Heath repair centre and, after extensive research use up to 1967 including fitting with a fly-by-wire electric servo system duplicating the conventional control circuits, was preserved at Cosford. The second 707A is now at the Museum of Science and Industry in Manchester.

Avro 707A
WD280 high
speed delta wing
experimental
aircraft, first
flown at
Boscombe
Down
by Roly Falk on
14 June 1951.
It was the third
of five such
aircraft and the
first of them
with wing root
engine intakes.

Meanwhile, major amendments were being made to the full scale Avro 698 during the detailed design phase, most notably the abandonment of wingtip fins and their replacement with a single vertical dorsal fin and rudder, with the addition of an elongated nose containing pressurised cockpit and crew stations. The 99 ft.-wingspan delta was an immensely strong structure, seven feet deep at the wing roots which merged around a 9 ft.-diameter circular section fuselage containing a vast 29 ft. weapons bay capable of accommodating a nuclear weapon or 21 conventional 1,000lb HE bombs. Retaining the frontal 'thinness' required aerodynamically for high speed flight the airframe offered sufficient internal space also for the four proposed 9,750lb-thrust Bristol Olympus turbojets in the wing roots, with fuel tanks and main eight-bogie undercarriage units in the wings themselves. Weighty, drag-inducing defensive armament turrets never featured in the design for an aircraft intended to reach its target at high altitude and speed.

Avro 698 component manufacture began at Chadderton in 1951. The structure, if

not the design, was relatively conventional, made from high strength light alloy with localised magnesium alloy for fin and control surfaces which were subcontracted to Armstrong Whitworth at Coventry. New techniques such as rigid bonded metal honeycomb were of such recent innovation as to be limited to detail parts. The wing structure was dominated by two huge spars within which the engines were contained by high tensile steel rings. Avro's Empire Works at Manchester made sheet metal components and the Bracebridge Heath works produced fin and rudder assemblies. Front and rear centre section sub-assemblies came together as a single 35 ft.-long unit at Chadderton where massive jigs were called for to compensate for soft ground beneath the factory. The centre-sections' 16-mile road journeys to Woodford for final assembly necessitated the local authority installing hinged lamp-posts along the route. At Woodford an overhead travelling crane lifted the centre-section, by then 65 feet from nose to fin, for mating up with the outer wings. The wing structures were deep enough for fitters to work inside much of their area.

All staff were under intense pressure to get the Avro 698 into the air for the 1952 Farnborough Air Show, ahead of Handley Page's HP80. Retired Avro Inspector Harold Ingham, of Poulton-le-Fylde, recalls members of the Avro workforce sleeping at the factory to complete the aircraft in time and food being served in the canteen by no less than Sir Roy Dobson himself.

Resplendent in overall white, the prototype was rolled out of the Woodford assembly hall at the end of August. Delays with its Olympus engines had required interim installation of four 6,500lb Rolls-Royce Avons and so powered it made its maiden flight on 30 August in the hands of Roly Falk. Amazingly, with the second pilot's seat amongst a number of items still to be fitted, Falk flew the five-crew aircraft single-handedly. Despite two undercarriage fairing panels being seen to flutter down, detached by the slipstream and flexing of the mighty wing structure, the aircraft showed great handling and performance potential from the start. An Avro 707 and

a Vampire were sent up to carry out visual inspection of the Vulcan's exterior before Falk was allowed to land. During the flight the factory and emergency service switchboards in the area were flooded with calls from local residents, alarmed by sightings of a huge alien craft in the sky. Road traffic was brought to a standstill. Falk, a flamboyant, vastly experienced former RAF test pilot, had a penchant for flying wearing an immaculate lounge suit, his only concession to piloting dress being a leather flying helmet. Only days later he stole the Farnborough Air Show with daily demonstrations of the massively elegant white bomber, still minus its undercarriage panels, patriotically flanked by red and blue Avro 707s flown by company pilots Orrell and Nelson. Each evening at the Air Show, and afterwards on the aircraft's return to Woodford, tests had to be carried out to ensure that no structural damage had been sustained to airframe bulkhead, pipework and micro-switches from the buffeting received as a result of flying without the

Roly Falk flies the Olympus-powered second Vulcan prototype VX777 ahead of the Sapphire-powered first prototype VX770, in formation with four Avro 707s en route to the 1953 Farnborough Air Show.

Second
production
Vulcan B.1
XA890 nearing
completion at
Woodford in
1955. Roly Falk
slow-rolled it at
Farnborough
that year, to the
astonishment of
spectators and
officials.

Opposite:
Third
production
Vulcan B.1
XA891 over
Crosby, with
Bootle and
Liverpool
beyond and the
whole of the
Wirral Peninsula
between the
Mersey and Dee
Estuaries and
Liverpool Bay,
around 1955.
Vulcan B.1s, of
which 45 were
built at
Woodford, now
incorporated the
'kinked' wing
leading edge.

panels. Harold Ingham and a colleague were given the job of modifying the original aluminium 'piano hinges' of the undercarriage fairings with much stronger mag-alloy castings. In October the aircraft was named **Vulcan**.

Intensive trials followed with the first prototype re-engined with 7,500lb Armstrong Siddeley Sapphires and the second with the intended 9,750lb Olympus engines. The unfamiliar outline of the Vulcan continued to generate reports of UFO sightings. Both prototypes flew at Farnborough in 1953 in formation with red, blue, orange and silver 707s. Falk was given considerable freedom to design the controls and cockpit layout. To match the Vulcan's fighter-like handling and manoeuvrability he opted for a pistol-grip control column rather than the conventional heavy aircraft 'spectacle' type. When in the climb he slow-rolled the second production Vulcan at Farnborough in 1955, ostensibly to demonstrate its exceptional structural integrity, the authorities and Sir Roy Dobson were reputedly not best pleased. Further rolls

were banned. Falk took Prime Minister Sir Anthony Eden for a more sedate flight later at the show, much to the delight of the PM who, in his 'thank you' letter, also urged Falk to "be careful of that roll!".

Availability of the powerful Olympus enabled flight testing up to maximum speed but also revealed severe buffeting not induced by the interim engines. Following experiments with the 707 this was solved aerodynamically by 'kinking' the Vulcan wing leading edges forwards at three quarters span and giving them a thinner, downward-drooping profile. This 'Phase 2' wing was incorporated in subsequent production aircraft from 1955 and earlier aircraft modified retrospectively.

Also in 1955, Avro concluded an order placed by the Ministry of Supply in November 1950 for construction of Canberra B.2 light bombers under licence from English Electric. The first flew at Woodford in November 1952, deliveries of 75 taking place between March 1953 and March 1955. A further 75 were cancelled due to pressures on the defence budget

and a relative easing of tension after the end of the Korean War in 1953. It cleared the way for full-scale production of the Vulcan B.1 which entered RAF service in 1956. In September a newly delivered Vulcan made a goodwill proving flight to New Zealand via the Middle and Far East but triumph ended in tragedy when on returning to land at London Airport in low cloud and rain it undershot and crashed. Initial design proposals for a jettisonable capsule for all the crew had been found impracticable as a result of which only the pilot and co-pilot were provided with ejector seats and survived: the rest of the crew seated in the fuselage below lost their lives. Provision for emergency evacuation of the Vulcan was a source of controversy throughout its life.

Vulcans, painted overall anti-flash white as evidence of their awesome capability, were soon familiar sights among the relatively few aircraft etching long white contrails across the clear blue skies over Britain nearly 50 years ago. It seemed fitting that No. 617 Squadron, RAF, who as the Dam Busters had used the Avro Lancaster in 1943 should be re-formed at Scampton to fly the Avro Vulcan in 1958. The 45th and final B.1 was delivered in 1959.

The B.1 airframe was capable of much further development and in 1955, designer J.R Ewans who replaced Stuart Davies after his resignation that year, began work on the B.2. The RAF wished to increase the operating ceiling of its nuclear deterrent spearhead and accordingly, in the Vulcan's Phase 2C wing, the span was extended from 99 to 111 ft. representing a 15 per cent increase in area. Two pairs of combined elevons replaced the previous elevators and ailerons and a new bulged tail housed electronic counter measures and radar. The first B.2, a modified B.1 prototype, was flown by Roly Falk in August 1957. Between 1960 and 1963 existing B.1s in service were withdrawn for conversion to hybrid B.1As, incorporating some of the B.2 features, work carried out mostly by Sir W.G. Armstrong Whitworth at Bitteswell. Between 1962 and 1964 all B.2s received 20,000lb-thrust Olympus engines and with all-up weight of 200,000lb could achieve heights in excess of 64,000 ft. over a range 25-30 per cent greater than the B.1.

In 1963 Sir Roy Dobson, Managing Director of Avro from 1941 and Managing Director of Hawker Siddeley from 1958, was appointed Chairman of the entire Hawker Siddeley Group, the constituent

Opposite:
The Shuttleworth Collection's Avro 504K 'E3404' (H5199) was rebuilt from a derelict 1920s' 504N by apprentices at Chadderton and Woodford in 1954-55. The restored aircraft was flown for the first time, on 19 August 1955, by Jimmy Orrell and starred in the 1956 film *Reach for the Sky* with Kenneth More as Douglas Bader. Over three decades separated the 504K from the overflying Vulcan B.1.

Three generations of Avro aircraft fly over Woodford around 1955 – rebuilt 504K 'E3404', a Shackleton and a Vulcan. Speed differentials would have meant a 'formation' of very limited duration.

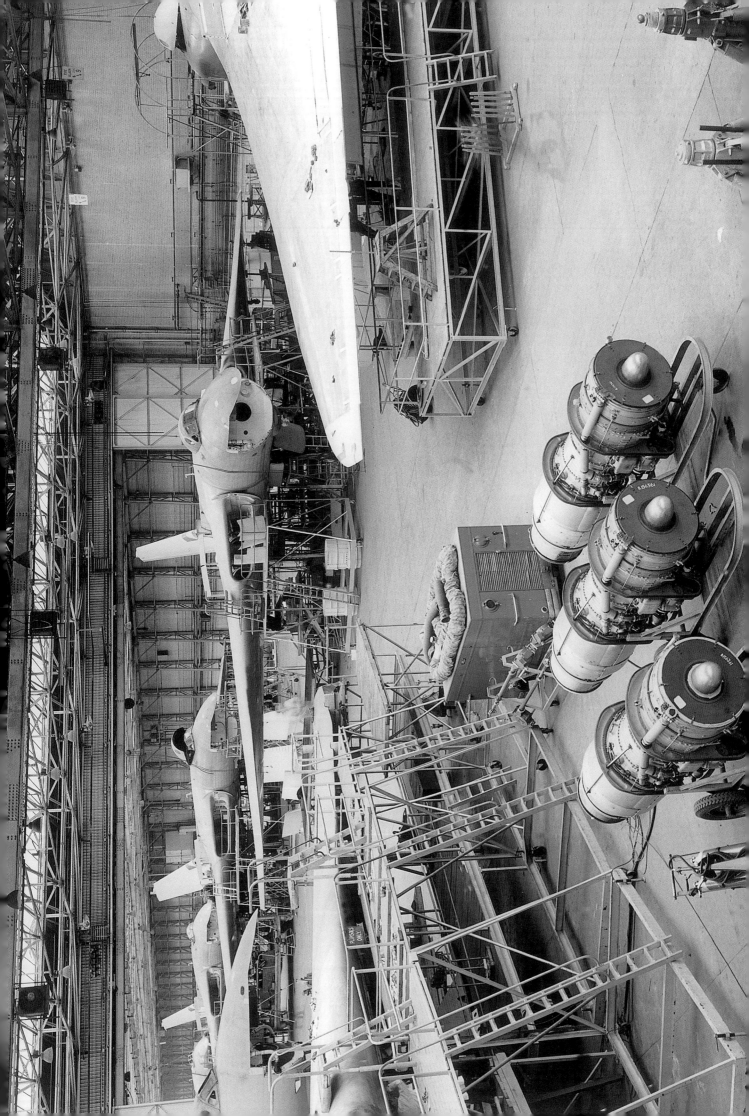

companies of which – Hawker, Armstrong Siddeley, Armstrong Whitworth, A.V. Roe, de Havilland, Gloster, Folland and Blackburn – were restructured into Hawker Siddeley Aviation (HSA) and Hawker Siddeley Dynamics (HSD). In a further strengthening of the Manchester connection between the names Avro and Whitworth, they were linked as the Avro-Whitworth Division of Hawker Siddeley Aviation. Sir Roy retired in 1967 at the age of 75 and died after only a year of retirement in 1968.

The reinforcement of defensive rings of surface-to-air missiles around targets in the Soviet Union prompted development of a stand-off missile, to be carried by RAF Vulcans and Victors, which eliminated the need for them to overfly or approach the target closely for 'free-fall' delivery of their bomb load. A Weapons Research Division had been established at Woodford in 1956 and, with an MoS contract placed, it was there that Avro designed and built **Blue Steel**, a 35 ft.-long, 13 ft.-span, 17,000lb nuclear stand-off missile powered by a Bristol Siddeley Stentor rocket motor capable of propelling it to over 70,000 ft. at 1,000mph. The combustion chambers for the Stentor were made by the Joseph Lucas Company of Burnley. Guided by an Elliott inertial navigation system the stainless steel missile was accurate to within 300 ft. over a range in excess of 100 miles. Apart from the warhead itself, Blue Steel's propellant of hydrogen peroxide and kerosene made it extremely dangerous to handle. Trials with Vulcan B.2s at the Woomera range in Australia and elsewhere began in 1959 and 57 of the weapons were ordered. Other trials which started in 1961 with the Douglas Skybolt, the world's first air-launched ballistic missile, were terminated when the Americans cancelled the project the following year. Special wing strengthening and Skybolt attachment hardpoints were fitted to Vulcan B.2s from the 40th production

aircraft onwards. The work was not entirely wasted as it contributed significantly to the Vulcan's future low altitude extended service life. Cancellation of Skybolt put paid however to designs for a larger 'Phase 6' or B.3 development of the Vulcan which had been intended to carry six of the strategic nuclear missiles. The entry into service of Blue Steel required airframe changes to be made to B.2s on the factory production line, the 26th to 61st aircraft, sometimes referred to as B.2As, built specifically to accommodate the weapon. In 1963 No. 617 Squadron became the first of three Vulcan Blue Steel squadrons operational at Scampton. In 1964 the combined strength of the V-force reached its all-time high with 50 Valiants, 39 Victors and 70 Vulcans. Altogether five Blue Steel squadrons were operational with a core strength of 24 Vulcan and 16 Victor B.2s equipped with the missiles. But increasing concern at the effectiveness of Soviet SAM missiles after the USAF U-2 of Gary Powers was shot down from 70,000 ft. over the Soviet Union in 1960 resulted in a major change in RAF tactics. Whereas Skybolt would have enabled Vulcans to stand off 1,000 miles from their target, Blue Steel still required them to approach within 200 miles. Accordingly, from 1964 Blue Steel became a low altitude delivery system, necessitating for the first time the application of a camouflage colour scheme to the upper surfaces of some Vulcans. The 89th and last B.2 was delivered to the RAF in 1965, all B.1As being withdrawn from service and replaced by B.2s between 1966-68.

During the 1960s the USSR had a highly capable bomber force but lacked any system comparable to the Vulcan, Victor and Blue Steel. When the USSR deployed low trajectory missiles in forward locations in Europe in the '60s it was necessary to keep Vulcans and their crews on Quick Reaction Alert (QRA), dispersing them in groups of four on Operational Readiness

Page 170 photo: Vulcan B.2 final assembly at Woodford around 1960 with Olympus engines awaiting fitting.

Page 171 photo: A view which emphasises the sheer expanse of the Vulcan's delta wing.

Opposite: Vulcan B.2s of No. 83 Sqn., lined up for Exercise *May Flight* at RAF Scampton on 11 May 1961. Few other photographs conjure up the awesome might of the RAF of the 1960s so effectively, a period when it possessed greater destructive power than at any other time in its history. Avro built 136 Vulcans at Manchester and Woodford, 89 as B.2s.

In another world – Vulcan B.2 XJ783 resplendent in anti-flash white, at high altitude.

Production of the Avro Blue Steel stand-off nuclear 'cruise' missile at Woodford. The red and white example in the background was for use in trials. Britain's primary nuclear deterrent for much of the 1960s, Blue Steel was deployed with Vulcans at Scampton (1963-69) and Victors at Wittering (1963-68) where the missiles were completed to operational readiness.

Vulcan B.2 XA903 displaying a Blue Steel stand-off missile test vehicle. On retirement from the RAF in 1961, Air Chief Marshal Sir Harry Broadhurst, formerly AOC-in-C of Bomber Command and Cmdr. Allied Air Forces, Central Europe, a survivor of the Vulcan crash at Heathrow in 1956, joined A.V. Roe as Managing Director. His responsibilities included the Blue Steel Project. He was a director of the Hawker Siddeley Group from 1968 to 1976.

Handley Page Victor B.2 XH675 participated in Blue Steel development trials at Woodford in the early 1960s. It was one of 24 Victors converted to K2 tankers at Woodford during 1970-76.

Platforms (ORPs) alongside runways. In this way, fully armed, fuelled and ready to go they could be airborne in less than half the four minutes warning time for incoming ICBMs, maintaining the credibility of an overwhelming retaliatory response as a deterrent to any attack. The record was four Vulcans airborne in 84 seconds. At the height of the Cuban missile crisis in 1962, as UK domestic life proceeded virtually as normal all around, for three days Vulcans and Victors stood ready to go from airfields of RAF Bomber Command until given the order to stand down to their everyday state of readiness. QRA was maintained throughout the decade with the Vulcan force becoming part of RAF Strike Command on the merging of Bomber and Fighter Commands in April 1968, until the primary responsibility for Britain's nuclear deterrent was transferred to the Royal Navy's Polaris submarine fleet on 30 June 1969.

To witness in the 1960s the push-button simultaneous 'mass rapid' engine start-up and take-off of a flight of four all-white 100-ton Vulcans on QRA, climbing steeply one after another, was equally awesome whether into a clear blue sky or disappearing abruptly into the overcast. It was a seismic event of two minutes' duration or less, leaving observers looking at an empty runway and a pall of smoke with the receding thunder of 16 Olympus engines beating in their chests. What foe could possibly threaten a Britain with such might at her disposal? But such displays of military strength at air shows in the 1960s served not just to thrill the crowds: they were also very public demonstrations to the USSR and its satellites of Britain's nuclear capability. Indeed, information that has come to light since 1990 shows the very great respect Soviet military strategists had for Britain's V-force of the 1960s.

Vulcan B.2s fly past the Fylingdales Early Warning Radar Station in North Yorkshire, opened in 1963 to provide early warning (four minutes) of missile attack to enable the V-force to become airborne in time to retaliate. The combined system comprised a viable and manifestly successful deterrent for a number of years until responsibility for the UK's nuclear deterrent was taken over by the Royal Navy's fleet of nuclear-powered Polaris ICBM-carrying submarines.

Victor B.2s under conversion to K.2 tankers at Woodford, 1970-76.

After 1969 it was decided to keep 60 Vulcans in service in the low-level penetration role made possible by the aircraft's immensely strong structure. Disruptive camouflage, previously applied to aircraft of the post-1964 low altitude Blue Steel force was now applied to all Vulcans, an essential though regrettable desecration of the graceful aircraft's former overall white. In 1973 nine Vulcans were modified to B.2 MRR maritime radar reconnaissance standard to counter a

Victor K.2 tanker XL231, newly converted at Woodford, around 1976.

Vulcan B.2 XM603 of No. 44 (Rhodesia) Sqn., Waddington, returning to Woodford on 12 March 1982 on its withdrawal from service. It was subsequently re-painted in its original anti-flash white and is still preserved today at Woodford by the '603 Club' of retired and present employees.

growing Soviet naval build-up, retaining this role until 1982. Others were kept as strategic bombers until replaced that year by Tornados.

Examples of all three types of V-bombers were converted to serve as aerial tankers in the later stages of their lives. Handley Page at Radlett converted a number of

Victors in the mid-1960s but, when more were required in 1969, the company's imminent liquidation required the contract to be placed with their arch-competitors, formerly Avro, at Woodford and Chadderton. There, between 1970 and 1976, HSA converted and practically rebuilt some 24 Victor 2s as K.Mk.2 tankers, the first being delivered to the RAF in 1972. It was felt that Sir Frederick Handley Page, who had died in 1962, must have turned in his grave. But the former Avro works did an excellent job: the Victors emerged with a long fatigue life, serving until 1993.

When Argentina invaded the Falkland Islands in 1982 it was essential to deny the Argentinian military the use of the airfield at Port Stanley for its potent Skyhawk, Mirage and Super Etendard strike aircraft. A force of five Vulcans was hurriedly prepared for deployment requiring the reactivation of their in-flight refuelling systems. After 26 years as a supremely successful deterrent, the five attack missions undertaken by Vulcans comprising Operation *Black Buck* were the only occasions they were ever used in action. The attacks on Port Stanley with 21 one thousand pound HE bombs were the longest bombing raids in military history involving return flights of 15¾ hours over the 3,900 miles from Ascension Island to the target. They required the support of ten of the Victor K.2 tankers converted at Woodford a decade before. It was ironic that in 1981 Argentina had unsuccessfully attempted to acquire surplus Vulcans from the RAF to replace their ageing fleet of Canberra bombers. Operation *Black Buck* was in the tradition of the raid by Avro 504s on Friedrichshafen in 1914 and by Avro Lancasters on the Ruhr Dams in 1943 when small forces of Manchester-built Avro aircraft had also been formed to undertake key precision strategic attacks.

Victory in the Falklands revealed the need for a larger RAF aerial tanker fleet to support supply flights to the islands and in April 1982 British Aerospace started work at Woodford on the conversion of six Vulcan B.2s into K.2 tankers. The first flew at Woodford in June and Vulcan K.2s served until 1984 when they were replaced by VC10 tankers. For Harold Ingham, who had started work with Fairey at Heaton Chapel at the beginning of 1935,

being brought back out of 'retirement' to work on Vulcans at the time of the Falklands War came at the end of a career spanning 50 years in the aircraft industry which concluded with his final retirement in 1984. During that time he had worked on some 40 different types of aircraft at locations also including Woodford, Ringway, Boscombe Down, Farnborough and Waddington.

Vulcans contributed to the development programmes of a number of other important aircraft and were used as flying test beds for Rolls-Royce Conway and Spey engines, Olympus engines for the TSR.2 and Concorde, together with the RB.199 for the Tornado. During their 28-year operational service with the RAF they became familiar sights worldwide and a number remain preserved on static display around the world as well as at the RAF Museum at Hendon and at the BAE Systems plant at Woodford where all 136 production aircraft and prototypes were assembled and flight tested. The last Vulcan on RAF charge, XH 588, was demonstrated by the Vulcan Display Flight at air shows until 1993 and is today maintained privately by the Vulcan Operating Company at Bruntingthorpe, Leicestershire. Hopes that it might fly again received a major boost with the offer in 2003 of substantial National Heritage Lottery Funding. It would be a fitting tribute to a North West aircraft that perhaps more than any other ensured Britain's security for nearly three decades.

So prolific was Avro's design department that during the company's long history three times as many aircraft types came off the drawing boards as entered production. The **Avro 720** was a mixed power-plant high altitude interceptor with D.H. Firestreak missiles which would have used an Armstrong Siddeley Screamer rocket to engage its target before returning to base under the power of an A.S. Viper turbojet. A prototype, using advanced Avro metal

Three of six
Vulcan B.2s
which
underwent
conversion to
K.2 tankers at
Woodford in
1982.

B.2 XH558 of
the RAF's Vulcan
Display Flight
enthrals the
visitors at a
sunny Woodford
Air Display in
1990. XH558
was one of the
six Vulcans
converted to K.2
tankers at
Woodford in
1982, but was
reinstated there
as a B.2 for the
Display Flight in
1985.

The prototype
Avro 720
XD696 mixed
powerplant
rocket and
turbojet
interceptor
aircraft, built
almost to
completion at
Chadderton in
1956 before
being scrapped
in defence cuts.

honeycomb panels, was built almost to completion at Chadderton before being cancelled, along with the projected **Avro 730** eight-engined stainless steel Mach 2 bomber, in government cuts at the time of the 1957 Defence White Paper. The **Avro Atlantic** was an abortive 1952 design for a 100-seat airliner based on the Vulcan.

Following the publication of Duncan Sandys' notorious 1957 Defence White Paper heralding the age of the missile, the end of manned fighters and no manned replacement for the V-bombers, Avro were among a number of manufacturers left seeking a future role. Ten years after their experience with the troubled Tudor, the company took the brave decision to look again at the civil market. In 1958 a team under J.R. Ewans began privately-funded design of a medium-sized rugged transport as a replacement for the ageing American Douglas Dakota, to be capable of landing on sub-standard airstrips around the world. Designated the **Avro 748**, it took shape as a low-wing, 95 ft.-span all-metal pressurised airliner to seat 44 passengers within a circular section fuselage. Power would come from two of the proven Rolls-Royce Dart 1,740hp turboprop engines mounted

on the upper wing surface to allow good ground clearance for the 12 ft.-diameter airscrews. The slim engine nacelles merged into bulged housings below the wings containing the main landing gear.

Early in 1959 work started at Chadderton on the construction of four prototypes, two for static testing and two for test flying. That year a series of fires devastated much of the works, destroying the company archive dating back to its earliest days. Vulcan production was held up and the second prototype 748 badly damaged.

Only 17 months after the decision to proceed, unscathed by the fires, the first prototype took to the air at Woodford on 24 June 1960 with a crew captained by Jimmy Harrison, Chief Test Pilot from 1958. The duration of nearly 2³/₄ hours was a world record for the maiden flight of any civil airliner, suggesting the excellence of the initial design. Orders had been received even before the first flight and an agreement was entered into for assembly of the aircraft in India by Hindustan Aeronautics Ltd. from components made in Britain.

The first (G-APZV in the background) and second (G-ARAY) Avro 748 prototypes. G-ARAY became the company demonstrator and was converted to the Series 2 prototype in 1961. G-APZV became the Avro 748 MF prototype in 1962-63.

RAF Andover C.MK.1 (Avro/HS.748 MF) production line at Woodford c.1965.

RAF Andover C.MK.1 XS605, one of 31 built, with upswept rear fuselage for the drop-down loading ramp and consequently high-set tailplane.

HS./BAe 748
Series 2A c/n
1761, C6-BEB,
one of four
supplied to
Bahamasair.

The first production 748 Series 1 flew at Woodford in August 1961, its wingspan increased slightly to 98 ft. 6 in. following ground tests and flight trials. Manufacturing was spread around several Hawker Siddeley Group companies, Avro making the fuselage and engine nacelles, Folland the wings, Armstrong Whitworth the tail and Hawker the ailerons, the whole being assembled at Woodford. This proved costly and entire production was later centred on Chadderton and Woodford.

A Series 2 version, capable of seating 62 passengers and operating from airfields at higher elevations, was flown in 1961 powered by Dart engines of over 2,000hp. The Avro sales team and 748 demonstrator scoured the world for orders, identifying such demand for short-medium range feeder airliners that the aircraft sold to some 80 operators in 50 countries, in every continent. In service the 748 matched handsomely the original concept, operating from frozen airstrips in the northern latitudes, in temperate regions and from jungle and desert landing grounds. Some were provided as optional or convertible passenger/freighters with a large cargo door on the rear fuselage side.

The Avro 748 was selected as the personal transport for 16 Heads of State. Legend has it that the weighty opulence of the interior specified by one potentate required localised strengthening of the airframe. The RAF received six Series 2 VIP versions, two of which joined the Queen's Flight.

Impressed by the 748's ability to operate from rough terrain, in 1962 the RAF ordered a heavier version with reinforced floor capable of carrying vehicles or up to 48 fully equipped troops. First flown in December 1963, the Hawker Siddeley 748 MF (Military Freighter), powered by 2,970hp Dart engines turning 14 ft. 6 in. propellers, was fitted with a rear loading door with ramp under a swept-up tail. Reviving a name last used by Avro some 40 years earlier, this became the **Andover C.Mk.1**, delivery of 31 of which started in 1965. The RAF operated them worldwide in tactical transport, communications and electronic calibration roles. Series 2 HS.748s in RAF service were designated Andover C.C. Mk.2s. Versions of the 748 were also operated by the Air Forces of New Zealand, Australia, Belgium, Brazil, Colombia, Equador and Malaysia. In 1967

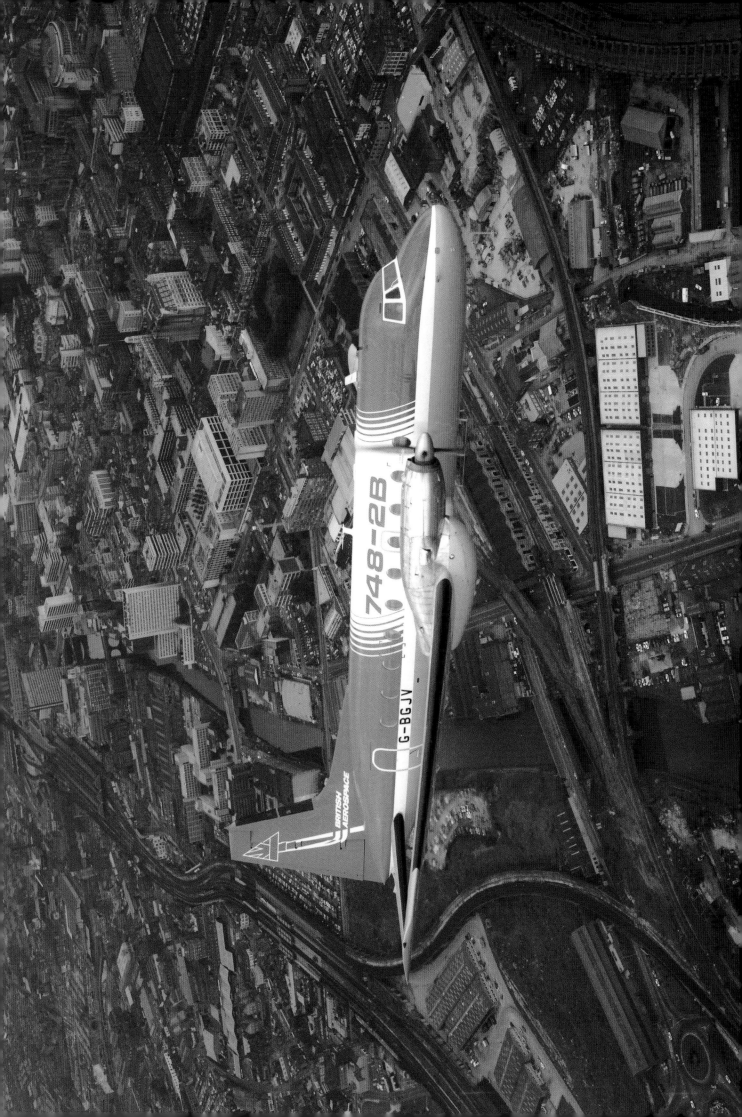

Avro introduced the Series 2A version with 2,290hp Dart engines. As previously described, HSA at Chester assisted Woodford by completing two 748s and converting another into the 'Coastguarder' maritime patrol aircraft which failed to attract orders and was re-worked in airliner configuration.

When Hawker Siddeley became part of British Aerospace in April 1977 the aircraft was designated the BAe 748. Further development saw the introduction of the Series 2B 'Super 748' in 1979 with a wider-bodied fuselage and wingspan extended to 102 ft. 6 in. When production ceased in 1988, a total of 380 of all versions of the extremely successful Avro 748 had been built, including 89 assembled in India from parts made in Britain. The 748's production run of 27 years was the longest of any Avro type, exceeding even that of the legendary Avro 504.

But as sales of the 748 eventually started to flag, British Aerospace took essentially the airframe of the Andover and lengthened it to accommodate up to 72 passengers. Amongst many other new features, Pratt & Whitney Canada 2,650hp turboprops were added with six-bladed reversible-pitch composite propellers turning relatively slowly in the interests of noise reduction. Pilots occupied a digital flight deck with an Electronic Flight Instrumentation System. In this form the 748 lived on in considerably updated and extended guise as the **British Aerospace Advanced TurboProp (ATP)**, 25 per cent of the content of which was BAe 748.

The ATP – dubbed with inimitable North West humour by some of the Woodford workforce as the 'Advanced Tater Pie' – first flew in prototype in 1986. The first production ATP took to the air early in 1987 and the first deliveries were made to British Midland Airways in 1988. British Airways were also customers and the regional airliner was supplied to other operators in Britain, Europe, Africa, the Far East and North America. Despite many advanced features the ATP failed to secure a market on the scale of its predecessor. After responsibility for assembly was transferred to Prestwick in October 1992 it was redesignated as the J61, part of the

Opposite:
BAe 748-2B demonstrator aircraft G-BGJV in British Aerospace house colours over central Manchester on 10 June 1981.

British Airways BAe ATP.

Jetstream family of regional turboprop aircraft, construction ceasing in 1994 with a total of 62 completed. The last was delivered in 1998.

In 1973, with Government support Hawker Siddeley Aviation announced a new venture to develop a 70-90 passenger short haul transport jetliner designated the **HS.146**. The international oil crisis and ensuing world recession resulted in its deferment for several years although limited design work was allowed to continue. A year after HSA was absorbed into British Aerospace, in 1978 the project was fully reactivated by BAe and the BAe 146 Series 100 made its maiden flight at Hatfield in 1981. It had evolved as a high-wing aircraft with 'T' tail, powered by four Lycoming high bypass-ratio turbofans slung on underwing pylons. A rugged main undercarriage retracted into fairings on the lower sides of a commodious 11 ft. 8 in.-diameter circular-section fuselage. The four engines, high lift flaps and rear fuselage air brakes allowed steep descent into airfields, excellent short field performance and economy of operation geared to low noise

levels with a cabin interior comparable with larger wide-bodied airliners.

Production commenced at the HSA (formerly de Havilland) factory at Hatfield where, in 1982, the BAe 146 Series 200 first flew with a fuselage lengthened by 7 ft. 10 in. capable of seating 112 passengers. A Series 300, lengthened by two such 'spacers' fore and aft of the wing, with accommodation for 128 passengers, flew in 1988. Whilst continuing at Hatfield, from 1988 assembly of the BAe 146 also began at Woodford where the first to be produced flew in May. The Chadderton factory contributed rear fuselages, electrical looms and assemblies. Some of the production test flying was shared with HSA at Broughton. Between 1985 and 1989 the Woodford plant was also engaged on a programme of avionics and armaments updates for 42 RAF Buccaneer S.Mk.2B strike/attack aircraft. Having once had both nuclear and conventional capability they subsequently used laser-guided weaponry in the Gulf War of 1991, served also in a maritime strike role and were finally withdrawn in 1994.

The Avroliner RJ 70, 85, 100, 115 family fly along the South Coast.

Avro RJ85 of Swissair/Crossair over the Honister Pass and Fleetwith Pike in the Lake District, with Buttermere and Crummock Water in the distance.

Avro RJ 85 of Northwest Airlines of the USA – built in England's Northwest.

In 1990 proposals were announced for a 146 successor range, the Regional Jetliner (RJ) Series, extensively upgraded with strengthened airframe and all-digital avionics, powered by 7,000lb-thrust Allied Signal turbofans. Like its predecessor, the RJ would be available in various sizes as the RJ 70, 85 and 100 capable of seating up to 112 passengers. All flew in 1992 and received certification in 1993. The ultimate RJ115 had capacity for up to 128 passengers.

When production of the BAe 146 ceased in 1993 a total of 221 had been completed,

165 at Hatfield and 56 at Woodford. Thereafter, following closure of the Hatfield plant, the RJ was produced only at Woodford where, reviving a name that many thought had disappeared for ever after the last 'real' Avro aircraft, the 748 airliner, BAe formed Avro International Aerospace as a division of British Aerospace Regional Aircraft Ltd. It would be responsible for the assembly, marketing and support of the new family of RJ aircraft. As a development of the BAe 146, itself regarded by many as the last 'real' design of de Havilland, there seemed a certain irony

when the new aircraft was given the RJ 'Avroliner' appellation for marketing purposes. In 1995 Avrotec was established at Woodford as the maintenance and refurbishment unit for regional aircraft with Avrotest responsible for flight and engineering test services. In January 1996 Avro International Aerospace became an integral part of Aero International (Regional) – AI(R) – a new European regional aircraft joint venture of Aérospatiale of France, Alenia of Italy and BAe of the UK, each with 33$^1/_3$ per cent interest. The new grouping offered marketing, sales and support for a wide range of aircraft comprising the ATR 42 and 72, Jetstream J41 turboprop regional aircraft, the Avro RJ regional jet series and 'out of production' HS.748, J31, J61 and BAe 146 types. AI(R) partners agreed dissolution of the company in April 1998, responsibility for regional aircraft support now resting with BAE Systems Regional Aircraft at Prestwick, Scotland, with Customer Training and Engineering at Woodford.

The first flight of a further upgrade, the Avro RJX, using composite materials and simplified systems offering greater operating economy, took place in April 2001. Little more than six months later with the onset of the international economic downturn in November it was announced that the RJX programme would close, related aircraft support services being consolidated under BAE Systems Regional Aircraft at Prestwick in Scotland. After the decision had been taken to cease production, the last commercial aircraft to be delivered from BAE Systems Regional Aircraft at Woodford, in 2004, was in fact the very first production BAe 146 Series 100 (E1001) which had made its maiden flight at Hatfield in 1981. Appropriately for the first of the 'whisper jets' this was originally registered as G-SSSH until, in 1987, when 'stretched' to become the first Series 300 (E3001) it was re-registered as G-LUXE. It remained a BAe development aircraft, heading north to be based at Woodford when Hatfield closed in 1993. Work began in 2001 on its conversion to a meteorological research aircraft known as the BAE Systems 146 Atmospheric Research Aircraft (ARA) which since 2004 has been operated by Directflight Ltd. of Norwich on behalf of the National

BAe 146 Atmospheric Research Aircraft G-LUXE, delivered to Directflight in May 2004, who operate it on behalf of the Facility for Airborne Measurements run jointly by the National Environment Research Council and the Met Office. It is historically significant as being the first production 146 Series 100 to have flown in 1981.

Environment Research Council (NERC) and the Meteorological Office. The 146 ARA replaces the previous UK met. aircraft, Hercules W.2 *Snoopy*, which gave excellent service in that role from 1973 to 2001. Some years previously in another interesting conversion, the second production BAe 146 (E1002) was re-modelled with a side-loading door as the Small Tactical Aircraft (STA) for military use, but after it failed to catch on was changed back into a Series 100 freighter. Altogether a total of 394 of the '146' family of aircraft was built, comprising 165 at Hatfield and 229 at Woodford, the latter made up of 56 BAe 146s, 170 Avro RJs and three RJXs. They continue to serve with some 60 operators worldwide including British Airways CitiExpress, Aer Lingus, Swiss, Air Canada Jazz, Lufthansa, Quantas, SN Brussels, United, Northwest and the RAF.

Today, the major programme at BAE Systems Woodford is the **Nimrod MRA4** maritime reconnaissance and attack aircraft. Woodford has had many years of involvement with the Nimrod going back to the mid-1960s when one of two unsold 'surplus' Comet 4C airliners was flown from the Hawker Siddeley Chester factory to Woodford for conversion as the second of two prototypes of the **HS.801 Nimrod.** The other Comet remained at Chester for conversion, flying from Hawarden as a Nimrod in May 1967 followed by the Woodford Nimrod in July.

Nimrod – taking its name from the Mighty Hunter of the Book of Genesis, the great-grandson of Noah – was the world's first land based four-engined pure-jet aircraft built for maritime reconnaissance and anti-submarine duties. The large, 115 ft.-wingspan aircraft carried mines, bombs, depth charges and torpedoes with an all-up weight of 192,000lb and top speed of 575 mph. As significant as its 'dash' speed was its ability to patrol at 230mph at low altitude for hours on end. On-board equipment included an ionisation detector to 'sniff out' surface shipping, a tail 'stinger' containing magnetic anomaly detection (MAD) apparatus to locate large metal objects on or below the surface, sonobuoys, searchlight and electronic countermeasures (ECM) pod. It had under-wing provision for missiles.

Hawker Siddeley HS.801 Nimrod MR.1 XV248 of No. 206 Sqn., RAF Kinloss, attracts attention from the starboard side of USSR *Kotlin Class* guided missile destroyer *453*, 2,900 tons, in the vicinity of the Orkneys.

The RAF ordered 46 Nimrod MR.1s for which the Chester factory made 41 sets of major airframe structures between 1966 and 1970. These were all transported by road to Woodford for final assembly and fitting with 11,500lb-thrust Rolls-Royce Spey turbofan engines. The first production example flew on 28 June 1968, the type entering service the following year. A decade earlier Woodford had produced all 191 of the Nimrod's predecessor, the Avro Shackleton and during 1970-71, with Nimrod new build under way, also modified a Shackleton MR.2 as the 'prototype' for a further eleven Shackleton AEW. Mk.2s converted at Bitteswell. Final deliveries of the Nimrod MR.1 were made in 1975.

Three of the series were produced for highly specialised classified 'calibration' duties, as Nimrod R.Mk.1s, in effect for covert electronic surveillance and intelligence gathering. The RAF equipped them itself in 1971 and from 1974, during the Cold War, operated them in international airspace close to the borders of the Soviet Union. They carried up to 28 specialist electronics operators and analysts. After modification with in-flight refuelling

they became R.Mk.1Ps.

In a major upgrading programme some 35 Nimrod MR.1s were extensively updated to MR.2 status at Woodford between 1975 and 1984. Work involved installing Searchwater computer-assisted radar, a new tactical computer which increased computing speed and power fifty times, new acoustic processing, inertial navigation and communication systems. Whilst retaining the Nimrod's 'dash' speed and low speed manoeuvring capability, the upgrade greatly enhanced capacity to detect and classify surface and submarine vessels in high sea states and at long range. The MR.2 played an important role in the Falklands and Desert Storm campaigns for which further modifications included in-flight refuelling probes, Harpoon anti-ship missiles and Stingray torpedoes. These and Electronic Support Measures in wingtip pods required the addition of aerodynamic tailplane finlets. Woodford undertook refuelling modifications on 16 Nimrods in record time for the Falklands, the aircraft being redesignated as MR.2Ps. More recently the Nimrod has participated in operations in Kosovo and Iraq and remains

RAF Nimrod
MR.2 No. 41,
XV241, over the
wreck of the oil-
carrying Danish
coaster *Bettina
Danica*, 1350
gross registered
tonnes, which
ran aground on
the south west
tip of the island
of Stroma in the
Pentland Firth
early in 1993.
The vessel's
crew scrambled
to safety ashore.
Although its
bunkers were
removed it was
never
completely
salvaged and,
increasingly
broken by the
waves, it remains
in situ.

RAF Nimrod
MR.2 No. 41,
XV241, passing
The Old Man of
Hoy in the
Orkneys.

Nimrod MR.2 No. 41 on patrol in Scottish waters.

Nimrod – The Mighty Hunter. MR.2 No. 54 casts a reassuring presence over the ocean.

Nimrod MR.2 No. 40 revisits its Woodford home.

in service to the present day.

During the 1970s NATO was bogged down in a protracted assessment of an airborne early warning system based on the American Boeing E-3 Sentry aircraft. With a view to replacing the Shackleton AEW.Mk.2 the British Government decided in 1977 to go it alone by converting surplus Nimrod and Comet airframes into a new Airborne Warning and Control System (AWACS) aircraft. Under British Aerospace (BAe), created as a nationalised corporation by the merger of the British Aircraft Corporation, Hawker Siddeley Aviation, Hawker Siddeley Dynamics and Scottish Aviation, the development programme started in 1977 with the conversion of a Chester-built Comet 4 as the development aircraft for the Nimrod AEW.Mk.3. Unlike the Sentry which used a fuselage-mounted revolving disc scanner, the Nimrod achieved 360-degree radar coverage by linking separate radars in bulbous nose and tail extensions with others housed in wingtip pods. At its core was a Variable Pulse Repetition Frequency radar system developed by GEC Avionics.

The first development aircraft for an anticipated fleet of eleven BAe Nimrod AEW.Mk.3s flew in 1980. During extensive trials it became clear that the combination of avionics and airframe did not represent a viable system. It was no reflection on either Woodford or the airframe. Problems with the radar, computer capacity and constant revision of requirement specifications proved impossible to deal with. Solving some merely created others. The need to dissipate heat generated by the avionics, using the aircraft's fuel as a heat sink, restricted usable fuel and hence endurance. In essence the requirements of the system exceeded the space available in the airframe. Escalating costs were the final straw and when the project was abandoned in 1986 the MoD had little choice but to opt for the Boeing E-3 Sentry.

But the Nimrod remained supremely successful in its established maritime patrol, reconnaissance and intelligence, anti-submarine and shipping, search and rescue roles. So much so that in 1996 the decision was taken to 'remanufacture' a number of existing aircraft to enhance the RAF's capability in the twenty-first century. In December BAE Systems was awarded a £2.4 billion contract to remanufacture 21 (amended to 18 in 2002) Nimrod MR.2 airframes as Nimrod MRA4s. By 1997 the complex and dispersed programme involved over 200 UK and overseas companies together with the prime contractor's sites at Farnborough, Filton, Warton, Woodford, Chadderton, Prestwick and Brough. In 1999 responsibility for conversion of MR.2 airframes and final assembly of the MRA4 was allocated to Woodford, the home of virtually all previous Nimrod new build and upgrades.

The excellent condition of the MR.2s allowed use of the term 'remanufacture' but in fact only parts of the fuselage, weapons bay and fixed tail surfaces are retained. Over 80 per cent of the content is brand new aircraft. Entirely new wings spanning 127 ft., with additional weapons hardpoints, have thicker roots to accommodate the four new Rolls-Royce Germany BR710 15,000lb turbofans. Giving a noise profile equivalent to a regional jet, these generate only a quarter of the take-off noise of the Spey-engined MR.2, yet will power the 235,000lb gross weight MRA4 at high subsonic speeds of over 600mph (Mach 0.77) at high level to a service ceiling of 42,000 ft. An un-refuelled range in excess of 6,000 nm and endurance of over 14 hours will enable MRA4 to remain on station for twice as long as its predecessor during search and rescue missions. A completely new undercarriage has been required to cope with the MRA4's additional weight. New systems throughout include hydraulics, environmental control, electrical, crew oxygen, automated fuel, flight control and auxiliary power unit. The cockpit includes many state-of-the-art systems in use on the latest Airbus airliners.

BAE Systems has teamed with Boeing to develop a Tactical Command Mission System. Multi-Mode Pulse Doppler Radar will provide greater range and improved target resolution. Electronic Support Measures will detect, localise and classify electronic transmissions. A Defensive Aids Sub-System will provide radar warning. Advanced sonobuoys will detect the quietest and deepest-running submarines as part of the Acoustics System. Other equipment includes an Electro-Optical Surveillance and Detection System and tail-housed Magnetic Anomaly Detector. A Communications Management System will include data-link and satellite capability for worldwide secure communication. MRA4 will be able to gather, process and display up to 20 times more data than the MR.2. The result will be greatly enhanced 'three-in-one' maritime patrol mission capability including Anti-Submarine Warfare (ASW), Anti-Surface Unit Warfare (ASUW) and Search And Rescue (SAR). MRA4 is

designed for use away from base and will be able to deploy worldwide for ten days without re-supply. Its operation will require a crew of ten compared with its predecessor's thirteen.

'Power On' was achieved with the Lead MRA4 (PA01), the first of three development aircraft, at BAE Systems Woodford in December 2001. The aircraft was given an informal 'roll-out' in August 2002. Delay to the first flight prompted an in-depth joint review of the programme with the MoD in 2002/3. As a result a restructured contract was announced in February 2003 which included a 'controlled production stop' on Aircraft 4 to 18 whereby the first three design and development phase aircraft were separated from production aircraft, the contract for which will be placed by MoD when sufficient overall risk reduction has been achieved and an acceptable level of confidence reached. All four BR710 engines were fired up for the first time on PA01 in April 2004, the aircraft commencing its low speed taxiing trials in June. On 21 July the Secretary of State for Defence announced that the UK's maritime

First outside appearance of the lead Nimrod MRA4 design and development aircraft, PA01, at BAE Systems Woodford, 16 August 2002.

Lead Nimrod
MRA4 PA01
undergoing
engine ground
runs and burning
off inhibitor oils
at Woodford,
April 2004.

Nimrod MRA4
PA02 in build
at Woodford,
May 2004.
Early in 2005 jigs
were installed at
Woodford for
the assembly of
MRA4 wings
and other major
components.

The modern
'glass cockpit' of
Nimrod MRA4.

Top:
Set against Woodford's pastoral backdrop, MRA4's new 127 ft. wing and large engine installations are apparent in this photograph taken during taxiing and runway testing.

Lower photos:
Lead Nimrod MRA4 PA01 ZJ516 lifts off on its inaugural flight from BAE Systems' Woodford site on the afternoon of Thursday, 26 August 2004. MRA4's flight trials programme is based at BAE Systems' Warton and Woodford sites. All preliminary manufacturing is concentrated at Woodford as is work on design modifications together with strip and survey work on other RAF Nimrod MR2 fuselages to permit remanufacture of further MRA4s.

Whilst retaining the distinctive 'double bubble' fuselage style of its MR.2 predecessor, MRA4 is 80 per cent a new-build aircraft.

reconnaissance requirement could probably be met in future by a fleet of 'around' 12 MRA4 aircraft. Witnessed by many of Woodford's 600 employees, MRA4 PA01 ZJ516 took to the air for the first time from Woodford on 26 August 2004. After a successful two-hour initial test flight captained by John Turner, BAE Systems' MRA4 Chief Test Pilot and a former Tornado ADV and Eurofighter Project Pilot, the aircraft landed at Warton in Lancashire to begin an extensive flight trials programme. The second design and development aircraft, PA02, made its first flight from Woodford to Warton on 15 December and the third, PA03, first flew on 29 August 2005. MRA4s will start replacing the RAF's existing Nimrod MR.2 fleet in 2009. They may well then operate as part of the RAF's intelligence, surveillance, target acquisition and reconnaissance (ISTAR) assets, with enhanced overland as well as maritime capability.

There has been speculation that MRA4's potential versatility as a platform might enable it to be used to carry the Storm Shadow cruise missile, in which event it would be the RAF's first long range heavy bomber since the demise of the Vulcan two decades ago. Those associated with the original Comet jetliner during the late 1940s would be astounded at the longevity of their basic design.

The English Electric Co. Ltd., English Electric Aviation Ltd., British Aircraft Corporation (BAC), BAC (Operating) Ltd., BAC Preston Division, BAC Military Aircraft Division, British Aerospace (BAe), BAe Aircraft Group Warton Division, BAe plc, BAe Military Aircraft Division, BAe Defence Ltd., BAe Military Aircraft Ltd., BAe Military Aircraft and Aerostructures, BAE Systems Air Systems: Strand Road, Preston, Samlesbury and Warton

By May 1945 MAP needed to effect substantial cut-backs in overall aircraft production without risking loss of excessive manufacturing capacity prejudicial to re-equipping the RAF with new aircraft, particularly the new jet fighters. English Electric's orders for Halifax bombers were

Opposite: Among many new airframe features of MRA4 are the wings, much enlarged intakes for the four new Rolls-Royce Germany BR710 turbofan engines and strengthened undercarriage.

Production of
the de Havilland
Vampire F.1 jet
fighter at
English Electric,
Samlesbury,
October 1945,
with work on
the last of the
Handley Page
Halifax aircraft in
the background.

terminated and production phased out by October. With just six completed of 300 **de Havilland D.H.100 Vampire F.1, 2 and 3** single-seat jet fighters then on order, production was maintained but at a reduced rate. Considerable spare capacity was released at Strand Road allowing reinstatement of diesel and electric locomotive, rolling stock and electric motor production. Even washing machines, electric cookers and fires were made until aircraft work again gathered momentum requiring transfer of domestic appliance production to Liverpool and the complete assembly of locomotives to the Vulcan Works at Newton-le-Willows.

For a company determined to remain in the aircraft business, Vampire output even at a reduced rate represented vital continuity until English Electric's own new designs could be translated into production. Indeed the Vampire was their sole new aircraft product between November 1945 and the completion of the English Electric A1 high altitude bomber, later named the Canberra, in spring 1949. However, in a contract which ran from

January 1946 to December 1948, Samlesbury also gained work by carrying out major electronics modifications to 200 Avro Lincoln heavy bombers. These were fitted with updated Loran, Rebecca and Gee radio navigation systems, H2S and rearward-looking radar which aimed the rear gun turret automatically.

A total of 1,369 Vampire F.Mk.1, 2, 3 and Sea Vampire F.Mk.20 fighters, FB.5 and FB.9 ground attack and fighter bombers was produced at Preston and Samlesbury between 1944 and 1952, mostly for the RAF and Fleet Air Arm but also for export to France, Norway, Sweden, Switzerland, Canada, India, South Africa and Italy. They served with the Second Tactical Air Force in Germany between 1946 and 1951 at the start of the Cold War and with the Vampire Wing of Fighter Command at RAF Odiham, Hampshire. In July 1948 four Preston-built F.3s of No. 54 Squadron, RAF, were the first jets to fly the Atlantic. English Electric's production comprised the largest single element of the total Vampire programme which continued in the North West with de Havilland themselves turning out 1,244 at Chester between 1949 and 1963 and Fairey Aviation building another 97 at Ringway during 1952-55. Altogether over 3,200 were built in Britain among a grand total of more than 4,300 worldwide with production in several European countries and Australia. Vampire F.Mk3 (VT812) built by English Electric in November 1947 is today displayed at the RAF Museum, Hendon.

English Electric made a key appointment when W.E.W. 'Teddy' Petter, formerly of Westland Aircraft of Yeovil, joined the company in July 1944. As Chief Engineer in charge of the small English Electric design team at 'TC' in Corporation Street, Preston, he was initially keen to develop ideas for a jet-powered fighter bomber. Because the Air Ministry was more interested in a high altitude light bomber, Petter was compelled to change course and preliminary designs progressed from a single-engined straight wing to a twin-turbojet swept-wing aircraft. The 6,500lb-thrust AJ.65 axial turbojet under development by Rolls-Royce at Barnoldswick seemed an ideal future power unit. Petter's design, designated the **English Electric A1**, firmed up as a twin-jet with outboard engines in the wing at a point where a broad parallel-chord centre section tapered almost symmetrically to cut-off wing tips.

A contract was received in January 1946 for the detail design and manufacture of four prototypes. As work progressed it became apparent that the expanding design team needed better accommodation and that more extensive flight test facilities were required than those available at Samlesbury. English Electric's eyes turned towards Warton, west of Preston, then recently vacated by the USAAF and used by the RAF for storage. Warton had seen intensive wartime use as BAD2 but the attraction lay not so much in its extensive dilapidated buildings as its 6,000 ft. asphalt runway capable of further lengthening, with unrestricted approaches along the Ribble Estuary and out to the Irish Sea.

In 1947 English Electric secured the services of Wg. /Cdr. Roland P. Beamont as Chief Test Pilot. Beamont had a distinguished war record both on operations and as a test pilot. Whilst awaiting completion of the A1 he undertook a series of research flights from Warton in a Gloster Meteor Mk.IV, an aircraft smaller though not unlike the A1 in overall configuration, investigating compressibility factors and handling at high subsonic speeds and altitudes. The tests showed conclusively that there was then no existing or proposed fighter anywhere

W.E.W. Petter at his desk at English Electric, the 1947-style austerity of his office personalised only by a model of the projected A1 (Canberra) in the foreground and a photograph of the Lysander, which he designed whilst at Westland in the 1930s, on the wall. Petter also had overall responsibility for the initial design of the supersonic English Electric P.1, later to become the Lightning, an aircraft as far removed from the 200mph Army Co-operation Lysander as could possibly be imagined.

in the world able to outclass the predicted performance of the A1 with its anticipated 10,000 ft. altitude 'advantage'. Spurred on by these findings was another group within the English Electric design team led by R.F. Creasey who, in response to MoS Experimental Requirement ER103 for a high speed research aircraft, had begun looking into development of a supersonic aircraft to be designated the P.1.

During summer 1948, with design of the A1 well advanced and manufacturing of parts underway at 'TC' and Strand Road, the design team transferred to Warton. Work also began there on provision of technical facilities including wind tunnels and a mechanical test department. As the aircraft took shape under considerable secrecy at English Electric's Strand Road factory, those 'in the know' were amused to hear rumours of an 'electric bomber' being developed. For much of this time Beamont also flight-tested production Vampires at Samlesbury. Early in 1949, with test-assembly of the A1 prototype almost completed at Strand Road, the company received orders for 132 bomber, photo-reconnaissance and trainer versions even before the aircraft had flown.

Dismantled at Strand Road and taken to Warton for reassembly, powered by two Avon RA.2 engines the blue-painted A1 prototype VN799 took to the air on 13 May 1949. The fact that it was also a Friday and that all the company's hopes for a long-term future in aviation rested on its success held no qualms for Beamont. The first and subsequent flights revealed an aircraft with excellent flying characteristics, requiring only straightforward modifications in order to meet all design aspirations for a maximum speed in excess of 500mph with a combination of high altitude manoeuvrability and complaisant low speed handling. To foster interest expressed earlier in the year by the Australian Government, the A1 was named the **Canberra**. In September Beamont demonstrated the prototype to spectacular effect at the Farnborough Air Show.

1950 saw the first production Canberra B.2 in the air and Australia's confirmation of its wish to build under licence. Increasing international tension and the outbreak of the Korean War in June resulted in the immediate expansion of the RAF with orders for the Canberra numbering 350 towards the end of the year.

A line-up of historic Canberras at Warton in the 1950s. Prototype T.4 trainer WN467 (foreground) first flew on 12 June 1952. Prototype B.5 VX185 crewed by Beamont, Hillwood and Watson made the first Atlantic return crossing on 26 August. The first production PR.3 WE135 flew on 31 July. Furthest away is second B.2 prototype VX169. Note the 'period' ground support vehicles including English Electric's Austin A40 van.

High Altitude Photographic Reconnaissance Canberra H.A.P.R. Mk.9 WH793 was converted from a PR.7 by D. Napier & Son at Luton in May 1954. Flown by R. Beamont in this photograph it shows the increased chord of the wing centre section.

Opposite: If it looks right, it flies right. Canberra B.6 WJ764 shows its superb lines, 1954/55.

Subcontracting arrangements had to be entered into with A.V. Roe at Manchester, Short Brothers & Harland at Belfast and Handley Page at Cricklewood, London, each of whom initially received instructions for 100 aircraft to supplement English Electric production at Preston.

Following expressions of interest and visits from American Government officials and US Air Force representatives, to whom Beamont demonstrated a prototype at

Burtonwood in 1950, in February 1951 an RAF-crewed B.2 crossed the Atlantic from Aldergrove (Belfast) to Gander at 40,000 ft. in just over 4½ hours, the first jet to do so direct without being refuelled. At that time the fastest Pan American Constellations took half as long again. Beamont subsequently pitted the same aircraft against the best that the Americans could offer in a flying competition at Andrews Air Force Base, Washington and

later displayed it at Martin Airport, Middle River near Baltimore, the home of the Glenn L. Martin Company. Beamont and the Canberra outclassed all other contenders, resulting in an agreement for the manufacture of the aircraft under licence by the Martin Company for service in the USAF as the Martin B-57. It was the first time that a British-designed military aircraft would be built in the US since the de Havilland D.H.4/9A, Handley Page 0/400 and Bristol F.2B of 1917/18.

At home, with Strand Road also busy with diesel and electric locomotive work, in 1950 English Electric acquired the vast former Bristol Hercules aero-engine shadow factory at Clayton-le-Moors. By early 1952, known as the English Electric Accrington Works, it was producing airframe parts for the Canberra, eventually including rear fuselages, flying control surfaces, tailplane and fin assemblies. Remarkably, much of the Canberra's tail fin was made of wood, forming a non-conductive dielectric panel housing the aircraft's RT aerial. It was as though English Electric were determined to retain some vestige of their traditional use of wood in tramcars and flying boats (and in the Vampire) in their latest aircraft. Termination of Vampire production enabled both Strand Road and Samlesbury to be devoted to the Canberra and thereafter Samlesbury, mid-way between Preston and Accrington, replaced Warton as the centre for Canberra final assembly and flight testing. From 1950, additional design capacity for later versions of the Canberra was located at the Napier factory at Acton, London which had become part of English Electric during the war.

RAF Bomber Command received its first Canberras in May 1951 when B.2s started to replace Lincolns of No. 101 Squadron at Binbrook. Two new versions, the PR.3 photo-reconnaissance and T.4 trainer appeared in 1952 followed by extended range PR.7 and B.6 variants in 1953/54. The B(1)8 interdictor low level and night attack version, notable for its offset fighter-type canopy for improved vision, was introduced in 1954. That year Napier at Luton began modifying a PR.7 as a prototype high altitude PR.9 with a wingspan extended from 64 ft. to 69 1/2 ft., subsequent production of which was subcontracted to Shorts. Altogether, 21 versions of the Canberra would come off the production lines with over twice that number of variants designated according to customer requirements.

The Canberra became synonymous with record-breaking flights worldwide and established a number of long distance point-to-point-records. In August 1952 a B.5 with up-rated 7,500lb-thrust Avon RA7s, crewed by Beamont, Hillwood and Watson made the first return crossing of the Atlantic in just over ten hours including a two-hour stop-over at Gander. Canberras held 22 records for flights to North America, Africa, the Middle East, Pakistan, Australia and New Zealand, attracting press coverage and celebrity around the world. In October 1952 four RAF Canberras undertook a 24,000 mile tour of South America as a precursor to major export sales. The England-New Zealand Air Race of October 1953 was won by an RAF PR.3 which covered 12,000 miles in under 24 hours at an average speed of 494.5mph, with just 80 minutes on the ground for fuel stops. The actual aircraft, WE139, is displayed today at the RAF Museum, Hendon.

Two B.2s were flown to Australia and another two to the US in 1951/52 as pattern aircraft for licensed production. Direct exports began in 1953 when aircraft were diverted from UK contracts to Venezuela, followed by orders from France, Ecuador, Peru, India, New Zealand and South Africa. Additionally, Rhodesia, Chile, West Germany and Sweden received aircraft diverted either from RAF use or stocks.

RAF Canberras were deployed against communist guerrillas in Malaya in 1955 and in the Suez Crisis the following year. Because of their imminent replacement by the 'V'-force of high altitude nuclear strike aircraft, in 1955 pure bomber versions of the Canberra ceased to be made although in 1957/58 some were modified to carry tactical nuclear weapons and from Cyprus provided strike potential to guard the southern flank of NATO and the Mediterranean, supporting the Central Treaty Organisation (CENTO). Production at Samlesbury switched to B(1)8 interdictors. Although outdated as a high level bomber by 1960, the Canberra would serve in the low level role for another ten years. RAF Canberra PR.9s continued to be used for high altitude photo-

reconnaissance, including observation of Russian convoys during the Cuban Missile Crisis of 1962. Others were converted into target tugs in the mid-1960s, capable of drawing a cable-towed Rushton target ten miles behind the aircraft.

In America, Martin B-57s served with the Strategic Air Command and some former USAF aircraft were supplied to the Chinese Nationalist Air Force. From 1965 USAF B-57s were active in Vietnam where they were joined by Canberras of the RAAF in 1967. Some B-57s, heavily modified for research and clandestine military reconnaissance, were able to cruise at heights of 80-90,000 ft. Canberras supplied to India by Britain and, as B-57s to Pakistan by America, briefly fought on both sides in the Indo-Pakistan war of 1965.

Canberras proved ideal research aircraft, particularly as engine test beds. One with Bristol Olympus engines established official world altitude records of 63,668 ft. in 1953 and 65,889 ft. in 1955. Some were used for high altitude monitoring of the British nuclear tests in Australia and Christmas Island in 1956-57. An Avro-built Canberra B.2, modified by Napier to carry a Double

Working on the Canberra in No. 4 Hangar, Samlesbury.

Modern and medieval history. Over six centuries separate Canberra B(1)66 F1028 – in 1970-71 immaculately refurbished for the Indian Air Force from the former 1950s Preston-built RAF B.6 WJ776 – and Piel Castle on Morecambe Bay. The fortress once guarded the anchorage for the Cistercian Furness Abbey with its illicit wool trade with Flanders.

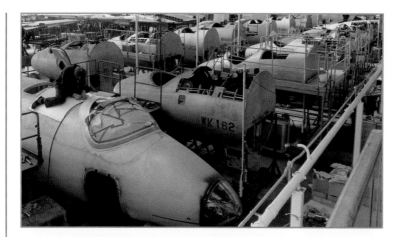

Late programme Canberra fuselage and wing refurbishment at Samlesbury. WK162 was from a batch built initially by Avro at Woodford.

Another view of Canberra refurbishment at Samlesbury.

The Vickers-Supermarine Spitfire was one of the relatively few major types of aircraft not manufactured in the North West. Between 1984 and 1986 however, Spitfire PR.Mk.XIX PS915 was completely rebuilt and fitted with a converted ex-Shackleton Rolls-Royce Griffon Series 58 engine by BAe apprentices at Samlesbury. It flew on 16 December 1986, subsequently joining the RAF Battle of Britain Memorial Flight. A second Spitfire was given a major overhaul. Ten Canberras can be seen on the airfield where refurbishment of the type continued until 1988.

Scorpion rocket engine in the bomb bay achieved a further record of 70,310 ft. in 1957. This aircraft, WK163, is currently preserved in flying condition albeit without the Scorpion.

The Canberra was under continuous manufacture for ten years by English Electric at Preston, Accrington and Samlesbury. They completed their 500th in 1956 but, as production started to slow down, an order for 80 placed by India in 1957 kept the line running until the end of 1959. The last new Canberra was built by Shorts at the end of 1960. But this was by no means the end of the story. 15 airframe assemblies built for stock were used to meet further export orders in the early 1960s, the final new-build Canberra being supplied to South Africa in 1964. Samlesbury continued to benefit also from a substantial workload of Canberra modifications and overhauls. Of even greater significance was the start in 1963 of major programmes of refurbishment often to the point of remanufacturing existing 'pre-owned' Canberras. Initially to meet RAF requirements, refurbished aircraft were subsequently exported to Venezuela, West Germany, Peru, Ethiopia, India and Argentina.

By then renamed the British Aircraft Corporation (BAC), the company re-purchased a number of Canberras in 1969 as a buffer stock for refurbishment. The RAF's decision taken in the 1970s to retain the Canberra in service into the 1980s as a 'Long Term Fleet' required BAC to refurbish no less than 50 between 1976 and 1982. Line-ups of stored Canberras were a routine sight on the airfield at Samlesbury where refurbishment and related work kept No. 2 Shed busy for the best part of 25 years until the late 1980s. During that time some aircraft were re-sparred twice. The Falklands War of 1982 resulted in two Canberras under refurbishment for Argentina being impounded at Samlesbury. Ironically two other former RAF Canberras built originally by Handley Page and Shorts, refurbished at Samlesbury as part of a batch of 12 delivered to Argentina in 1970-71, were shot down in the Falklands by missiles fired from a Royal Navy Sea Harrier and HMS Exeter.

The total of 1,376 new Canberras built comprised 631 by English Electric, 144 by Short Brothers and Harland, 75 each by A.V. Roe and Handley Page, 403 by Martin

Canberra T.4 WJ874, painted and re-serialled to represent the Canberra prototype VN799, flies from Warton on 13 May 1999, commemorating the 50th Anniversary of the prototype's first flight. *Postscript:* WJ874 again overflew Warton and Samlesbury on 1 September 2005 to mark its own forthcoming retirement after more than 50 years of service with the RAF.

in the USA and 48 by the Government Aircraft Factory of Australia. Of the 925 UK-built aircraft, 782 were for the RAF and 143 for export. All export aircraft were Samlesbury-produced, as were another 112 refurbished for overseas customers. Canberras and Martin B-57s served with 20 air forces worldwide.

Today, seven Canberras remain in RAF service on strength with No. 39 Squadron, No. 1 Photographic Reconnaissance Unit (1 PRU), based at Marham in Norfolk. Five are Canberra PR.9s from a batch of 23 produced by Shorts during 1958-60. They have worldwide capability and, as the only aircraft combining multiple photographic systems, high service ceiling and long endurance, have seen action over Kosovo, Afghanistan and Iraq where, in 2003, amongst other missions they were deployed to reconnoitre possible Scud missile sites. The other two aircraft are Canberra T.4 trainers, WH849 and WJ874, both built by English Electric at Preston and first delivered to the RAF over 50 years ago in 1954. On 13 May 1999, resplendent in blue livery to simulate the Canberra prototype VN799, WJ874 visited Warton to commemorate the 50th anniversary of the prototype's first flight. No. 39 Squadron Canberras are now among the oldest aircraft remaining in operational military service anywhere in the world, eloquent testimony to the brilliance of W.E.W. Petter's original design. It is almost unbelievable that the Canberra, in 1949 the first product of a design team which itself had only existed for five years, remains in service in the twenty-first century and is likely to continue to do so for several years to come. For an aircraft that first flew on Friday 13th it proved the success story of the immediate post-war British aircraft industry and went on to become one of the all-time outstanding successes of British aviation.

Concurrently with detail design and initial build of the A1 (Canberra) prototype, in

1948 a Warton design team under Ray Creasey, who had been recruited from Vickers, was working on the aerodynamics of an experimental transonic research aircraft. Designated **P (Project) 1**, by 1952 it had evolved as the **P.1A** research design and its **P.1B** derivative to meet Ministry of Supply specification F.23/49 for a supersonic fighter.

Throughout the industry designers working at the threshold of supersonic flight were grappling with problems of compressibility drag which could induce extreme buffeting, instability or even catastrophic structural failure. To lessen the build up of shock waves approaching Mach 1, English Electric incorporated exceedingly thin wings swept back at 60 degrees with a tailplane set low on the fuselage. As these features were somewhat at variance with advice then emanating from the RAE at Farnborough, a nervous MoS commissioned a low-budget interim research aircraft, the SB.5, from Short Brothers & Harland of Belfast, with wing and tail layout capable of being varied between test flights. In proving the soundness of the P.1 design it also provided useful low speed handling data without delaying the overall project.

With design work advancing, early in 1950 W.E.W. Petter resigned to join Folland Aircraft Ltd. His position as Chief Engineer was taken by F.W. 'Freddie' Page who would have the challenging responsibility for detail design of the P.1 and its development for operational use by the RAF. English Electric became one of the first to use early computers in aircraft design and also developed a supersonic wind tunnel. In April 1950 the company was awarded a contract for two flying prototypes and one static test airframe. The first P.1A was in advanced build by late 1953. In February 1954, recognising the complexities involved in developing all the systems required to convert the original research concept into the RAF's first operational supersonic fighter, the MoS ordered no less than 20 P.1B development aircraft.

The prototype P.1A, WG760, was completed in May 1954 and, with facilities at Warton still not fully adequate, was transported to the A & AEE at Boscombe Down for initial flight tests. Although the wing and tail design gave away its advanced aerodynamics, the aircraft was unlike the needle-sharp supersonic darts designed by other companies such as Fairey Aviation with their competing FD.2. Though clean-lined it was of bluff appearance with a large 'ovoid' nose intake to ingest the quantities

of air required by two Armstrong Siddeley Sapphire turbojets, mounted one on top of the other in a 57 ft.-long slab-sided fuselage. They would propel the 14-ton aircraft well beyond the speed of sound. Roland Beamont piloted the prototype on its maiden flight on 4 August, taking it to 15,000 ft. It exceeded Mach 1 on its third outing, becoming the first British aircraft to do so in level flight. Performance and handling showed excellent promise, only four minutes separating 'brakes off' on the runway to 30,000 ft. From September the aircraft was back at Warton where test flights, reaching Mach 1.22 over the Irish

English Electric P.1A prototype WG760 first flew on 4 August 1954, went supersonic on its third outing on 11 August and here poses for air-to-air photography for the first time from an accompanying Meteor 'chase' plane in September.

Test pilot Peter Hillwood flies English Electric's first aircraft, the S.1 Wren, restored for the Shuttleworth Trust, over P.1A WG760 which Roland Beamont is preparing to fly at Warton in July 1957.

Sea, revealed the need for an enlarged tail fin for improved directional stability. The second prototype, WG763, flew from Warton in July 1955. It undertook many supersonic research flights over the next few years, attaining Mach 1.53 and is today preserved at the Museum of Science and Industry in Manchester.

By 1956 three P.1B prototypes were being assembled at Strand Road and manufacturing was taking place of the 20 development aircraft. Arrangements were in hand for production aircraft and a two-seat trainer version was at the design stage. The first P.1B, XA 847, powered by reheated Rolls-Royce Avons, made its maiden flight from Warton in the early afternoon of 4 April 1957 when in the space of 25 minutes from take-off to return Beamont took it beyond Mach 1.2. As it cooled down back at Warton, later that very afternoon Duncan (later Lord) Sandys, Minister of Defence in the Conservative Government, rose to deliver his infamous 1957 White Paper *Defence. Outline of Future*

Policy to the House of Commons. Against a perceived need to rein-in defence expenditure in a thermonuclear age, it proclaimed a change of emphasis from manned combat aircraft to less expensive missiles. Fighter aircraft would be superseded by defensive guided weapons, strategic bombers by ballistic missiles. Given the progress in guided weaponry the RAF would be unlikely to require further manned combat aircraft after the Vulcan and Victor strategic bombers and the P.1B interceptor fighter. Absurd at the time, Sandys' unilateral policy was further discredited in the years to come. It wrought serious damage on the British aircraft industry for the next decade and, although not axed like many other programmes, the early potential of the P.1B was inevitably retarded by the scaling-down both of development funding and RAF fighter procurement. Certainly the P.1B's oft-quoted sobriquet 'the RAF's last manned fighter' did nothing to promote its export potential at the time.

XA847 continues its circuit, with undercarriage doors opening, over the River Ribble with the River Douglas joining from the right. Nearly half a century ago, more heavily industrialised than today, a somewhat murky Preston appears in the distance.

The sonic boom became a sensitive issue, not only on the mainland but also in the Isle of Man. To minimise its effects the English Electric flight test team used a narrow south to north corridor, 'Test Run Alpha', over the Irish Sea from the Great Orme headland in North Wales to the south of Dumfries, between the Isle of Man and the Cumbrian coast. Along this route, in July 1957 XA847 unofficially exceeded the world speed record of 1,132mph set by the Fairey Delta 2 the previous year. On 25 November 1958 at 40,000ft off St. Bees Head, P.1B XA847, by then named the **Lightning**, piloted by Beamont became the first British aircraft to fly at Mach 2 (1,250mph). From North Wales to the Scottish coast and round to the Southern Lake District had taken under eight minutes. Rather less than a year after the death of Sir Alliott Verdon-Roe it was a measure of the progress made in little more than 48 years of aviation since the Blackpool flying meetings of 1909/1910 and the exploits of pioneering aviators on the Lancashire coast.

Visible changes to the P.1B/Lightning's appearance included a circular nose intake with a centre cone for improved air induction at supersonic speeds and capable of accommodating radar. A fuselage spine ran from a redesigned cockpit canopy to an enlarged tail fin. On the underside, actual *curves* appeared in the form of a 250-gallon faired ventral fuel tank. Some had two Firestreak missiles on lower front fuselage pylons. The Lightning T.4 two-seat trainer prototype flew at Warton in May 1959, its 12-inch-wider front fuselage detracting virtually nothing from the performance of the single-seater. By September 1959 some 23 prototype and development Lightnings were in the air, the ranks of English Electric test pilots including Beamont, Hillwood, de Villiers, Dell and Squier later augmented by Ferguson, Hall, Isherwood and Knight. Distant sonic booms out over the Irish Sea from 'Test Run Alpha' were not uncommon.

The first production Lightning F.1 flew in October 1959 and deliveries to the RAF started in June 1960. At last, six years after

the USAF got the F-100 Super Sabre, five years after the Soviets the MiG-19 and three years after the Super Mystère entered service in France, the RAF had a supersonic jet fighter. And what a supersonic fighter it was – capable also of breaking the sound barrier whilst in the climb. What had become almost a national disgrace was quickly forgotten as the RAF, unlike other air forces, progressed overnight from subsonic to Mach 2 supersonic capability with no Mach 1 intermediate aircraft. But the Lightning's one-to-one power to weight ratio reheated performance came at the price of heavy fuel consumption: endurance was initially little more than one hour. This was improved by a flight refuelling probe on the F.1A, provision for two 260-gallon jettisonable over-wing tanks primarily for ferrying purposes on later F.3s and F.6s, together with the latter's much enlarged ventral tank. The Lightning's other 'weakness' proved to be its complexity

which was to present an ongoing challenge for RAF service and maintenance crews.

Lightning front fuselages and wings were manufactured at Strand Road, the main fuselage, fin and tailplane at Accrington. These were married up on the production line at Samlesbury from where the aircraft were flown to Warton for final flight testing. Some T.4s were also assembled at Warton. The Lightning F.2 with improved electronic systems and fully variable engine reheat entered service in 1962. The F.3 represented a far more significant advance with Ferranti AIRPASS radar and D.H. Red Top air-to-air missiles. Distinguished by a larger, purposeful tail fin with a squared-off top, the F.3 had Avon engines of up to 16,300lb thrust giving RAF pilots access to speeds in excess of Mach 2 when it entered service in 1964. Front fuselages for a new F.3-based trainer, the T.5, were made at BAC's Filton Division when some limited redistribution of work was made within the Group in 1962.

In 1964 Warton designers started to look at developing the aircraft in a multi-role capacity to include ground attack and reconnaissance. At the same time the Government of Saudi Arabia began showing interest in the Lightning and BAC embarked on a major marketing initiative to meet Saudi needs with a comprehensive package of air defences including aircraft, ground-to-air anti-aircraft missiles, radar systems, training and support services. Related to both these developments, the ultimate Lightning, the F.6, flew at Samlesbury in June 1965. A cambered and kinked wing leading edge with increased lift enabled the aircraft to carry more weight in the form of a much enlarged 600-gallon ventral fuel pack which could also be shared with ADEN cannon. Typical endurance was doubled to two hours whilst over and under-wing hard points allowed additional fuel tanks, rockets or bombs to be carried as well as the usual Firestreak or Red Top AAMs. 1965 was the peak year for Lightning production with 50 aircraft built. An order for 40 Lightnings and 25 Strikemaster trainers for Saudi Arabia announced in December provided a further production lifeline in a year that saw the cancellation of the TSR.2 (described later), up to then considered BAC Preston Division's principal future project. The £125 million Anglo-American Saudi defence contract was then the UK's largest export order, worth over £100 million to Britain including £65 million to BAC. The Lightnings comprised 34 F.53s and six T.55s, derivatives of the F.6 and T.5, the first six supplied from RAF stocks in the expedited *Magic Carpet* sub-programme. Twelve months later, in December 1966 Kuwait ordered 14 Lightnings comprising twelve F.53Ks and two T.55Ks worth over £20 million.

The last Lightning F.6 was completed in June 1967 and new deliveries to the RAF ceased six months later. However, Warton worked on modifications to interim F.6s and on a conversion programme for 30 F.2As, virtually to F.6 standard, for the RAF from 1967 to 1970-71. Deliveries to Saudi Arabia started in July 1968 where the aircraft entered service in 1969 and saw action for the first time in ground attacks on the border with South Yemen. Deliveries to Kuwait started in December 1968, both contracts being completed in 1969 apart from a replacement F.53 for Saudi Arabia, the last Lightning of all, completed at Samlesbury in June 1972.

In their definitive *English Electric Aircraft and their Predecessors* (Pub. Putnam, 1987) Ransom and Fairclough indicate that 10,000 Lightning test flights had been made from Warton by mid-1968, three-quarters of them at supersonic speed. Of individual test pilots, Beamont contributed 1,300 and Dell, de Villiers, Knight and Ferguson each over 1,000.

RAF Lightnings, ultimately able to climb to 30,000 ft. in 1½ minutes on reheat and 40,000 ft. in two minutes, with a maximum speed of Mach 2.3 and service ceiling of 60,000 ft., provided vital defence for the UK, being regularly 'scrambled' to intercept long-range Russian bomber and reconnaissance aircraft probing Britain's airspace over the North Sea. Tupolev Tu 95 Bears flew frequent missions from the Kola Peninsula, round North Cape and over the Norwegian Sea down into the Atlantic through the Iceland-Faroes Gap, often en route to Cuba. Interception to 'guide' them away from NATO airspace became a regular routine, on occasions Russian crew members waving pin-up magazines and even copies of the *RAF News* journal at the closely formating Lightning pilots. Lightnings and later Phantoms and Tornado ADV fighter aircraft formed a Quick Reaction Alert (Interceptor) Force – (QRAI) – on constant 24-hour standby equivalent to the QRA of the RAF's force of 'V' bombers. Elsewhere Lightnings served with the Second Tactical Air Force in Germany, in

Opposite: Cold War warriors. Lightnings and some of their test pilots of the 1960s: *from left to right,* Desmond de Villiers, Peter Hillwood, Jimmy Dell, Don Knight and Roland Beamont.

Cyprus and with the Far East Air Force in Singapore. Availability of the Jaguar from 1974 allowed redeployment of the RAF's Phantom force for air defence, seemingly spelling the end for the Lightning. However, an RAF reassessment backed up by satisfactory fatigue tests carried out on an F.6 at Warton allowed it to continue in service into the 1980s until finally replaced by the Tornado ADV. The RAF finally retired the Lightning in 1988. It had been in service for over 28 years, longer than any other RAF fighter. The Royal Saudi Air Force replaced its Lightnings with 72 Tornados under a deal agreed with British Aerospace in 1985 (described later). In the UK, Lightning F.6 XS928, retired on the disbandment of No. 5 Sqn. RAF at the end of 1987, went on to fly with the Tornado ADV trials programme at BAe Warton until March 1992. It was subsequently restored and preserved for static display at Warton by volunteer members of the BAe North West Heritage Group.

The Lightning, which celebrated its 50th anniversary in August 2004, was the last jet fighter of all-British design and build. A total of 341 was produced, including prototypes and development aircraft, 54 of which were exported. Technically brilliant

but complex, highly regarded by pilots if not always ground crews, several factors conspired to limit the success that it deserved. In a post-1957 missile-orientated Britain it had been starved of investment at a critical stage of its development from a research aircraft to a military system. Moreover it was at a time when the Americans and French were able to market more versatile aircraft. By the mid-1960s, when the folly of the 1957 Defence White Paper had become obvious even to politicians, as the brakes came off and the F.6 and F.53 started to show something of the Lightning's multi-role and improved range potential, it was too late. Cheaper-to-buy-and-maintain competitors such as the Phantom were available and work was under way on the next generation of multi-role combat aircraft. The Lightning proved excellent and got even better but was not developed to its fullest potential in time to generate substantial export-led production.

Small scale production of a light utility aircraft, the **Lancashire Prospector E.P.9**, by the Lancashire Aircraft Co. Ltd. at Squires Gate, Blackpool and Samlesbury between 1958-61 was in marked contrast to the military jets made there by Hawker and English Electric.

Lightning F.6s in three different colour schemes, with over-wing fuel tanks, hustle over BAe Warton in a farewell fly-past on 16 December 1992. The lead aircraft, XP693, first flew on 16 June 1962 and for many years was the manufacturer's Lightning development aircraft and chase plane for development of the later MRCA/Tornado. Following are XS904 (foreground) and XR773.

It was in 1932 that an Australian, Captain Edgar W. Percival, established the Percival Aircraft Co. Ltd., manufacturing the Gull series of light aircraft at Maidstone, Gravesend and, from 1936, at Luton. Between 1940-45, F. Hills and Sons Ltd. built large numbers of the Percival Proctor trainer derivative at Trafford Park and Barton Aerodrome. In 1944, at Luton, Percival Aircraft became part of the Hunting Group, from 1954 Hunting Percival Aircraft Ltd. E.W. Percival left the company, establishing Edgar Percival Aircraft Ltd. at Stapleford Aerodrome, Essex. There he designed the single-engined E.P.9 as an agricultural crop-spraying and fertiliser-spreading aircraft for which he foresaw considerable demand from Commonwealth countries.

Samlesbury Engineering Ltd., makers of aircraft components, were the post-war occupants of the former Burnley Aircraft Products hangars on a small part of Samlesbury Airfield on the opposite, south side from English Electric. In 1954 they built Donald Campbell's Bluebird K7 jet hydroplane speedboat in which the record-breaker lost his life on Coniston Water in

1967, the boat subsequently being recovered from the lake bed over 34 years later in 2001. In 1958 Samlesbury Engineering bought out Percival's interests, in the process of which acquiring some 20 aircraft in various stages of completion and establishing the Lancashire Aircraft Co. Ltd. at Squires Gate, Blackpool. Work was transferred to Samlesbury in 1960, a total of 28 aircraft being completed as Lancashire Prospector E.P.9s, the majority assembled or built in Lancashire including a single Series 2 aircraft in which the standard 295hp Lycoming engine was replaced by a 375hp Armstrong Siddeley Cheetah. Production ceased in 1961.

Following on from the Canberra and Lightning, the next major project initiated by the English Electric Company's Aviation Division would prove one of the most controversial chapters in the history of the British aircraft industry. Even today, 40 years on, **TSR.2** remains an emotive issue amongst former employees.

English Electric were considering a replacement for the Canberra from the mid-1950s, spurred on by the Air Ministry's circulation of draft proposals for a supersonic successor in 1956. Drawing on experience with the P.1, in February 1957 the company responded with a proposal designated P.17A, the key design personnel for which being R.F. Creasey, B.O. Heath and G.F. Sharples working under the Division's Chief Engineer, Freddie Page. Elsewhere, among a number of other interested companies, a team at Vickers-Armstrongs (Aircraft) Ltd. at Weybridge, under the direction of H. Gardner and G. Henson, were working on a concept with fully integrated systems known as the Vickers (Supermarine) V571. But the whole issue was about to be thrown into the melting pot by the 1957 White Paper on Defence. *Inter alia,* as far as bomber aircraft in particular were concerned, it effectively scotched any further work on the Type 730, an eight-engined stainless steel Mach 2 strategic bomber then taking shape on Avro's drawing boards at Chadderton.

Only days before Sandys unleashed his White Paper, the Air Staff finalised a first draft of General Operational Requirement (GOR) No. 339 for a supersonic tactical strike and reconnaissance aircraft to succeed the Canberra. Its timing could not have been less auspicious, but although delayed by the hiatus that followed Sandys' announcement, GOR 339 would be the only new military aircraft project to survive the defence review. Significantly the Government also had a further agenda. As well as proposing the abandonment of manned combat aircraft it also desired the rationalisation of the British aircraft industry then comprising 20 separate airframe and six aero-engine companies. Even in the penurious post-war years, new prototypes proliferated like mayflies at the annual Farnborough Air Shows, often with comparable life expectancy. The Government intended its radical defence review to achieve restructuring of the industry by forcing companies to merge in order to compete more efficiently for a

smaller number of projects. Laudable industrial objectives were however about to be marred by the arbitrary butchering of some of the most promising aircraft projects anywhere in the world, some of which had been designed and would have been built in the North West.

At an historic meeting in London on 16 September 1957 between Government officials and industry leaders including H.G. (later Lord) Nelson of English Electric, Sir Roy Dobson and Sir Frank Spriggs of Hawker Siddeley, Sir George Edwards of Vickers, Sir Frederick Handley Page and others, the industry was left in no doubt that the Government would only entertain submissions for GOR 339 arising from collaborative ventures and preferably amalgamations of companies. Who should merge with whom was left entirely to the industry, although the Government would favour balanced groupings with military, civil and wider industrial interests. Only this way was it felt that Britain could compete in the future, particularly with America. Tempestuous in conception, future development of GOR 339 would prove even more heated and controversial.

From autumn 1957, interest expressed by the Ministry of Supply in VTOL was explored jointly by English Electric and Short Brothers & Harland of Belfast who, already subcontractors to EE for Canberra production, were about to fly their SC.1 VTOL research aircraft. A complex joint submission emerged for a composite project involving launching and retrieving the P.17A from a VTOL platform powered by no less than 56 Rolls-Royce RB.108 lift engines. In view of the likely development time-scale the submission also proposed that the P.17A should operate conventionally in the interim.

By 1958 officialdom was retreating from use of VTOL for GOR 339. Moreover the Air Staff were disposed towards P.17A in conventional mode but incorporating the integrated systems of Vickers' Type 571.

Accordingly, MoS moved to secure co-operation between the EE and Vickers teams. With Shorts now out of the running, on 1 January 1959 the Government announced that the aircraft, designated TSR.2[3], would be developed jointly by Vickers-Armstrongs and English Electric. The main contract would go to Vickers as lead firm, with work shared equally. A joint project team would be established at Weybridge. Shotgun marriages in the industry were the order of the day and in order to cement another, the Government ruled that the TSR.2's engines would be developed by Bristol Siddeley Engines, newly formed by the Government-backed merger of Bristol Aero-Engines and Armstrong Siddeley Motors, hitherto subsidiaries of the Bristol Aeroplane Company and the Hawker Siddeley Group respectively.

Four revisions of GOR 339, with ever more demanding specifications, appeared in 1958 culminating in the issue in March 1959 of OR 343, virtually written around the EE P.17A / V571. It required all-weather low level radar penetration at speeds of Mach 1.1, Mach 2 at high altitude to avoid interception, with an operational radius of 1,000 miles. It defined a strike aircraft for support of ground forces, capable of delivering nuclear or conventional bombs and air-to-surface missiles, as distinct from a strategic bomber. Short take-off performance would be necessary from rough strips. An advanced design and structure would provide low turbulence and gust response in the interests of crew comfort and handling at low level. All this, plus the capability to carry advanced navigational and terrain-following equipment meant an aircraft of increased size, weight and complexity requiring extensive research and development at several leading edges of technology. Implications for time-scale and cost, with no chance of shared offsetting against other projects thanks to the cuts,

were potentially enormous. Most worryingly of all, TSR.2 was that riskiest of aviation ventures – a new airframe mated with a virtually new and unproven engine.

On 9 January 1959 the establishment of English Electric Aviation Ltd. was announced, comprising the former Aircraft Division's research, design and development headquarters at Warton. The production sites at Strand Road Preston and Accrington, together with Samlesbury Aerodrome, at that stage remained parts of the main EE company. It meant that both EE and V-A now had aviation subsidiaries capable of being merged and it was announced on 12 January 1960 that English Electric Aviation Ltd. and Vickers-Armstrongs (Aircraft) Ltd., together with Bristol Aircraft Ltd., would amalgamate to become the British Aircraft Corporation (BAC) Ltd. BAC became a legal entity on 1 July and later in the year also achieved a controlling interest in Luton-based Hunting Aircraft Ltd. The new company was initially owned jointly by the English Electric Company (40 per cent), Vickers (40 per cent) and Bristol (20 per cent).

Overall TSR.2 design started at Weybridge at the beginning of 1959. It was agreed that Vickers would be responsible for detail design, build, assembly and equipping the fuselage nose, forward and aft centre sections, together with electrics and avionics. English Electric, whose design team returned to Warton in October, had charge of the rear fuselage, wing, tail, engine fit, hydraulic and fuel systems and overall aerodynamics. Manufacturing began in 1960, including complete tailplane and fin assemblies and parts for the rear fuselage and wings at Accrington, other rear fuselage parts and rear fuselage assembly at Strand Road, Preston, with Samlesbury undertaking wing assembly from parts made at all three plants. A contract for nine flying development aircraft and two for ground and structural testing was received in October 1960, followed by one for eleven

[3]The designation linked the aircraft's operational roles to its maximum speed of Mach 2. In 1933 Fairey Aviation built a torpedo bomber, spotter and reconnaissance biplane, the TSR.I, which after modification as the TSR.II became better known as the Fairey Swordfish.

TSR.2 prototype
XR219
undergoes
ground testing at
Boscombe
Down, Wiltshire,
summer 1964.

Roland Beamont
taxies the TSR.2
for its first flight
at Boscombe
Down, Sunday
27 September
1964.

pre-production aircraft in June 1963. The first wing, rear fuselage and tail assemblies were despatched from the Lancashire factories to Weybridge in March and April 1963, where final assembly of development aircraft was to take place. By then the English Electric Aviation Ltd. subsidiary of BAC had taken over the Warton, Preston and Samlesbury plants, only Accrington remaining part of the English Electric Company. The name English Electric Aviation Ltd. was extinguished in January 1964 when it became BAC Preston Division. When GEC took over English Electric in 1968 the industrialist Arnold (later Lord) Weinstock became an influential figure in the aircraft industry, even more so after GEC's new 40 per cent interest in BAC became 50 per cent following their joint acquisition, with Vickers, of Rolls-Royce's (formerly Bristol's) 20 per cent holding from the R-R Official Receiver in 1972.

The A & AEE at Boscombe Down in Wiltshire, 60 miles from Weybridge, was selected for TSR.2's first flight, Vickers' two runways at Brooklands and nearby Wisley being too short for safety. Weybridge was

reluctant to surrender flight testing to
Warton, 200 miles away, despite the latter's
extensive facilities and expertise in test
flying fast jets. But Boscombe involved
setting up a completely new final assembly
and flight test centre to receive the major
sub-assemblies from Weybridge, adding
considerably to other cost and time
overruns. After ground tests, engine runs
and taxiing trials, XR219 crewed by BAC's
then Deputy Chief Test Pilot Roland
Beamont and Chief Test Navigator Donald
Bowen, took to the air on 27 September
1964. It was 18 months behind schedule.

Well before the flight, serious problems
had manifested themselves with the TSR.2's
new Mk.320 Bristol Olympus engines,
explosions of which having wrecked both
the manufacturer's test house and an Avro
Vulcan flying test bed. The prospect of
uncontained catastrophic failure of one or
both engines, tightly confined with their
jetpipes side by side in the TSR.2's
rectangular section, 90 ft. fuselage, was
made even worse by the fact that the
engine tunnels passed through the main

fuselage fuel tanks. Traced only a month
before the first flight to failure of the low
pressure compressor shaft, with onset
heralded by severe resonance, it was
estimated that modifications could take
two months. Rather than delay the flight it
was decided to go ahead, but with
restricted use of reheat and keeping out of
the resonation range by limiting the
engines, already de-rated to 20,000lb st, to
97 per cent rpm. A second restriction
concerned the undercarriage which, not
having been certified for retraction, had to
be left down during initial flight testing.

A delta wingform had been adopted, thin
in section and spanning only 37 ft., with
powerful trailing edge blown flaps for short
take-off performance. Downturned wing
tips enhanced stability. The tail unit
comprised an all-moving fin and tailplane,
the latter with 'taileron' flaps combining
elevator and aileron control. An aluminium
silicate windscreen was proofed against
birdstrike at low level supersonic speeds.
Despite use of advanced weight-saving
structures, machined panels, chemically-

A Meteor 'chase' plane is already aloft as TSR.2 XR219, with reheat pouring from its Olympus engines, takes off from a wintry Boscombe Down in December 1964. TSR.2 would have been capable of carrying nuclear stores on inner and outer wing pylons and in the weapons bay.

Jimmy Dell was at the controls of TSR.2 on this, its 13th flight from Boscombe Down, on 16 February 1965.

etched skins and materials such as aluminium-copper, aluminium-lithium and titanium alloys, depending on the exposure to heat of various components, changing specifications for increased range and equipment had seen its gross weight rise from under 30 to over 45 tons. When fully equipped, TSR.2 would have had fully automatic all-weather nav/attack systems with inertial platform, Doppler and sideways-looking radar and full reconnaissance fit. An automatic flight control system and automatic updating of data would all have been linked by digital computer. Terrain-following radar looking 20 miles ahead would automatically maintain altitude at 2-300 ft. The crew had head-up and moving map displays. TSR.2's potential would range from battlefield support, with four air-to-surface rockets, to long range conventional and nuclear strike, with computer-controlled bombing by free-fall 'lobbing' or parachute-retarded 'lay down' techniques.

Engine limitations required that early test flights be made with the aircraft as lightly loaded as possible, with minimum avionics on board. Although confirming the engine vibration and identifying serious undercarriage problems, the maiden flight revealed an aircraft of outstanding performance, stability and flawless handling. The manufacturer solved the principal engine vibration by the second flight in December 1964 but, perversely, a secondary vibration caused by a reheat fuel pump took until the fourth flight to cure. Reluctant undercarriage retraction and severe runway landing oscillation by the main bogies were solved by the tenth flight. On its fourteenth outing, en route from Boscombe to Warton where the remainder of the test flying was scheduled to take place, on 22 February 1965 over the Irish Sea, Beamont took the TSR.2 to just over Mach 1 at maximum dry thrust. He then eased it to Mach 1.12 with minimum reheat on one engine. Later tests included an impressive Mach 0.9 low-level flight over the Pennines.

Just as teething troubles were getting sorted out, powerful forces were growing increasingly critical of TSR.2. The project had faced Treasury opposition from the start, fuelled by time and cost overruns from early in the programme. There had been no adequate unified project management system on the part of manufacturer or customer. Much of the procurement had been made by the Ministry of Aviation, removing cost control from the manufacturers who also had to stand more than their fair share of R & D costs. Excessive bureaucracy had seen a proliferation of committees with inadequate industry representation. The TSR.2's complexity begged the question whether it was the most appropriate first project for the union of English Electric and Vickers, given some inevitable initial tensions between the two.

Significant orders beyond the 150 expected from the RAF might well have silenced the critics. The Australian Government had expressed interest in purchasing 30 but in 1963, suspecting that the project might be cancelled in Britain on political and cost grounds, opted instead for the apparently cheaper American Lockheed F-111 swing-wing aircraft. They may also have been influenced by the Chief of the Defence Staff, Admiral Lord Mountbatten, a strong supporter of the excellent, though subsonic, Blackburn NA.39 Buccaneer low-level strike aircraft then about to enter service with the Royal Navy. In Australia he frequently asserted that five Buccaneers could be had for the price of one TSR.2. The Royal Navy was implacably opposed to TSR.2, believing that Buccaneers should replace the RAF's Canberras, bringing benefits of reduced costs to both Services. The Navy believed that TSR.2 had survived so far only as 'compensation' to the RAF for the impending loss of its nuclear deterrent to the Polaris Fleet. Moreover the United States had kept a close watch on TSR.2 and its prospective export markets for several years. Ostensibly interested in purchasing it, a team from the Pentagon came to Britain in 1960 to assess the aircraft. It is more likely that it was a fishing expedition to gather information, fearing that if TSR.2 proved as successful as the Canberra – which the US had had to manufacture under licence – it could seriously threaten worldwide prospects for the F-111.

At home, encouraged by Australia's decision to cancel, an increasingly hostile press railed against an aircraft 'which had made only five flights in five months without being able to retract its undercarriage'. By 1964 with an uncertain Conservative Government and a Labour administration-in-waiting, TSR.2 with an estimated cost of anything up to £5 million per aircraft had become a political football, electioneering pawn and the subject of

After the initial nine development aircraft, BAC were to have built eleven pre-production followed by 30 production TSR.2s at Samlesbury. This photograph, taken early in 1965, shows the first pre-production aircraft XS660 taking shape in the Samlesbury jigs.

internecine bickering between politicians, Ministries and Service Chiefs. During the 1964 General Election campaign a handbill circulated round Preston claimed that a Labour Government would not cancel TSR.2 and that jobs would be guaranteed. After the Election the new Labour Government under Harold Wilson delayed a decision for six months, a period marked by intense lobbying by all parties and a mass march on Whitehall by 10,000 BAC and other aircraft workers. Key personalities including the new Government's Chief Scientific Adviser, the eminent zoologist and scientist Sir Solly (later Lord) Zuckerman and Treasury allies, lost no opportunity to press for cancellation. In the media, vociferous contributors to the debate including Mary Goldring of *The Economist* maintained a constant anti-TSR.2 barrage, interpreted by many as suggesting that the UK Government should procure all its future aircraft requirements from the USA. Several published accounts have since alleged that in a crucial Defence Committee meeting, the then Minister of Defence, Denis (later Lord) Healey remarked: "By the way Prime Minister we think you should know that the wing of TSR.2 broke under test at Farnborough yesterday". In fact this was under routine structural testing to destruction, after the wing had already withstood many times the loading it would encounter in service.

Amidst deepening gloom in the industry, the Chancellor of the Exchequer, James Callaghan, announced the cancellation of TSR.2 in his Budget speech on 6 April 1965. Within hours Denis Healey announced that an option had been taken to buy the F-111. An order for 50 F-111Ks was mooted. Thereafter it was always denied that cancellation was the price exacted by the US for its support of Sterling at the time. BAC at Weybridge were instructed to destroy immediately the TSR.2s on the production line, together with their assembly jigs. Of five airframes fully or substantially completed, only the prototype XR219 had flown. It later joined XR221 and XR223 as gunnery targets at the Proof and Experimental Establishment at Shoeburyness, Essex. XR220 and XR222 were spirited away from such ignominious destruction and today can be seen preserved at the RAF Museum at Cosford and Imperial War Museum at Duxford respectively. Other airframes at varying stages of assembly at Weybridge and Samlesbury were scrapped.

Before cancellation, in December 1964 it had been announced that final assembly of eleven pre-production and initially 30 production TSR.2s would take place at Samlesbury with flight testing at Warton. The potential had been immense. The loss of its sole surviving major military aircraft project was a body blow to Britain's – particularly Lancashire's – aircraft industry,

Government-prescribed Olympus engines, rather than equally powerful though lighter and more economical by-pass turbofans such as the Medway or Conway, have proved the right choice? Would the tightly-packed engine installations have presented long term problems for access, on-board servicing and maintenance, or removal? Such questions are academic: it would be unrealistic to compare TSR.2's potential serviceability with modern aircraft such as the Tornado or Typhoon in which such aspects are specified as part of the design. What is fact is that TSR.2 was a prodigious driver of technology. Its reheated Olympus engines were further developed to give many years of excellent service in Concorde. TSR.2 was a major advance in solid-state electronics, all main avionics systems having been installed in the third development aircraft at the time of cancellation. Even afterwards, its avionics, nav/attack system and digital computer continued to be developed by Elliott Automation, Ferranti, EMI, Smiths and Decca to benefit later projects such as the British Phantom, Jaguar, Harrier and Nimrod. TSR.2 gave over 1,000 subcontractors the opportunity to participate at the forefront of technological advance. It was Sir Sydney Camm, formerly of Hawker, who would later remark: "All modern aircraft have four dimensions: span, length, height and politics. TSR.2 simply got the first three right."

TSR.2 was the last major all-British military aircraft programme. Cancellation terminated the most advanced military aircraft of its time in the world. So advanced that if it was rolled out for the first time today, 40 years on, and presented in a blaze of publicity as the latest product of the industry, many would stand in awe of its futuristic appearance.

Sir George Edwards, Chairman and Managing Director of BAC, lost no opportunity to stress to the Government the serious consequences of cancelling

TSR.2 for employment and the future viability of the Preston Division. But although the repercussions would be felt for a decade to come, their impact was mitigated by three principal sets of factors. The first was the reallocation of work on a number of different aircraft projects within the BAC group. Second was the winning of immense export orders from Saudi Arabia. Thirdly, following its decision to cancel, the Labour Government pushed the industry hard down the road of European collaboration. The European route would lead to major collaborative work programmes which have now sustained the Lancashire aircraft factories for some 40 years.

From 1959 English Electric contributed to various studies for a supersonic airliner as input to the Supersonic Transport Aircraft Committee of the RAE. When this developed as the **Concorde SST** collaborative project between BAC at Weybridge and Filton, and Sud Aviation of Toulouse, Warton was responsible for the design of the fin, rudder and part of the rear fuselage. As a result, rear fuselages and engine nacelle intakes were built at Strand Road and Samlesbury for Concorde prototypes until pressure of work on Lightning and TSR.2 required the transfer of Concorde work to Weybridge.

Preston Division also gained from the placing in the 1960s of subcontract manufacture of rear fuselages for **McDonnell F-4 Phantoms** for the Royal Navy and RAF, following the cancellation of various British aircraft. The requirement that they be fitted with Rolls-Royce Spey engines rather than the standard J79, for extra take-off thrust from smaller British aircraft carriers, together with British electronics, necessitated major airframe modifications.

Of even greater significance was the transfer of the **Jet Provost** line to Preston (and wing manufacture to Hurn) after BAC closed the Hunting Aircraft factory at

Luton in 1966. Some rationalisation within the group was inevitable after TSR.2, but the demise of Preston with over 20 years of expertise in design, manufacture and flight testing of military jet aircraft was unthinkable. At the time of its closure, Luton had produced over 400 Jet Provost T.Mk.1, 2, 3, 4 trainers primarily for the RAF. As the successor to the earlier piston Provost of which Hunting Percival had made over 460, the Jet Provost was designed for seamless all-jet training from *ab initio* to front line aircraft for RAF pilots of the 1950s. The first 'JP' flew in 1954, powered by a 1,640lb-thrust Armstrong Siddeley Viper 5. Designed initially as an expendable engine for the Australian Jindivik target drone, the Viper proved remarkably durable and reliable, contributing greatly to the success of the 'JP' family.

Financed by BAC, an initially private venture proposal by Hunting Aircraft for the H.145 development of the 'JP' was worked up by Warton as the BAC145 Jet Provost Mk.5. Retaining the side-by-side pilot-pupil seating of its forebears, the Mk.5 was given a pressurised cockpit, extended nose housing improved avionics, additional internal fuel tankage and an up-rated Viper engine, the whole providing much enhanced high altitude pilot training. With a view to exports, a new stronger wing with longer fatigue life, capable of carrying weapons in the strike attack trainer role, was fitted. The T.Mk.5 first flew on 28 February 1967, 110 being delivered to the RAF between 1969 and 1972, together with five armed T.55 versions to Sudan. Two Preston-built T.Mk.5s used by HRH Prince Charles for jet pilot training operated under the call sign 'Golden Eagle', one of them (XW323) being displayed today at the RAF Museum, Hendon. A radio, navigation and instrumentation refit of 157 earlier 'JPs' began in 1973 for the RAF, armed variants of which having been supplied to Ceylon, Kuwait, Sudan, Iraq, South Yemen and Venezuela. From 1988 the RAF's 'JPs' started to be replaced by the winner of a design competition for a successor, the Shorts S.312 Tucano, based on a product of the Brazilian EMBRAER organisation. 130 Tucanos, the last complete aircraft to be built by Shorts at Belfast, were supplied to the RAF and another 28 armed versions to overseas countries by 1993.

British Aerospace 167 Strikemaster Mk.88 NZ6361 of the New Zealand Air Force flies over Poulton-le-Fylde and Thornton. It carries underwing fuel drop tanks and Matra rocket launchers.

An improved export version of the 'JP', the **BAC 167 Strikemaster**, was first flown at Warton by project pilot Reg Stock on 26 October 1967. Powered by a 3,410lb-thrust Viper 20, generating over twice the power of the 1954 'JP' prototype's Viper 5, the Strikemaster had additional airframe and landing gear strengthening, with side-by-side Martin Baker ejection seats. It offered low cost, multi-role pilot and weapons training and extreme ruggedness for ground attack and reconnaissance. A 3,000lb mixed weapon load could be lifted off grass or laterite-surfaced strips over a range of 1,400 miles with an endurance of five hours. The concluding of the Saudi Arabian Defence Contract at the end of 1965, specifying 40 Lightnings and 25 Strikemasters, the latter increased to 41 by 1976, was a major boost. Altogether, from 1969 156 Strikemasters were delivered by Warton to Saudi Arabia, South Yemen, Oman, Kuwait, Singapore, Kenya, New Zealand, Ecuador and Botswana. Orders from Sudan were discharged by British Aerospace at Hurn in 1984 after assembly was relocated from Warton.

In December 1964 the Wilson Government set up the Plowden Committee of Enquiry into the Aircraft Industry. It was no surprise that when the Committee reported twelve months later it echoed strongly the evolving Government view that the industry must address the issue of collaboration with other European countries. If politicians and their advisers had been less than

supportive of TSR.2, credit must go to Denis Healey – for whatever wider European political or other objectives – for strongly projecting the industry into Europe initially through collaborative ventures with the French. The first case in point, Concorde, proved hugely expensive but survived largely because of inextricable Treaty agreements with the French Government and the likelihood of cancellation facing imposition of punitive damages at The Hague. Although TSR.2 had been axed and Healey had ordered military aircraft such as the Phantom and Hercules from America, the point had not been lost on the Government that the British aircraft industry, particularly military work at Preston and civil at Weybridge, was far too valuable in employment, critical mass expertise, high value-added and strong export potential to be allowed to go to the wall. Even before TSR.2's cancellation, discussions had started with the French about feasibility studies into two new projects, an advanced trainer and variable geometry or 'swing-wing' multi-role aircraft. Ultimately these would lead to two major programmes of enormous significance for BAC and its successors at Preston – the Jaguar strike aircraft and Tornado strike and air defence fighter. By 1967 BAC was busier than anyone including the most optimistic might have imagined in the dark days two years before. At Preston Division, under F.W. Page as Chairman and Managing Director, the last Lightning was delivered to the RAF as work increased on refurbishment of the evergreen Canberra. Elsewhere in the Corporation civil work was at a healthy level with VC10, BAC111 and Concorde airliners proceeding at Weybridge and Bristol. BAC gained Queen's Awards for Export in 1966 and 1967.

During the early 1960s both France and Britain had requirements for an advanced training aircraft. France designated theirs the École d'Appui (ECAP), to bridge the gap between the Magister and Mirage III. In Britain the more prosaic Air Staff Target (AST) 362 envisaged a replacement for the Gnat and Hunter. In France Breguet won a design competition for an aircraft which by 1964 had developed into a strike trainer with tactical capability in single and two-seat versions for combat and photo-reconnaissance, the Breguet Br.121. They redesignated it as École de Combat et d'Appui Tactique (ECAT).

In Britain, TSR.2 was then still in progress but increasingly sophisticated, expensive – and vulnerable. As the straitjacket imposed by Sandys' 1957 White Paper started to loosen, the Air Staff believed that another way forward would be a fast twin-engined trainer with potential for an attack role flying at up to Mach 1.7. This was even more advanced than the already enhanced, but still relatively basic, cheaper and marginally subsonic French ECAT. Keen that an Anglo-French collaborative project should lend credence to its bid for membership of the Common Market, the British Government signed a Memorandum of Understanding with the French in May 1965 for 300 aircraft. For political reasons it was deemed acceptable that Breguet should retain lead partner status in airframe design but to avoid problems of collaborative working as experienced with Concorde, a joint company – Societé Européanne Production de L'Avion ECAT (SEPECAT) – was established in France between Breguet and BAC in May 1966, with production facilities at Vélizy-

Villacoublay near Paris and at Warton. To be named **Jaguar**, the resulting advanced supersonic strike fighter, ground attack and trainer aircraft would be much more potent and closer to the RAF's requirements than the more basic ones of the French. Most of the necessary redesign was carried out by a team headed by Ivan Yates at Warton, from 1971 to be renamed the BAC Military Aircraft Division, where cancellation of TSR.2 had released considerable capacity. For its new Gnat-replacement trainer the RAF would have to await the evaluation of smaller designs submitted by BAC and Hawker Siddeley, eventually manifested as the HS.Hawk.

To provide the necessary extra power, Jaguar's engines were also developed as a joint venture combination of Rolls-Royce's RB.172 and Turboméca's T.260. Now with an afterburning requirement, the French SNECMA company was also included. The resulting Rolls-Royce Turboméca Adour bypass or turbofan engine, initially of 5,200-7,400lb thrust, linked Rolls' traditional use of river names for its engines with the part-French product. With most of the Jaguar's slim fuselage taken up by two engines and fuel tanks there was no provision for a bomb bay. Instead, shoulder-mounted wings combined with a long, rugged undercarriage allowed external under-wing carriage of disposable stores. Under arrangements which avoided duplication of manufacturing, Breguet built front and centre fuselage units including cockpits, and BAC the wings (at Samlesbury), rear fuselages and tails. The major components were transported to each other's assembly lines at Toulouse and Warton. In Britain the Jaguar's power flying control system was made by the Fairey Hydraulics Ltd. subsidiary, Fairey Engineering, at Stockport.

Each country initially ordered 150 Jaguars in 1966, increased to 200 the following year, the RAF specifying 110 two-seat Jaguar 'B' trainers and 90 single-seat 'S' strike versions. A Defence Review of October

1970 more than reversed this allocation to 35 two-seater T.Mk.2s and 165 single-seat GR.Mk.1s, with a further two T.Mk.2s later acquired by the Empire Test Pilots' School and one by the RAE.

The first Jaguar to fly, from a batch of five French prototypes, took to the air at Istres near Marseilles on 8 September 1968. A month later both Jimmy Dell of BAC and his French counterpart had flown it supersonically. The first British Jaguar, the prototype GR.Mk.1 tactical support aircraft, flew at Warton on 12 October 1969 followed by another on 12 June 1970. The third, final British prototype, a T.Mk.2 trainer, flew on 30 August 1971. The first production Jaguar, a French aircraft, flew in November 1971 and deliveries to the L'Armée de l'air commenced in 1972.

Production GR.Mk.1s started to come off the Warton line in June 1973 for delivery to the Jaguar OCU at Lossiemouth in September and to No. 54 Squadron in March 1974. Of eight operational RAF Jaguar units, four were based at Brüggen in Germany as part of the Second Tactical Air Force. Britain's 203 Jaguars were assembled at Warton between 1973 and

Jaguar T.Mk.2 production in full swing at Warton.

The 50th production Jaguar GR.Mk.1 XX738 at Warton.

235

1978. To demonstrate their STOL and tactical deployment potential, on 26 April 1975 a GR.Mk.1 flown by BAC test pilot Tim Ferguson landed on the then unopened M55 Preston-Blackpool motorway to be 'bombed up' for a loaded take-off under reheat. With its Jaguars the RAF gained a first class force of interdiction and reconnaissance aircraft capable of Mach 1.1 at low level and Mach 1.5 at higher altitudes. GR.Mk.1 equipment included a Marconi-Elliott digital navigation and weapons aiming sub-system (NAVWASS) projecting a Head up Display (HUD), with moving map display. Ferranti laser ranging and marked-target seeker avionics were housed in a distinctively chisel-shaped nose. With armament of two 30mm cannon and 10,000lb of weaponry on external stations, radius of action was up to 800 miles. At the same time its designers effectively addressed issues of ease and speed of maintenance in the field: 400 quick release panels covered 30 per cent of the aircraft's surface. Jaguar remains today a potent tactical strike weapon able to carry out precision 'single pass' attacks.

Jaguar proved capable of even further development. In 1974 the Adour engines were up-rated to give nine per cent more thrust at take-off and 27 per cent more in the Mach 0.8-0.9 range under combat conditions at low level, later increased to 15 and 40 per cent respectively. Anti-shipping and overwing Matra Magic dog-fight missiles, night sensors and multi-purpose Thomson 'Agave' air-to-air, sea and ground radar were added. The resulting **Jaguar International**, developed by British Aerospace Aircraft Group Warton Division, responsible for assembly of all Jaguars for export as well as for the RAF, achieved significant success in overseas markets. The first production Jaguar International flew on 19 August 1976. Warton built 94 for export to Ecuador (12), Oman (24), Nigeria (18) and India (40). In 1978 the order for India, to replace IAF Canberras and Hunters, was confirmed by the signing of an 'Intention to Proceed' by representatives of the Indian Government and Mr F.W. (later Sir Frederick) Page, by then Chairman of British Aerospace Aircraft Group and a former Joint

Jaguar International demonstrator aircraft XW563 over Blackpool, carrying twin over-wing Magic AAMs, twin Matra rocket pods and 1,000lb bombs together with a single centreline drop tank.

Chairman of SEPECAT. It was followed by an agreement for Hindustan Aeronautics to manufacture under licence. Mr R.H. (later Sir Richard) Evans, then Commercial Director at Warton and a Director of SEPECAT, until recently Chairman of BAE Systems PLC, had responsibility for the associated support organisation. In 1979 he was appointed Director-in-Charge (India) for setting up the Jaguar manufacturing programme there. The first Indian-produced Jaguar flew in 1982 and 106 had been completed by 1999 with work starting on a further 17 with improved nav/attack systems.

In a development of huge technological significance for the future a GR.Mk.1 was withdrawn from RAF service to be extensively modified as a demonstration aircraft for Active Control Technology (ACT). Its conventional manual control rod linkages were substituted by a 'fly-by-wire' (FBW) system with four independent computer-controlled electrical channels activating flight control surfaces. After first flying in October 1981 the FBW demonstrator was re-modelled with large leading edge wing strakes or extensions and ballast added to the rear fuselage to

create an aerodynamically unstable but potentially highly manoeuvrable aircraft. In this form it flew again in 1984, the FBW/ACT technology proving highly successful in effecting virtually instantaneous control corrections. Experience gained from 96 test flights comprising the Jaguar FBW/ACT programme up to September 1984 was vital input for the development of the Experimental Aircraft Programme (EAP) and the subsequent European Fighter Aircraft (EFA) and currently the Eurofighter Typhoon. After several years' use for instructional purposes at Loughborough University the FBW/ACT Jaguar demonstrator was placed in the RAF Museum Cosford in 1996.

BAC modified part of the Jaguar force with external photographic reconnaissance pods in 1976 and between 1978 and 1984 RAF aircraft were brought up to Jaguar International standards of engine power. From 1983 avionics improvements brought about redesignations as GR.Mk.1A, 1B, T.Mk.2B, GR.Mk.3 and T.Mk.4. Jaguars have seen successful deployment in regional conflicts including the Gulf War and in the Balkans. Today they remain an important part of the RAF's strength and in a programme extending from 1998 to 2005 Warton is engaged on fitting improved engines to provide some 96 Jaguars with ten per cent further increase in thrust.

The Anglo-French Jaguar occupies a unique position as the first combat aircraft produced by international collaboration to enter service with the RAF and the L'Armée de l'air. Its success and continued potency is all the more remarkable given its gestation in complex international political circumstances and the significantly different initial requirements of the two air forces concerned. Given such capability, the UK Government's recent decision to retire the RAF's Jaguar fleet by 2007, taken as part of its Defence Restructuring Review of 2004, has been received with disappointment in many quarters.

'Big Cats' in current service – Jaguar GR.3As of the RAF Coltishall Jaguar Wing of No. 6 (foreground), 41, 54, and 16 Sqns. *Photo: Geoffrey Lee.*

Jaguar upgrade work at Warton.

Since 1945, at Weybridge and elsewhere, the remarkable Dr. (later Sir) Barnes Wallis had been studying variable geometry (VG) or 'swing wing' technology. With wings outstretched it offered the prospect of enhanced lift during take-off, landing and at low speeds, combined with the aerodynamics of fully swept wings for high speed flight. Wallis proceeded using models as part of the *Wild Goose* and *Swallow* research projects. Variable geometry was considered for application to the TSR.2 as early as 1958 but then rejected as a technology too far. Vickers and later BAC continued to keep it under active consideration. In yet another tie-up between the pioneering Wallis and Lancashire, in 1964 all such work was transferred from Weybridge to the Preston Division of BAC at Warton. The move was overseen by N.W. Boorer, formerly Vickers' Chief Designer (R & D) reporting to Wallis. Warton immediately applied the principles of VG to the design of the P.45, a projected two-seat fighter bomber.

With development costs increasing relentlessly, the need to design a single aircraft capable of discharging multiple military functions was fast becoming a holy grail within the industry. VG seemed a sure way forward. Moreover, in the 1960s prevailing climate of multi-nation collaboration, the combination of circumstances offered the irresistible prospect of European production runs to rival those of America. In 1965 Britain and France jointly agreed to proceed on a second military collaborative project, this time the Anglo-French Variable Geometry (AFVG) multi-role Mach 2.5 aircraft. With the P.45 as a sort of precursor, BAC took the lead in airframe design and a full-scale mock-up was built at Warton. AFVG work ended prematurely in July 1967 when France pulled out of the joint working arrangements to pursue a totally French VG alternative involving Dassault alone. France remained committed to ECAT (Jaguar), for

which Breguet had the airframe design lead, as the sole surviving Anglo-French collaborative military aircraft project.

When announcing France's withdrawal from AFVG, Minister of Defence Denis Healey indicated that work would continue in Britain on development of variable geometry wing design. The same year he signed up to the so-called European F-104 replacement programme which, also involving Canada, was looking into a variable geometry multi-role combat aircraft to enter service in 1975 – the MRCA-75 – to succeed the American Lockheed Starfighter then in service with West Germany, Italy, Belgium, the Netherlands and Canada. In January 1968 the escalating costs of the F-111 compelled Britain to drop its option to purchase the American aircraft, pushing it further down the MRCA-75 line. At the same time however, Canada, Belgium and the Netherlands, who principally required an interceptor, dropped out.

The practicalities of VG had been receiving close attention at Warton and by 1968 a team led by Ray Creasey had designed and seen manufactured and tested a wing pivot with PTFE 'Teflon'-plated bearing. There appeared to be no insuperable barrier to either its large scale production or reliability in service. The MRCA programme was launched in December and by the end of January 1969 a Joint Feasibility Study was concluded. On 26 March the remaining partners – Britain, Germany and Italy – formed a joint company, Panavia Aircraft GmbH, registered at Munich two days later. Healey announced the MRCA Memorandum of Understanding in Parliament on 14 May. It indicated potential demand for over 1,000 aircraft, one third of which for the RAF to replace Vulcans, Buccaneers and Phantoms in the tactical strike/reconnaissance, air defence and maritime strike roles. The statement made no reference to MRCA as a replacement for the Canberra –

something the RAF still wanted. Perhaps it was too soon after cancellation of TSR.2 to risk officially associating the three aircraft. In fact MRCA would evolve into a very different aircraft to the TSR.2, its multi-role potential providing a single replacement for nearly all the types of front line combat aircraft then in service with the RAF. Moreover, RAF requirements had changed with the Service's considerably reduced commitments 'East of Suez.' Considering its potency, MRCA would be remarkably small in size, scarcely more than half the length of TSR.2, and its 28-45 ft. wingspan in marked contrast to the massive 111 ft. Vulcan.

Panavia represented three companies nominated by the national partners, each with a shareholding reflecting the aircraft numbers required. Initially Messerschmitt-Bolköw-Blohm had 50 per cent (later, as Dasa, 42.5 per cent), BAC 33 per cent (BAe 42.5) and Fiat 17 per cent (Aeritalia-AIT-Alenia 15). Similarly, a second consortium, Turbo-Union Ltd. comprising Rolls-Royce, Turbien Union (MTU) and Fiat was established in London in September 1969 to develop MRCA's engines. IWKA-Mauser of Germany were appointed to develop a fast-firing cannon as the aircraft's basic armament. From 1970 Panavia also took overall responsibility for avionics, with EASAMS (UK) reporting directly to them and co-ordinating work done by SIA in Italy, ESG in Germany and their many suppliers. An organisational tier known as the NATO MRCA Management Organisation (NAMMO) was formed in Panavia's Munich offices as the interface between Panavia, Turbo-Union, Mauser and the three Government partners. In effect NAMMO and its agency NAMMA were the customer with Panavia the prime contractor for the entire programme.

A Definition Phase authorised by the tripartite Memorandum of Understanding of May 1969 was completed by April 1970. MRCA variants would be expected to perform close air-to-ground support,

battlefield interdiction and interdictor strike, countering any breakthrough by Soviet ground forces in Central Europe, together with reconnaissance and land-based maritime strike. At higher altitude they would excel at interception and air superiority. MRCA would also be required to provide operational training in all roles. It was a tall order.

Under co-Chief Designers Oliver Heath and Helmut Langfelder, MRCA emerged as a two-seat supersonic combat aircraft with high-set continuously variable geometry wings offering up to 67 degrees leading edge sweep-back, hydraulically powered on a PTFE-plated pivot with a ballscrew mechanism. An ingenious system of pneumatic rubber wing root seals and fan-like overlapping plastic plates on the upper surfaces protected the moving wings' airframe slots. A sophisticated mechanical system of high lift leading edge wing slats and trailing edge slotted flaps was preferred to a thrust-consuming blown system. With two Turbo-Union RB.199 three-spool turbofan engines of 8,700-14,840lb thrust, reheat and thrust reversers, the arrangement offered STOL capability of take-off in 3,000 ft., landing in 1,500 ft. at slow speed, with quick response time from dispersed or partly incapacitated airfields. Transonic at low level, MRCA would have high manoeuvrability and low gust response, a long penetration range and all-weather day and night capability with appropriate radar and nav/attack systems. It would have flexible load-carrying ability for weapons and external fuel tanks, pivoting on under-wing pylons for retained alignment during wing sweep. The engines would provide high specific excess power for rate of climb and acceleration to Mach 2 for interception or evasion during reconnaissance, combined with good fuel consumption and extended loitering ability in the air superiority role.

In July 1970 a further Memorandum of Understanding authorised the

Development Phase. Production of nine prototypes, four in Britain, three in Germany and two in Italy, began in November. The initial requirement of 600 aircraft for Germany, 385 for the UK and 200 for Italy was adjusted to 400, 400 and 100 respectively. A full development contract was awarded to Panavia in August 1972 and in March 1973 NAMMA announced the authorisation of preparatory production work. During this time Vulcan, Buccaneer and Lightning test bed aircraft, the latter two types based at Warton, were engaged on development of the engines, radar/avionics/nav/attack systems and proving the Mauser cannon respectively. Six pre-production aircraft were ordered in 1974 to follow the prototypes.

Ground-running tests began in Germany in April 1974 and the first MRCA (PO1) flew from the MBB flight test centre at Manching, near Munich, on 14 August piloted by BAC Military Aircraft Division Chief Test and Project Pilot Paul Millett. He flew the second aircraft (PO2) at Warton on 30 October. It was the start of an intensive flight test programme involving all 15 prototype and development aircraft at the three flight test centres of the partner countries and the sharing of information between all three. MRCA, then known as the Panther, was officially named **Tornado**. The third to fly, the British PO3, took off from Warton on 5 August 1975 in the hands of BAC Chief Test Pilot Dave Eagles and his Deputy, Tim Ferguson. The first Italian Tornado flew at Caselle, near Turin, on 5 December.

Full scale production was authorised in July 1976. A total of 809 Tornados were then required, 385 for the RAF comprising 220 interdictor strike (IDS) and 165 air defence (ADV) variants, 324 for Germany comprising 212 for the Luftwaffe and 112 for the Marineflieger, and 100 for Italy. Of the total, 137 would be dual control trainers retaining full operational capability, 68 of these for the RAF. Tornado MRCA was the world's first supersonic truly multi-

Opposite:
The first British MRCA prototype PO2 XX946 undergoing ground tests and engine runs prior to its first flight by Paul Millett at Warton on 30 October 1974. The aircraft carried tri-national British, German and Italian insignia, with PANAVIA-AIT-BAC-MBB partner credits beneath the distinctively large tail fin. This aircraft is now preserved at the RAF Museum, Cosford.

MRCA prototype PO2 flies north along the seafront to take a close look at some engineering of a different era. Behind Blackpool Tower can be seen the Winter Gardens complex.

MRCA prototype PO2 takes fuel from No. 55 Sqn. Victor K.2 XL160, in 1975 then just recently converted by Hawker Siddeley at Woodford for the RAF's tanker fleet.

role combat aircraft. Its production was then Europe's largest ever military aircraft programme and largest collaborative industrial project, providing work for 500 firms and up to 70,000 people, half of whom were in the UK. In 1977, Mr. F.W. Page was appointed Chairman of Panavia.

There was no duplication of production. Each national partner was responsible for manufacturing specific sub-assemblies for all 809 aircraft – the UK for front and rear fuselage including nose section, cockpits, engine bays, fin and tailplane; Germany the centre fuselage including wing pivots; Italy the wings. Each had its own assembly plant and flight test centre to where the appropriate number of sub-assemblies were delivered. In Britain major sub-assemblies were erected at the BAC Military Aircraft Division plant at Samlesbury from smaller components made there and at Preston, with final assembly and flight testing at Warton where a major new assembly hall was under construction. By 1976 the UK's

workshare stood at 47.6 per cent. Construction was surprisingly conventional given the aircraft's advanced design which incorporated VG, FBW control system with mechanical back-up, pitch and roll control by all-moving differential tailerons (there being no ailerons). Tornado was of all-metal conventional alloy-build save for a titanium wing carry-through box. 35 per cent of the aircraft's surface comprised access panels to key equipment with servicing facilitated by a Line Replaceable Unit system. Costs estimated at £1.5 million per aircraft in 1969 had increased to £5.3 million by 1977, largely due to the high inflation of that period. In 1977 BAC was absorbed into the newly created, nationalised British Aerospace (BAe).

By the end of August 1978, Tornados had cleared 90 per cent of the flight envelope in over 2,000 hours of flying. Weapon loads of over 16,000lb had been carried, speeds well over Mach 1.9 attained at height with a climb performance of brakes off to 30,000 ft. in well under two minutes.

Lancashire-built Tornado F.3 ZE835 of No. 111 'Treble One' Sqn. RAF intercepts a Tupolev TU-95/142 'Bear F' long range maritime surveillance aircraft of the Soviet Naval Air Force. Up to six such interceptions per week took place during the 1980s, some up to 500 miles north of RAF Leuchars in Scotland requiring aerial refuelling from Victor tankers. *Photo: Cpl. Kevin Jones © Crown Copyright/ MOD.*

Tornado ADV and GR.1 variants, Jaguar, Lightning, Strikemaster and Canberra pass by the Lytham Yacht Club in November 1984.

Tornado F.3 ZE835 of No. 111 Sqn. and another of No. 43 Sqn. escort a Soviet Ilyushin IL-78 'Midas' tanker. The pylon-mounted missile-like appendages under the tanker's wing and on the rear fuselage are in fact UPAZ Sakhalin ram-air turbine units for rapid delivery of fuel along hoses extended to refuelling aircraft. *Photo: Cpl. Kevin Jones © Crown Copyright/MOD.*

Tornado GR.1A 6620 tactical reconnaissance variant of the Royal Saudi Air Force, with three internally-mounted infra-red sensors and a comprehensive video recording system providing horizon-to-horizon coverage at low level, high speed and in all weather conditions, day and night.

Assembly of the first RAF production aircraft, ZA319, commenced in the new facility at Warton in September, the aircraft flying on 10 July 1979. A new Tri-National Tornado Training Establishment (TTTE) at RAF Cottesmore became operational in 1980 and Tornados entered operational service in the UK on 1 June 1982 with No. 9 Squadron at RAF Honington, followed in 1983 by No. 617 (The Dam Busters) and No. 27 Squadrons at Marham. In addition to their stated duties, Marham Tornados are believed to have had a strategic nuclear role. By May 1983 over 200 Tornados had been completed in the three countries. Based at Laarbruch and Brüggen, eight of the 15 squadrons comprising RAF Germany started to receive Tornado GR.1s from November 1983.

The first of three ADV prototypes, some 4½ ft. longer than the IDS to hold different radar, air-to-air missiles and extra fuel, was flown at Warton on 27 October 1979 by Chief Test Pilot Dave Eagles, exceeding Mach 1 on the first flight. Designated F.2 by the RAF, it was a long range interceptor required to complement its IDS sibling's NATO roles in Central Europe under SACEUR (Supreme Allied Command Europe) and over the Eastern Atlantic under SACLANT, by patrolling far out over the North Sea and North Atlantic approaches. 400 miles from base, it was intended to keep airspace and sea lanes free of enemy aircraft, particularly supersonic Soviet bombers carrying stand-off weapons from bases in the Kola Peninsula. As a replacement for Lightnings and Phantoms, the ADV could launch Sky Flash and Sidewinder missiles fitted under its fuselage at multiple targets over 25 miles distant. To do this, instead of IDS terrain-following Texas Instruments radar, the ADV employed GEC-Marconi Foxhunter Air Intercept radar. Delays with the system required early aircraft to be flown with ballast in the nose, referred to facetiously as 'Blue Circle' radar after the well-known

concrete manufacturer. In fact the ballast used was steel bars. The F.2 entered service at RAF Coningsby in 1985 with interim radar but began to be replaced by the F.3 with more powerful engines and improved avionics in 1986.

In September 1985 the Saudi Arabian and UK Governments signed the £4 billion *Al Yamamah 1* 'Bird of Peace' defence contract involving the Warton Division (from 1986 the Warton Unit of the Military Aircraft Division) of British Aerospace supplying 48 Tornado IDS and 24 ADV aircraft. The package also included 30 Hawks, 30 BAe/Pilatus PC-9s and two Jetstreams. It followed the sale of BAC Lightnings and Strikemasters to Saudi Arabia twenty years earlier as part of a £100 million air defence system contract, a 1973 Saudi Support Contract for £253 million and its renewal in 1977 worth in excess of £500 million. The 1985 contract was itself followed in 1988 by *Al Yamamah 2* for a further 12 IDS and 36 ADVs, later changed to 48 IDS aircraft, making a total of 120 Tornados sold to Saudi Arabia. Together with the Indian Jaguar Contract of 1979, these were all occasions when Warton was credited with winning the largest-ever single export orders in Britain.

The main Tornado production run, with final assembly at Warton from sub-assemblies supplied by Samlesbury and components from Strand Road, ended in 1993 on completion of RAF and *Al Yamamah 1* requirements. The assembly line closed, jigs were dismantled and tools dispersed. *Al Yamamah 2* had been cancelled in 1990 but was reinstated in 1994 for 48 Tornado IDS aircraft. Manufacturing of front and rear fuselages, fins and tailerons had to be cranked up virtually from scratch again at Samlesbury, the external supply chain reactivated and the Tornado workforce re-grouped involving, in some cases, the return to work of retired personnel. It was a complex operation, made all the more difficult by the fact that the Strand Road factory had closed in 1993. Nevertheless Warton was able to deliver the last Tornado of all to the RSAF in September 1998. By then a total of 992 Tornados had been built by the partner countries, 557 by BAC and BAe at Warton and the balance of 435 in Germany and Italy. Of those produced at Warton, nine were prototype and development aircraft, 398 for the RAF (228 IDS and 170 ADV) and 120 for Saudi Arabia (96 IDS and 24 ADV).

In RAF service the Tornado has been designated GR.1 all-weather, day and night interdictor strike, close air support, counter air and defence suppression; GR.1A tactical reconnaissance; GR.1B long range maritime attack; F.2 interim long range air defence fighter; F.3 long range air defence fighter with GR.4/4A updates of the GR.1/1A. The GR.4 is an extensive £700 million mid-life avionics and systems upgrade with GPS global positioning, forward-looking infra-red and night vision equipment, maintaining its superiority in fast, covert low-level penetration operations into the twenty-first century. It first flew on 29 May 1993, delivery of the first of 142 GR.4/4As upgraded at Warton starting in May 1998 in a programme completed in 2003. In the most graphic terms, GR.4 has the capacity to attack targets with pinpoint accuracy in the toughest conditions, including flying through mountainous terrain in blizzard conditions at night. GR.4 can now carry the TIALD laser designation pod for delivery of Paveway laser-guided bombs, the RAPTOR reconnaissance pod and the Storm Shadow cruise missile. It is also to be fitted with the Brimstone anti-armour weapon system. It is likely to remain in service until 2020. Work on upgrading the F.3 to carry ASRAAM and AMRAAM missiles began in 1997, the aircraft re-entering service in 1998 with its life at the forefront of UK air defence extended until Eurofighter Typhoon is fully operational.

Since entering service Tornado has been deployed in several war zones and campaigns including the 1990-91 Gulf War, Operations *Desert Shield* and *Desert Storm*, policing no-fly zones over Iraq, in Bosnia and the Balkans and most recently in Operation *Iraqi Freedom 2003*. A small contingent remains on station to defend the Falkland Islands. In a remarkable reversal of their Cold War duties, in 2004 RAF Tornado F.3s were among several NATO aircraft types engaged on short-term deployment and exercises at former Soviet Air Force bases, protecting the airspace of new NATO member countries in the Baltic States and Hungary. When it entered service in 1982 the RAF not only got its replacement for the Canberra (albeit 23 years after the placing of the contract for TSR.2 and 17 years after its cancellation) but also for the Vulcan, Buccaneer, Lightning and Phantom – virtually all its front line combat strength other than specialised types such as the Jaguar and Harrier. Tornado has been one of the most remarkable chapters of British and European military aviation.

One of the aircraft most frequently seen in the skies over Lancashire today is the **BAE Systems Hawk** advanced trainer and light combat aircraft. Much associated now with Warton and Samlesbury, historically Hawk owes its initial design and manufacture to Hawker Siddeley plants at Kingston and Dunsfold in the South of England and Brough in Yorkshire. Today Brough is the principal manufacturing centre from where the aircraft are transported to Warton for final assembly, wing attachment and flight testing.

The origins of the Hawk date from the RAF's requirement of the 1960s for the replacement of its Gnat jet trainer, specified in 1964 by the previously referred to Air Staff Target (AST) 362. Even after the advent of the Jaguar trainer, the basic requirement remained unfulfilled and in 1968 Hawker Siddeley began looking at a

Tornado GR.1B of No. 617 Sqn., armed with Sea Eagles makes rapid ascent. (See also below).

With wings fully swept – Tornado GR.1B of No. 617 'Dam Busters' Sqn. in maritime attack configuration armed with Sea Eagle sea-skimming anti-ship missiles with a capability to strike over 400 miles from base and at stand-off range of over 70 miles. No. 617 Sqn. relocated from Marham, Norfolk to Lossiemouth, Moray, in the 1990s.

RAF Tornado GR.1 of No. 9 Sqn., Brüggen, Germany, in vertical power climb. (See also below).

With wings extended – RAF Tornado GR.1 Interdictor Strike aircraft of No. 9 Sqn., Brüggen, Germany, carrying three Defence Suppression Air Launched Anti-Radar ALARM missiles on fuselage pylons, Electronic Counter Measures ECM Pods on outboard pylons and external fuel tanks, c.1992.

Two Warton-based Tornado GR.4 upgrade development aircraft, promotionally liveried, on test over the Northern Fells in the mid-1990s.

Tornado GR.4 of No. 9 Sqn., RAF Marham.

subsonic trainer designated the P.(HS.)1182. At Warton, BAC submitted proposals for its P.59. The RAF chose Hawker Siddeley's design in 1972 and production contracts were awarded. To be named the Hawk, the aircraft made its first flight at Dunsfold on 21 August 1974. Powered by a single Adour turbofan, it was characterised by an elevated tandem rear seat position giving the instructor an excellent field of view over the head of his pupil. Hard points beneath the wings and fuselage afforded tactical weapons training capability. The Hawk T.Mk.1, of which 176 were ordered, entered RAF service in 1976, proving immediately successful. The RAF *Red Arrows* aerobatic display team has used the Hawk since 1979, their appearances worldwide having been a significant factor in the aircraft's subsequent export sales to some 20 countries.

Hawk 50 and 60 Series two-seat flying and weapons trainers for export, which first flew in 1976 and 1982 respectively, were superseded by later generation Hawk 100 two-seat advanced weapons trainers

and ground attack aircraft (1987) and Hawk 200 single-seat lightweight MRCA ground attack and light combat fighters (1986). From late 1988 the BAe Flight Test and Development Centre at Warton was increasingly involved in the Hawk programme, fitting the Hawk 100 company demonstrator ZA101 with a new seven-station combat wing and uprated Adour engine developing 5,845lb thrust. ZA101, the eighth production Hawk, had been built originally as a Hawk 50 at Dunsfold in 1976 and modified there as the Hawk 100 prototype in 1987. Meanwhile in 1981 a derivative of the Hawk 60 had been selected as the advanced sea-going carrier trainer for the US Navy. As the T-45A Goshawk, arrangements were agreed for the building of some 200 under licence by McDonnell Douglas as US prime contractor and BAe as the principal subcontractor. The Goshawk first flew in 1988, deliveries following from 1992 under workshare arrangements whereby about half the airframe was built at Samlesbury (including the centre fuselage) and Brough,

RAF Tornado GR.4 crosses the North Norfolk coast near Brancaster. *Photo: Geoffrey Lee.*

Early production
HS.Hawk Mk.1
XX164 of
No. 4 Flying
Training School,
RAF Valley,
Anglesey, on a
training sortie
over Snowdonia
in July 1990. The
aircraft is
following the A5
from Betws-y-
Coed to Bangor,
above Llyn
Ogwen at the
head of the
Nant Ffrancon
Pass.
Photo:
Terry Blacow,
BAe Warton.

Left bottom:
The Royal Air
Force Aerobatic
Team, the *Red
Arrows*, formed
in 1965, have
flown the BAe
Hawk T.Mk.1
(T.1A) since
1979. Their
Hawks were
converted for
display purposes
at BAe's
Bitteswell
factory.
Photo:
Geoffrey Lee.

Right bottom:
T-45A
Goshawks
engaged on
Carrier
Qualification
Training for the
US Navy.

the remainder in the USA most recently with manufacture and final assembly by Boeing at St. Louis.

In the UK, up to 1991 Hawk build was at Kingston and Brough with final assembly and flight testing at Dunsfold. Thereafter, design and build was concentrated at Brough with all final assembly and flight testing at Warton. Between 1991 and 1999 Warton was responsible for fully assembling and testing 190 Hawk 100/200 Series aircraft. Since then, Hawks produced at Brough have been transported to

Warton for wing attachment and flight testing. Hawk assembly has also taken place in Finland and Switzerland.

In 2004 Hawk celebrated the 30th anniversary of the maiden flight of the first of its type, XX154, at Dunsfold in 1974. Subsequently, a total of 736 Hawks were produced up to the end of September 2003 and by March 2004 some 922 were either in service, ordered or selected by 19 air forces worldwide. The T.Mk.1A remains the RAF's current principal Advanced Jet Trainer (AJT) but is to be succeeded from

Hawk 200 ZJ201 single-seat lightweight multi-role fighter and ground attack aircraft, which first flew on 13 February 1992, was the first Hawk to come off the final assembly line established at Warton in 1991. Component manufacture remained mostly at Brough. Here it is shown in air superiority configuration with data-link pods on inboard pylons and Sidewinders on wingtip rails. It was the first radar-equipped Hawk, becoming BAe's Radar Development and demonstration aircraft.

The first production Hawk Mk.108 for Malaysia, ZH745-MT003/M40-03 at Warton, January 1994.

2006 by the new 'digital' Hawk Mk.128.
Orders for 20 Hawks, with an option for a
further 24, were placed by MoD in July
2003. Following negotiations spanning 15
years, in 2004 the Indian Air Force ordered
66 Hawk Mk.132s, 24 of which to be built
by BAE Systems 'ready to fly' and 42 under
licence by Hindustan Aeronautics in
Bangalore, India.

Hawk is now the world's most successful
aircraft of its type. Reputedly Britain's first
aircraft designed solely using metric
measurements, there is something of an
irony in the fact that it is today the only
British military jet aircraft still in production
not to have originated as a multi-nation
collaborative project. Export orders
resulting from high profile marketing
missions undertaken by Hawk
demonstrator ZJ100, now configured with
Lead-In Fighter (LIF) avionic system and
cockpit enhancements for training aircrew
for current and future front line combat
aircraft, are likely to prolong that success
even further.

Despite originating with Hawker Siddeley
elsewhere, like the Hawk, production of the

**British Aerospace/McDonnell Douglas
Harrier** has been closely associated with
the Lancashire aerospace industry at
Warton and Samlesbury for over a decade.
The Harrier 'jump jet' traces its ancestry to
the Hawker P.1127 vertical take-off and
landing (VTOL) aircraft developed from
1957 by a team at Kingston under the
direction of Sir Sydney Camm, together
with Bristol Siddeley Engines under
Dr. (later Sir) Stanley Hooker. It was a
highly successful marriage of Hawker's
airframe and Bristol Siddeley's Pegasus
turbofan engine, VTOL being achieved by
vectoring, or swivelling the engine's thrust
out of two pairs of pivoted nozzles.
Stability in the hover and during low speed
manoeuvring was provided by another four
jets in the nose, tail and wingtips, expelling
compressed air bled from the engine.

Thanks to the 1957 Defence White Paper,
the early design proceeded without official
support from the British Government.
Sustained mainly as a private venture, the
project did however attract backing from
the NATO Mutual Weapons Development
Team, largely financed by the USA, for the
development of its engine. The P.1127

Another view of RAAF Hawk Mk.127 over the Ribble Valley, with Longridge in the background, in 2000.

The Hawk Mk.115 CT-155 provides the fast jet training element of the NATO Flying Training School in Canada (NFTC) Programme at Moose Jaw, Saskatchewan and Cold Lake, Alberta. The first was delivered in 2000, for Advanced Jet Training and Tactical/Fighter Lead-In Training, equipping pilots to progress onto aircraft such as the F-16, F-18, Jaguar, Tornado and Eurofighter Typhoon.

Opposite:
Hawk 100 Series Advanced Jet Trainer (AJT) demonstrator aircraft ZJ100 over Warton in 1997.

Hawk ZJ100 in special livery as the BAE Systems Hawk Lead-In Fighter (LIF) demonstrator.

BAE Systems Hawk New Demonstrator Aircraft (HNDA) ZJ951, powered by the new uprated Adour Mk.951 turbofan engine with Full Authority Digital Engine Control (FADEC), takes a look at the company's marine interests at Barrow-in-Furness, Cumbria, in 2003. Nearly a century earlier, in 1910 Claude Grahame-White made an aerial inspection of the same shipyards, then Vickers Sons & Maxim, flying from Blackpool in his Farman biplane. *Photo: BAE SYSTEMS Creative Media.*

Auxiliary Oiler (AO) and Landing Platform Dock (LPD) vessels on BAE Systems' Naval Ships Superberth Facilities at Barrow-in-Furness, where since 1871 the yards have produced a vast range of armaments, ordnance, warships, conventional and nuclear submarines, passenger and cargo ships – and airships. The Devonshire Dock Hall, seen in the distance, inaugurated in 1986, extending over 25,000 sq.m (269,000 sq.ft.), with a height of 51m, can completely accommodate a nuclear submarine or Type 42 Destroyer. To the left are the Jubilee Bridge, Walney Channel, and Island.

made its first, tethered hovering trial in October 1960 at Dunsfold, where it hovered untethered a month later. Having remained convinced of its potential, in May 1962 the US and West German – by then joined by the British – Governments announced that they would jointly fund nine evaluation aircraft, to be named Kestrels. A three-nation evaluation squadron was established and the first Kestrel, with Pegasus uprated from 11,300 to 15,200lb thrust, flew in March 1964.

A supersonic version on the drawing board, the HS. P.1154, was cancelled in 1965 as the UK Government's price for continuing to support the extensive further design and development necessary to bring the subsonic Kestrel into operational service. The Pegasus engine was further uprated to 19,000lb thrust and the aircraft, then named Harrier, entered service with the RAF in 1969 and, as the Sea Harrier, with the Royal Navy in 1979. In May 1969, two Harriers of No. 1 Squadron RAF made

Hawk HNDA ZJ951 over Morecambe Bay and Grange-over-Sands, *en route* back to Warton in 2003. *Photo: BAE SYSTEMS Creative Media.*

international news in the *Daily Mail*[4] Transatlantic Air Race from London to New York after taking off vertically from a coal yard near St. Pancras in London, refuelling several times in flight over the Atlantic and landing vertically in Manhattan.

US interest in the Harrier remained keen and in 1969 Hawker Siddeley signed a licence agreement allowing it to be made by McDonnell Douglas at St. Louis. As the AV-8A, orders followed for 102 for the US Marine Corps but, despite the licence, it was considered more economical to manufacture them in Britain. The first was delivered to the USMC in 1971. In service the Americans developed 'Vectoring in Forward Flight' or 'VIFF' as a means of rapid deceleration, enhanced turn rates and agility in flight. The technique of 'Viffing' subsequently proved invaluable under combat conditions.

Hawker Siddeley and McDonnell Douglas began design and development of a second generation 'Harrier II' in 1973, both progressing somewhat independently until the signing of a Memorandum of

Understanding between McDonnell Douglas and, by then, British Aerospace in 1981. This agreed production workshare splits of 60 per cent and 40 per cent respectively for future aircraft for the USMC and 50/50 for those for the RAF, with McDonnell Douglas as prime contractor. The wing, forward fuselage and tailplanes would be built in the US, rear fuselage, fin, rudder and tailplane in the UK. The Harrier II was the world's first production combat aircraft to make large-scale use of composite materials with carbon fibre comprising over a quarter of its airframe weight. 232 US-assembled McDonnell Douglas/British Aerospace AV-8B Harrier IIs started to enter USMC service in 1984. The RAF received its first Harrier IIs, designated GR.5s, in 1986. In due course BAe at Samlesbury assumed responsibility for manufacture of major units for the Harrier AV-8B II (Plus), FR.S2, T.Mk.10 and GR.7 variants including fin and tailplane rudders using composites. After McDonnell Douglas became part of Boeing, the Boeing Partnership with BAe was responsible for production of the Harrier II and II (Plus), together with the Goshawk. Also Boeing-related was the manufacture of Rolls-Royce engine struts and pylons at Samlesbury for the Boeing 747. To the present day, BAE Systems Military Air Solutions & Support at Warton, Samlesbury, Woodford and Chadderton provide a wide range of support services to operators of products including Canberra, Jaguar, Nimrod, VC10, Harrier, Hawk and Tornado at home and overseas. This includes US Business Support and the delivery of major aircraft units and support services for Goshawk and Harrier training and combat aircraft operated by the US, Spain and India.

In operational use by the RAF in Germany and elsewhere it was found that by using a short take-off run the Harrier could carry a heavier weapon load in STOVL mode – short take-off, vertical landing – rather than VTOL or V/STOL. The principle was developed further by the Royal Navy with the now famous 'ski' ramp a feature of carrier decks. RAF and RN

Harriers operating jointly from HMS *Invincible* and *Hermes* played vital roles in ground attack, anti-shipping and air-to-air combat in the Falkland Islands campaign of 1982 and have since been deployed in Bosnia, Kosovo and Iraq. Since 2000, RAF GR.7s and RN F/A.2s have operated as a Harrier Joint Force. US AV-8Bs were extensively involved in the *Desert Storm* Gulf War of 1991. Other operators of the Harrier have included the Indian, Italian, Spanish and Royal Thai navies.

A grand total of 831 Harriers of all types has been manufactured in the UK and USA. Of these, the last 'second generation' aircraft to come off a British assembly line were 13 Harrier T.Mk.10 two-seat trainers with full operational capability assembled at Warton between April 1994 and October 1995 from components received from Dunsfold, Brough, Samlesbury and McDonnell Douglas. Warton has also upgraded 30 GR.7s to GR.7As with replacement uprated Pegasus engines and is engaged on updating GR.7s and 7As to GR.9s and 9As, and T.10s to T.12s, with

Harrier T.Mk.10 ZH653, one of 13 assembled at Warton during 1994-95.

more powerful engines and avionics/ weapons fit including integration of the Raytheon Paveway IV precision guided bomb on the GR.9/9A. The GR.9 contract alone is worth £500 million to BAE Systems.

As a replacement for RAF Lightnings and Phantoms, during the late 1970s British Aerospace started to give consideration to an advanced fighter aircraft with a performance at least equal to the American General Dynamics F-16 Fighting Falcon. International collaboration had become the established way forward for major aircraft projects as demonstrated by Concorde (Aérospatiale), Airbus (Airbus Industrie), Jaguar (SEPECAT) and Tornado (Panavia). Studies undertaken by BAe and Messerschmitt-Bölkow-Blohm (MBB) put forward the **European Combat Fighter (ECF)** and later, with MBB and Dassault, the **European Combat Aircraft (ECA)**. With no particular support expressed by the various Governments, in 1981 BAe came up with a private venture proposal for a

smaller, cheaper version, the **P.110**. Further discussions with MBB developed this into the **Agile Combat Aircraft (ACA)** which progressed to a full-size mock-up but still failed to attract official support. Significantly, in October 1981 the Jaguar Active Control Technology (ACT) 'fly-by-wire' (FBW) demonstrator aircraft flew for the first time.

Matters progressed when ACA was unveiled to the public at the 1982 Farnborough Air show and the UK Government announced that it would contribute financially to an **Experimental Aircraft Programme (EAP)** technology demonstrator based on refinements of joint studies into an agile combat and air superiority aircraft undertaken by BAe, MBB and Aeritalia. A contract was signed in May 1983 with costs shared between the UK Ministry of Defence, BAe, Aeritalia and partner equipment companies in Italy, Germany and the UK including Dowty, Ferranti, GEC Avionics, Lucas, Rolls-Royce and Smiths Industries. Design evolved as a

Opposite:
Experimental
Aircraft
Programme
(EAP)
Demonstrator
ZF534 streaks
down the
Fylde Coast
during handling
trials on
6 July 1987.

single-seater with all-moving foreplanes, an advanced compound-sweep delta wing, constructed from new lightweight materials, powered by two Turbo-Union RB.199 Tornado engines. Build started in September 1983.

In December, alarmed at progress in the USSR with the MiG-29 and Sukhoi Su-27, the British, German and Italian Air Staffs issued a European Staff Target (EST) for a new air combat aircraft along the lines of the ACA. Spain and France joined the group in 1984 but in 1985 France, requiring greater emphasis on a ground attack role, disagreed with the other four about the conclusions of a joint feasibility study into the EST and withdrew to pursue the Rafale project independently. During 1985-86 the remaining four nations and their lead companies, BAe, MBB, Aeritalia and CASA, implemented the Definition Phase for what was then named the **European Fighter Aircraft (EFA)**.

BAe's Warton Division had been carrying out research into the potential, design and manufacture of Carbon Fibre Composite (CFC) structures since 1966. They teamed up with the similarly-experienced Aeritalia, both companies sharing design and manufacture of the EAP's CFC wing. The CFC materials were produced by a Ciba-Geigy system containing Toray and Courtaulds fibres. The resulting co-bonded structure, with torsion box spars cured and bonded directly to the lower skins in an autoclave, gave a greatly strengthened wing with considerably reduced need for mechanical fasteners. Aeritalia produced the left-hand wing, detail manufacture and co-bonding of the right-hand wing torsion box taking place at BAe Warton Division's Samlesbury site.

Inherent aerodynamic instability was at the core of EAP's design, instantaneously controlled by the world's first full authority quadruplex digital 'fly-by-wire' system developed from the Jaguar ACT programme. It co-ordinated the

symmetrical operation of the all-moving foreplanes and wing trailing edge surfaces to artificially maintain stability in pitch, together with asymmetric deflection of trailing edge devices for roll. EAP had a fully-integrated cockpit with computer-controlled systems, all data shown on multi-function colour displays.

The single EAP aircraft ZF534, assembled at Warton, was unveiled there on 16 April 1986 by Sir Raymond Lygo, BAe's Chief Executive, in the presence of the Rt.Hon. George Younger MP, Secretary of State for Defence. Considerable emphasis was given to the fact that it brought together in a single airframe all the latest aerospace technologies previously partially developed in isolation. The Secretary of State said: "Whilst the EAP is not a prototype aircraft, we expect that the knowledge gained in its design, construction and operation, will make a significant contribution to the European Fighter Aircraft (EFA) Programme".

In July the four company partners formed a joint company, Eurofighter/Jagdflugzeug GmbH, based in Munich. Along similar lines to the Tornado programme, Eurojet Turbo GmbH – comprising Rolls-Royce (UK), Motoren und Turbinen-Union (Germany), Fiat Aviazione (Italy) and Sener-ITP (Spain) – was established to design, develop, manufacture and support EFA's intended two-spool reheated turbofan engines. Euroradar – representing GEC Marconi, Dasa Sensor Systems, FIAR and ENOSA – would later produce its all-new ECR 90 radar, now named CAPTOR.

Dave Eagles, Warton's Executive Director Flight Operations, piloted EAP to Mach 1.1 at 30,000 ft. during its highly successful first flight from Warton on 8 August. An intensive flying programme culminated in its public debut the following month at the Farnborough Air Show. EAP completed the last of 259 flights in an extremely valuable five-year test programme on 1 May 1991 after which it was taken to

In July 1988, EAP,
Hawk 100,
Hawk 200,
RN Sea Harrier
FRS.1,
RAF Harrier II
GR.Mk.5,
Tornado
GR.Mk.1 and
Tornado F.3
made up this
formation off
Blackpool.
*Photo:
Geoffrey Lee.*

Loughborough University to be used for technical training purposes.

A further milestone was passed in September 1987 with the finalisation of the EFA European Staff Requirement for Development confirming the basic specification for a lightweight single-seat supersonic fighter of great agility, incorporating elements of stealth technology, powered by two 20,000lb-thrust Eurojet EJ200 turbofans. The partner countries signed a Development Phase contract in November 1988 for the design, build and flight testing of eight prototypes including two two-seaters. Funding was geared to anticipated national shares of total production estimated at 765 aircraft i.e. BAe (later BAE Systems) 33 per cent, MBB (DaimlerChrysler, Daimler-Benz Aerospace, Dasa, EADS-Deutschland, EADS-Military Aircraft Germany) 33 per cent, Aeritalia (Alenia Aerospazio) 21 per cent and CASA (EADS-CASA Spain) 13 per cent.[5]

But political events, notably the tearing down of the Berlin Wall and ending of the Cold War in 1989, the reunification of Germany the year after and the German domestic economic problems that came in its wake, threatened to derail the whole project. Both Germany and Italy looked like withdrawing. Moreover there was considerable debate between the companies and national agencies concerning EFA's radar and weaponry specifications. After a radical four-nation review which even considered cheaper, lighter, single-engined alternatives, matters were resolved with the issue of a revised European Staff Requirement at the end of 1992. In fact EFA had passed the point of no return. With considerable sums already spent, returning to the drawing board at that stage to design a different 'cheaper' aircraft would have merely added to the overall cost. With outright cancellation impracticable due to the likelihood of huge compensation penalties, international collaboration in the complex political circumstances either side of 1990 had at

[5] *DaimlerChrysler, CASA and Aérospatiale combined as EADS in 2000.*

The first British-
assembled
Eurofighter
2000, DA2
ZH588, flew for
the first time at
Warton on
6 April 1994
piloted by
Chris Yeo.

Eurofighter 2000
DA2 ZH588
makes a slow,
wheels-down
pass over the
BAe Warton
plant during its
first flight.

once served both to increase costs and delay, yet preserve the project. Proposed development of a slightly less costly version, renamed the **New EFA** and subsequently **Eurofighter 2000**, was finally agreed by the Chiefs of Air Staff of all four nations in January 1994. In essence it was defined as an extremely agile single-seat twin-engined fighter with optimal performance in Beyond Visual Range and

Close Combat, with significant ground attack capability.

The first two Eurofighter 2000 prototypes were flown within two weeks of each other, DA1 by Peter Weger in Germany on 27 March and DA2 by Chris Yeo at Warton on 6 April 1994, both with interim Rolls-Royce RB.199 Tornado engines without thrust reversal. They have since been used by EADS-Military Aircraft for handling and

engine development and by BAE Systems for envelope expansion and carefree handling. The first to fly with EJ.200 engines was the Italian DA3, used by Alenia for digital engine control integration. The first two-seater, DA4 built at Warton, has been used as the development aircraft for radar. The German DA5 is an avionics and weapons integration aircraft. DA6, the Spanish two-seater used by EADS-CASA for avionics and systems development was, in August 1996, the first two-seater actually to fly but was subsequently lost as a result of an engine failure in November 2002. Both crew ejected safely. The Italian DA7 is used for weapons integration and performance development. All had flown by March 1997.

Further concerns about costs, particularly in Germany, together with reassessment of the number required by each country, generated more uncertainty. Workshare arrangements were revised in January 1996 and it was not until January 1998 that Eurofighter GmbH and NETMA, the NATO Eurofighter and Tornado Management Agency, signed Production Investment, Production and Support contracts for 620 aircraft with another 90 on option. Of these, Britain is to receive 232, Germany 180, Italy 121 and Spain 87. The first metal was cut for production by Dasa at Augsburg in May 1998, for the centre fuselage. Alenia were responsible for the left wing, outboard flaperons and part of the rear fuselage, CASA the right wing and leading edge slats. BAe at Samlesbury were to produce the front fuselage, titanium canards, windscreen and canopy, dorsal spine, vertical stabilizer, inboard flaperons and another section of the rear fuselage. Germany would provide the flight control system. Four final assembly lines were laid down at Warton, Manching, Caselle near Turin and Getafe near Madrid, all of which receiving components from Samlesbury on a 'Just in Time' (JIT) basis.

70 per cent of the airframe surface was of

CFC, the remainder mainly aluminium, superplastic-formed titanium and glass-reinforced plastic. Unlike metal, CFC once formed cannot be reshaped, requiring manufacturing to be right first time. It demanded major investment in modern production techniques including high levels of automation using CATIA for designing tools and programming numerical controlled machines. Japanese manufacturing and production techniques were introduced including lean manufacturing and the establishment of manufacturing cells, in effect businesses within businesses. Gearing up for Eurofighter manufacturing was accompanied by work on other projects including Airbus, Hawk, Goshawk, Harrier and Boeing 747. Following the signing by BAe and Saab Military Aircraft in 1995 of a joint marketing and production agreement to offer the **JAS 39 Gripen** fighter internationally, Samlesbury also attracted work on the Gripen's composite wing. The digital fly-by-wire Gripen, with fully integrated avionics, is significant as the world's first fourth-generation Mach 2 low cost multi-role/swing-role combat aircraft to enter service. Capable of use from roads and dispersed bases it has been operational in the Swedish Air Force since 1997 and 28 have been ordered by South Africa (together with 24 Hawks) and others by Hungary and the Czech Republic. Gripen International, owned 50/50 by Saab and BAE Systems, was formed in 2001 to market, sell and support the aircraft worldwide, outside Sweden, as a natural progression of the Joint Venture Agreement.

The decision to focus on Samlesbury as a wide ranging competitive manufacturing facility had been taken at the end of 1990. Following a comprehensive review of business, markets, threats and opportunities arising from the ending of the Cold War and the resulting 'Peace Dividend', taking account of the likely decline in demand for

DA2 ZH588, now with new EJ.200 engines, flies the full length of the Fylde Coast, turning in over the Ribble Estuary towards Warton. (Pages 270-272).

military aircraft and increasing competition in the airframe sector, particularly from the Far East, the BAe Military Aircraft Division concluded that a reduction in its manufacturing capacity was inescapable. A leaner, fitter and more efficient structure was essential and the company announced their intention to vacate the historic Strand Road factory in the centre of Preston where the doors finally closed on 30 September 1993. Recent investment there in highly efficient hard metal machining and sheet metal facilities was transported to Samlesbury where it joined composites, superplastic-forming, diffusion bonding and precision boring capacity as the basis for a future world-class manufacturing centre of excellence. Activities would encompass Machining with Treatments, Fabrication, Commercial Assembly and Tooling. The Strand Road 'East' Works was subsequently demolished and the site redeveloped for residential and business uses. Today, new roads such as Kerr Place and Beamont Drive testify to its 130-year history of railway and aeronautical engineering. The

'West' Works, for many years used by GEC and Alstom, still stands.

A £3 million Engineering Assembly Building opened at Samlesbury in September 1997. Over £14 million went into high technology tooling, £8 million into two five-axis machining centres, £7 million into three Mitsui Seiki five-axis horizontal machining centres and £5 million into two Interchangeability (ICY) machines. With Eurofighter panels and fittings requiring to be accurate to 70 microns (three-thousandths of an inch), 40 per cent of machine tool investment was funded by MoD. Flexible manufacturing was facilitated by a unique system of false flooring beneath which accessible service runs permitted total freedom of location and movement of machinery, jigs and associated equipment. Altogether, over £50 million was invested at the plant in the 1990s. Having embraced every appropriate modern business and process technique, including Direct Line Feed (DLF) and JIT, Samlesbury is indeed now one of the world's most cost-effective aerospace

manufacturing centres. Machining of Eurofighter centre fuselage frames for delivery to Dasa started in September 1998, the same month that the aircraft was re-styled as the **Eurofighter Typhoon,** initially for greater impact in potential export markets.

At Warton, a £10 million conversion of the former Tornado Assembly Hall began in March 1999 and was completed the following year. It now provides a magnificent state of the art 'clean room' assembly facility for Eurofighter Typhoon, with a full-length collocated team area first-floor balcony overlooking the nose-in dock staging for aircraft at various stages of completion. Automated computer-controlled equipment including laser alignment is employed to marry-up major fuselage sections. Altogether around £100 million has been invested at Warton and Samlesbury.

The first Instrumented Production Aircraft assembled by BAE Systems, IPA1 ZJ699, flew on 15 April 2002. In September

Eurofighter was officially named Typhoon at Farnborough 2002. No. 17 (R) Squadron RAF, the Typhoon Operational Evaluation Unit (OEU), located at Warton in December 2003, together with No. 29 (R) Squadron, the Typhoon Operational Conversion Unit (OCU). Both units would benefit from immediate access to the manufacturing facility during the initial period of entry into service and instructor pilot training, under the joint industry/RAF training programme code-named 'Case White'. In 2005 the squadrons moved to RAF Coningsby with operational Typhoon units likely to be established there and at RAF Leuchars. In order to expedite pilot training, initial production has comprised two-seater versions and the RAF accepted its first aircraft, Typhoon T.1 ZJ803/AA at Warton on 30 June 2003. Flying started at the beginning of 2004 with the OEU having received four Typhoons and the OCU two by the end of June. On 17 December 2004, UK Secretary of State for Defence Geoff Hoon confirmed the signing of a four-nation contract for the second batch

Back at
Warton, the
new Eurofighter
Assembly Hall
can be seen
beneath the
aircraft's port
Sidewinder.

Eurofighter Typhoon ZH588, carrying ASRAAM missiles, departs RAF Leuchars where it underwent airflow measurement tests in 2000. The aircraft was painted in a special black finish to conceal the 490 pressure transducers applied to the airframe surfaces. In deference to No. 43 Sqn., based at Leuchars with Tornado F.3s, the Squadron's gamecock badge was applied to ZH588's fin.

Typhoon T.1 ZJ699 Instrumented Production Aircraft (IPA1) wastes no time in lifting its undercarriage on take-off from Warton in 2002, trailing a spectacular reheat backwash.

Inspection of Typhoon front fuselage in Ditmeco jig at BAE Systems' Samlesbury production facility.

Typhoon Final Assembly Hall, Warton. (Pages 274-277).

of 236 Typhoons for the air forces of Britain, Germany, Italy and Spain. BAE Systems are responsible for manufacturing major units including front and rear fuselages. The Tranche 2 contract is worth £4.3 billion to BAE Systems and £750 million to Rolls-Royce. At peak production Typhoon will help sustain 5,000 and 4,000 jobs respectively at the two companies. BAE Systems at Warton will assemble all 232 aircraft which the RAF is ultimately expected to receive from the Typhoon programme. Of these, 55 are already on order as Tranche 1, with Tranche 2 representing a further 89 for the RAF.

Events of recent years have demonstrated the need for aircraft with precision ground attack capability. Yet at the same time air superiority remains the absolute prerequisite for successful surface operations both on land and at sea and, although optimised for air-to-air combat, Typhoon has emerged as a genuine multi-role aircraft also with ground attack and reconnaissance capability. Moreover, with fully integrated avionics, airframe, missile and weapons system it has 'swing-role' ability to translate from one to another within a single mission. Without having stealth as its overriding design objective, Typhoon incorporates significant stealth characteristics without sacrificing flexibility of weapon load, manoeuvrability or performance. Its radar signal is a quarter of the size of that of the Tornado. Typhoon has 13 weapon carriage points, four on each wing and five on the fuselage. It can carry Advanced Short Range Air-to-Air Missiles (ASRAAMS), medium range (AMRAAMS) and the highly advanced Meteor Beyond Visual Range AAM, Air Launched Anti-Radar Missiles (ALARM), 2000lb., 1000lb. and 500lb. bombs, laser bombs, anti-armour weapons (Brimstone is to be integrated on Typhoon as well as Harrier and Tornado) and external fuel tanks. Maximum weight at take-off is 46,000lb. With a combat thrust-to-weight ratio in excess of 1.2 to 1, maximum speed

is given as Mach 2 with brakes off to Mach 1.6 at 36,000 ft. achieved in under two minutes thirty seconds. The aircraft can produce nine 'g' almost instantly and sustain it almost indefinitely. The ergonomically designed cockpit, full authority 'fly-by-wire' flight control system, fully integrated airframe, materials and engines offer the pilot 'carefree handling' whereby maximum performance is available without overstressing the aircraft structure or causing the aircraft to depart from controlled flight. In combat conditions it will enable him to concentrate 100 per cent on his adversary who can be electronically detected and engaged without being aware of the Typhoon's presence. Direct Voice Input (DVI) designed by Smiths Industries enables the Typhoon pilot to communicate with his aircraft by voice for certain functions rather than just manually. A Helmet Mounted Symbology System (HMSS) provides a range of data through the pilot's visor, his helmet also incorporating night vision.

Changing geopolitics and operational requirements, coupled with less than flexible workshare arrangements and technological complications notably with flight control software, have all combined to delay the aircraft by ten years and more than double the project's initial estimated cost of £20 billion. At times, seemingly unwilling to acknowledge the full impact of such complex issues on major leading edge defence projects, some elements of the media have given the Typhoon a rough ride over the years. Although the Cold War imperative that determined the original need for the aircraft may itself have evaporated, other imperatives have since materialised. In the out-turn, delays to the programme have proved adventitious for Typhoon's incorporation of even more advanced technologies. As a result it is now a much more comprehensive and flexible defence and attack weapons system than originally envisaged, with Multi-Role/Swing-Role capabilities and potential

Opposite: Line-up of the first production Typhoons, all two-seater T.1s, to enter RAF service carrying the 'gauntlet' insignia of No. 17(R) Sqn., the Typhoon Operational Evaluation Unit (OEU) based at Warton during 2003-5, along with No. 29 (R) Sqn. Typhoon Operational Conversion unit (OCU). Aircraft c/n BT001, 'AC' of No. 17 (R) Sqn., s/n ZJ800, the first of 232 Typhoons for the RAF, made its maiden flight at Warton in March 2004.

now including Air Superiority, Interdiction/Strike, Close Air Support, Reconnaissance, Suppression and Destruction of Enemy Air Defences, and Maritime Attack roles. Scope for future development during its production life includes the addition of vectored thrust jetpipe nozzles, presently being investigated by Eurojet partners ITP in Spain and MTU in Germany. Typhoon is likely to prove capable of even further development during its anticipated operational life extending from 2005 to 2050.

The Typhoon production programme has surpassed even that of its predecessor, the Tornado, to become Europe's largest ever defence contract. At peak it will provide high-tech jobs for over 120,000 Europeans. Percentage workshare is now apportioned as UK/BAE Systems (37), Germany/EADS-Deutschland (30), Italy/Alenia Aerospazio (20) and Spain/EADS-CASA (13). To date, in addition to the 620 aircraft already on order for the four partner nations, Austria has confirmed an order for 18, Greece has selected Typhoon for its next generation fighter, Singapore has shortlisted it and a number of other countries have expressed interest. In the early stages of its entry into service Typhoon is receiving a rapturous welcome by all those responsible for flying and operating it. Indeed Typhoon is already being spoken of as the spiritual successor to iconic RAF aircraft such as the Spitfire, Hunter and Lightning. At Warton, the 'Case White' training programme exceeded all expectations. In March 2005 the RAF took delivery of its first production single-seater and, in April, Samlesbury completed its 100th Typhoon front fuselage.

With the bulk of Typhoon manufacture still to take place, BAE Systems at Warton and Samlesbury are already engaged on other advanced products for the future. The most significant is the **F-35 Joint Strike Fighter (JSF)** under development by Lockheed Martin, Northrop Grumman and Pratt & Whitney of the USA, since 1997

teamed with British Aerospace/BAE Systems and Rolls-Royce in the UK. Three variants, designated X-35A, B and C comprise, respectively, a conventional take-off and landing (CTOL) aircraft for the USAF, a short take-off and vertical landing (STOVL) aircraft for the USMC and the UK, and a carrier take-off and landing (CV) version for the US Navy. Initial plans are for the UK to buy 150 F-35s for the RAF and Royal Navy by whom, as their first 'stealth' aircraft, it will be known as the Joint Combat Aircraft (JCA). In appearance, generically and in configuration, the F-35 resembles a three-quarters-scale version of the Lockheed Martin Boeing F-22A Raptor air dominance fighter which the USAF is now starting to receive. Two Concept Demonstrator Aircraft have been built, the first as an X-35A subsequently modified to X-35B which successfully tested the type's unique shaft-driven Integrated Lift-Fan Propulsion System (ILFPS), all three versions flying during 2000-2001. JSF will ultimately replace A-10, AV-8 Harrier, F-16 and F/A-18 aircraft currently in service and, in the UK, the RAF's Harrier GR.7/9s and the Royal Navy's Sea Harrier F/A.2s.

Only time will tell whether, 50 years on from the Lightning, the F-35 might prove to be a more realistic contender for the title of 'the last manned fighter...'

In 2001 an $18.9 billion System Development and Demonstration (SDD) contract was awarded to the 'aircraft' team and one of $4 billion to the 'engine' team involving production of an initial 22 aircraft,

Typhoon T.1s of
No. 29(R) and
No. 17(R) Sqns.
in formation,
based at
Warton.

Typhoon cockpit
view.

FLT LT ELLIOTT

Typhoon cockpit view.

Typhoon T.1s 'BE' (ZJ806) and 'BF' (ZJ807) of No. 29 (R) Sqn. 'cleaned up', carrying no external stores, pictured over the Middle East on a promotional deployment to Singapore in June 2004. The patterns on the ground are irrigated desert 'crop circles'.

A unique photograph – five fast jets in close formation, operated by the Fast Jet and Weapons Operational Evaluation Unit based at RAF Coningsby. It comprises a Typhoon T.2, Tornado F.3, Tornado GR.4 and Jaguar GR.3A, all built in Lancashire, with a Harrier GR.7 in the foreground. *Photo: © Cpl. Chris Ward Crown Copyright/MOD.*

Beyond the Typhoon – the F-35 Joint Strike Fighter STOVL variant required by the US Marine Corps and the UK. F-35 represents major business for BAE Systems at Warton, Samlesbury and elsewhere. Work is already underway on long-lead production of components.

long-lead part manufacture for which having already started. Over 2,500 aircraft will be required by the partner countries with an export potential estimated at 3,000. The F-35 JSF is expected to be operational in 2010 and in the UK in 2012. Business of such magnitude is likely to be worth $1.6 billion (£1.1 billion) to BAE Systems in the UK for the SDD Phase and potentially $16.5 billion (£11 billion) for the Production Phase, excluding export sales. Both Samlesbury and Warton sites will be major beneficiaries of the programme. The rear fuselage, tail and fin units for each aircraft will be designed, engineered and built at Samlesbury, benefiting from the plant's investment in advanced manufacturing technology and lean manufacturing as well as BAE Systems' overall STOVL experience with the Harrier.

From 2005 these units will be shipped from Samlesbury to Lockheed Martin's Fort Worth, USA plant, there to be joined with wings and forward fuselages from Lockheed Martin and centre fuselages from Northrop Grumman. BAE Systems will also be extensively involved with JSF avionics, weapons system and other aspects elsewhere in the UK and North America.

But even JSF will not conclude the story of aerospace production in Lancashire and the North West. There will be further developments in civil aviation arising from the Airbus programme and its military element the A400M. Although wing production of the A400M is to be at Filton, Broughton will have responsibility for building the all-new carbon fibre composite wing for the A350 widebody long-range twin-engine 250-300 seat 'hub-to-point' aircraft due to enter service in 2010 to face competition from the Boeing 787 'Dreamliner'. BAE Systems and Rolls-Royce have a long record of partnership with Boeing and the 787 also represents a major

potential business opportunity for the North West aerospace industry.

Militarily, it is foreseen that Typhoon and JSF could jointly underpin a Future Offensive Air System (FOAS), comprising an integrated warfare network of satellites, airborne early warning, air, ground and sea forces with satellite and infra-red-controlled missile systems such as Storm Shadow, parts of which are produced at the MBDA[6] plant at Lostock, Bolton. All this possibly in conjunction with unmanned air vehicles (UAVs) and armed combat versions (UCAVs). All are likely to be components of a fully integrated 'Global Information Grid' (GIG), in effect a military internet encompassing all military systems and command structures. Referred to in the USA as Network Centric Warfare, in the UK MoD together with BAE Systems are progressing an aligned Network Enabled Capability (NEC) incorporating all the elements required to deliver precise military effect rapidly and reliably, notably sensor systems, the network and strike assets.

If, as now forecast, piloted combat aircraft such as Typhoon and JSF remain in service towards the mid-point of the century as part of a mixed defence network, the 1957 White Paper on Defence will by then have assumed a prematurity of staggering proportions. By then the political interventions of the 1950s will be ancient history to an age routinely making use of combined cycle supersonic jet engines, hypersonic ramjets, anti-gravity engines and innovations as yet unknown. Against such a background, with ongoing Air Systems Programmes, FOAS, UAV and related work, BAE Systems' facilities in Lancashire are likely to remain at the centre of Future Systems, Projects, Concepts and New Business developments in the years to come.

[6] MBDA was formed in 2001 by the merging of Matra BAe Dynamics, EADS-Aérospatiale Matra Missiles and AMS missile activities, with BAE Systems holding a 37.5 per cent share. It is a world-leading missile systems company with a portfolio including Storm Shadow, Meteor, ASRAAM, ALARM, Rapier, Seawolf and Exocet.

Chapter 7
Postscript

However optimistic their views on the future of aviation, the pioneers of flight at the Blackpool 'Flying Week' and 'Flying Carnival' of 1909 and 1910 could hardly have foreseen the scale of the industry that would develop in Lancashire and the North West. In their day, industries such as cotton, coal, heavy engineering, steam, shipping and railways, with road transport industries still to be motorised, drove the regional economy. When Grahame-White overflew the Barrow-in-Furness airship hangar and shipyards of Vickers Sons & Maxim in his Farman in 1910 it probably never occurred to him to question their future. Had he done so he could not possibly have imagined that nearly a century later, still in operation, they would be part of a wide-ranging defence group the size of BAE Systems, itself a much later product of an aircraft industry then only just established by his contemporary A.V. Roe in Manchester.

From the dawn of aviation, used to hand-building aeroplanes in ones or twos, Roe saw huge advances during the First World War as the new industry, including the National Aircraft Factories, employed thousands of people in the production of some 4,500 aircraft across the region. His successors, Roy Chadwick and Roy Dobson, at the forefront of civil aviation in the ensuing peace, were among those instrumental in expanding the industry during the 1930s. As a result, including the Shadow Factories, the region contributed 30,000 aircraft to the 1939-45 war effort.

Roe saw his name and that of the company he founded become synonymous with the most successful bomber of the war, the Lancaster, and the post-war Vulcan, both designed and produced in the region. Lancashire and the North West played a major role in the winning of the Second World War by making Lancaster, Halifax, Wellington and other aircraft in quantity and the region's contribution to winning the 'Cold War' was equally immense. The awesome might of a relatively small force of Avro Vulcans, armed with Blue Steel, spearheaded Britain's policy of national defence through deterrence for much of the perilous 1960s. Moreover the Canberra, Lightning, Nimrod, Jaguar, Tornado and now the Typhoon are all products of the North West. Additionally, in the civil sector, exports and balance of payments have benefited from aircraft including the 748, 125 and 146/RJ Series and, most significantly of all, the Airbus wing operation at Broughton. Although Airbus is in neighbouring North Wales, its labour force and supplier catchment areas extend over a wide area of the North West.

Industrial heritage is no longer just the preserve of 'traditional' industries dating back to the Industrial Revolution, most of which have long since been supplanted by what is now universally termed the aerospace industry as the principal driver of the regional economy. At the start of the second century of manned, powered flight, aerospace today is sufficiently long established to have its own almost overwhelmingly diverse heritage of personalities, factories and aircraft. The extent is shown by the thriving aircraft heritage centres in the region run by current and retired employees of the industry who voluntarily give their time to preserving company photographic and other archives and artefacts, restoring historic aircraft, supplying information, publishing magazines and newsletters. The BAE Systems North West Heritage Group at Warton has equivalents at Woodford and Chadderton. In Manchester, the Aviation Hall of the Museum of Science and Industry provides an increasingly regional focus for aerospace heritage. The North West branches of the Royal Aeronautical Society address heritage, present and future aspects of the industry in their programme of events. There are flourishing local aviation societies and established researchers and writers throughout the region. In *Rapide* the region has its own quality magazine for vintage aviation.

The legacy is that of countless individuals – designers, industrialists, test pilots, aircrew and thousands of production workers. Over the decades they have striven to harness new technologies and materials, to respond to the demands of politicians, Service Chiefs and airline operators in war and peace, in times of relative isolation and as partners in European and transatlantic collaborative ventures. It is a tribute to them all, especially those who laid down their lives in building that industry, in flight testing or subsequent service use of the aircraft it has produced. Altogether their efforts and those of more than 30 producers in the region amount to a total output approaching 50,000[7] aircraft representing over 150 different types in the North West since 1910.

The facts and figures of today's industry are dazzling. After more than four decades of rationalisation and consolidation, primes such as BAE Systems, Rolls-Royce Aero-Engines and Airbus are now at the core of the largest cluster of aerospace, defence and related companies in the UK, a world-scale centre of excellence quite the equivalent of Seattle in the USA or Toulouse in France. BAE Systems' sites in the North West have an annual turnover of £4billion, about one third of the company's total, sustain 35,000 jobs in the region and remain fundamental to Britain's ability to defend itself. Some of BAE Systems' highest profile aircraft programmes such as Eurofighter Typhoon, Nimrod and the Joint Strike Fighter (JSF) are proceeding in the region. Altogether the cluster of primes, OEMs, subcontractors and suppliers represents a critical mass of advanced technology, production capacity, expertise and skills employing on the most conservative of estimates 60,000 people. Its gross annual output exceeds £6 billion, a third of total UK aerospace production.

The Northwest Aerospace Alliance (NWAA) represents over 800 companies in aerospace, high technology engineering and supporting supply chain activities. Industry-led and founded in 1993 as the Consortium of Lancashire Aerospace to provide a voice and focus for the industry, the NWAA was re-branded under its present name in 1999 to reflect the aerospace interests of the region as a whole. The NWAA has the strong support of regional bodies such as the Northwest Regional Development Agency (NWDA) and local authorities including Lancashire County Council, one of its founder members. The whole is strengthened by the existence in the region of the highest

[7] *See Production Appendix 1. The figure of nearly 50,000 represents complete aircraft manufactured or fully assembled in series in factories in the region. Accordingly it excludes:*

1. Non-factory small scale amateur production of aircraft.

2. Supplementary production of spare components and sub-assemblies for repair purposes, possibly equivalent to an additional 25 per cent of production.

3. Production of major sub-assemblies for incorporation in final assembly operations elsewhere, notably over 3,500 wing sets to date by Airbus at Broughton.

4. Final assembly of substantially complete aircraft and kits imported from the USA under Lend-Lease during WW2 at centres including Speke, Hooton Park, Hesketh Park, Burtonwood and Warton. Without reliable records, estimates range between 30-40,000 additional aircraft having been turned out at such locations.

concentration of Further and Higher Education Institutes in Europe, with 62 FE and 17 HE establishments, the latter including eight world-class universities. North West academia offers the widest range of aerospace-related capability and expertise in teaching and research. The aerospace infrastructure is complemented by two of the fastest growing international airports, Manchester and Liverpool, whilst Blackpool, so closely involved with many early aviation achievements, is a flourishing regional airport also with services to international tourist destinations.

Aerospace is identified by the NWDA as a priority sector in the North West Regional Strategy. But despite the industry's size, none of the parties involved is in any way complacent about the future. The need to compete efficiently with producers in Europe, North and South America and the Far East is paramount. For these reasons the various representative organisations, working with the industry, Central Government and the DTI have established an Aerospace Innovation Centre (AIC) in the region to maintain the momentum of aerospace well into the twenty-first century. The AIC is to become fully operational in 2005.

Triplane to Typhoon encapsulates the region's story at the forefront of every technological advance in nearly a century of aircraft development. It is a story of industrial achievement second to none. When the North West's latest major project, the Nimrod MRA4, took off on its maiden flight on 26 August 2004, it evoked a production heritage of 50,000 aircraft comprising 150 different types. But as it climbed past Christ Church, Woodford, where rest Roy Chadwick, Sir Roy Dobson and their colleagues, powerful engines of nostalgia were muted by the possibility that the occasion might also prove significant as the last 'first flight' of a *large* new aircraft in the UK. It would be fascinating to have the perspectives of the early designers and planemakers – Chadwick, Dobson and Sir Edwin Alliott Verdon-Roe – on this and many other aspects of the industry today. Not least on Eurofighter Typhoon as it powers through the same skies over the Lancashire coast into which Roe tentatively coaxed his Triplane in 1910.

Nimrod MRA4 PA02, ZJ518, freshly painted in RAF light grey, flies over Woodford on 12 May 2005.

Page 288: Nimrod MRA4 PA02, ZJ518, having landed at Woodford on 12 May 2005.

Appendix I
Aircraft produced by factories in Lancashire and the North West of England from 1910

Pages 290, 322
Warton-built
Typhoons of
Nos. 17 and
29 Sqns. fly in
formation with
Hawks of the
RAF's Display
Team the
Red Arrows over
the Lancashire
Coast in 2004.

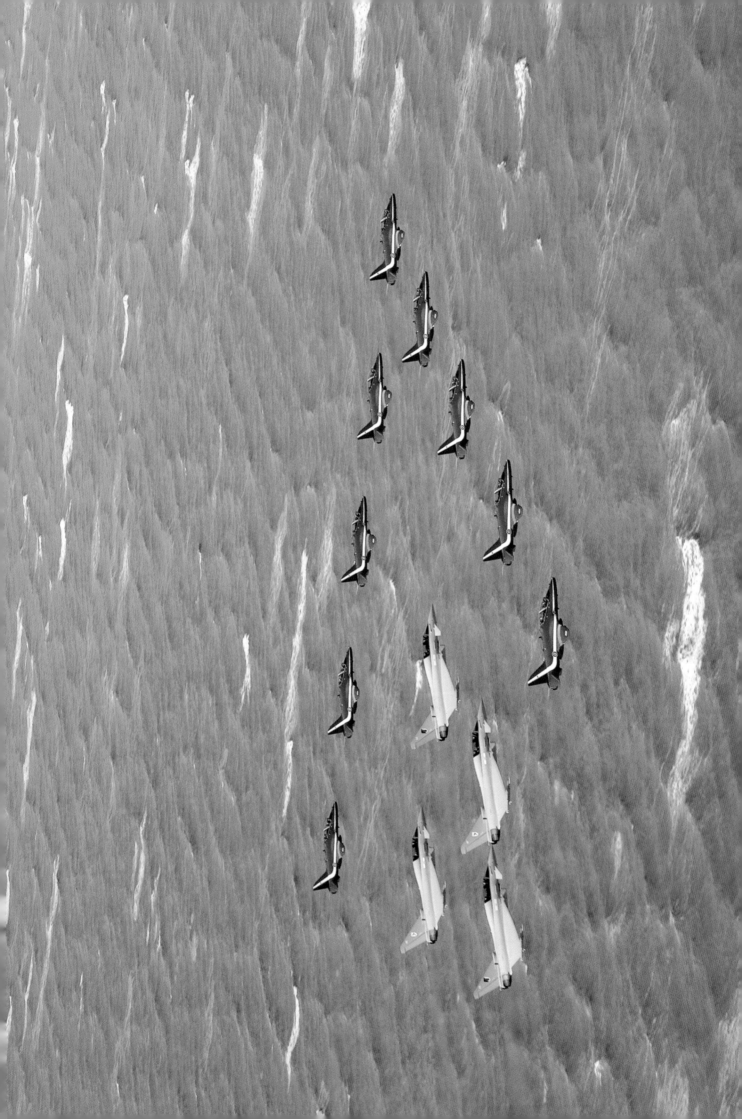

1 Aircraft Type	2 Producer	3 Location(s)	4 Production Dates (at Locations in Col. 3)	5A North West Locations (Col. 3)	5B Grand Total (all UK and Worldwide)	6 Notes
Roe II Triplane single-seater	A.V. Roe & Co.	Brownsfield Mill, Ancoats, Manchester; Brooklands, Surrey	1910	2	2	Roe I Biplane built at Putney, London, 1907-8. Roe I Triplane built at Putney and Lea Marshes 1909. Second machine fitted with engine at Blackpool 1909. First Roe II Triplane named *Mercury*.
Roe III Triplane two-seater	A.V. Roe & Co.	Brownsfield Mill, Ancoats, Manchester; Brooklands, Surrey; Blackpool	1910	4	4	Third machine assembled at Manchester and Blackpool.
Roe IV Triplane single-seater	A.V. Roe & Co.	Brownsfield Mill, Ancoats, Manchester; Brooklands, Surrey	1910	1	1	
Roe Biplane Farman-type	A.V. Roe & Co.	Brownsfield Mill, Ancoats, Manchester	1910	1	1	Built for M. Edwards, Bolton.
Empress Monoplane Blériot/Antoinette-type single-seater	C. Fletcher; Empress Motor Company/ Empress Motor Car and Aviation Company Ltd.	Stockport Road, Manchester	1909-1910	2	2	
Empress Biplane single-seater	C. Fletcher; Empress Motor Company/ Empress Motor Car and Aviation Company Ltd.	Stockport Road, Manchester	1910	1	1	
HMA No. 1 *Hermione 'Mayfly'* rigid airship	Vickers Sons & Maxim Ltd.	Barrow-in-Furness	1910-1911	1	1	

| 1 Aircraft Type | 2 Producer | 3 Location(s) | 4 Production Dates (at Locations in Col. 3) | 5 Production Numbers | | 6 Notes |
				5A North West Locations (Col. 3)	5B Grand Total (all UK and Worldwide)	
Gnosspelius Hydro-monoplane No. 1 Blériot-type single-seater	Borwick & Sons	Bowness-on-Windermere, Westmorland	1910	1	1	
Gnosspelius Hydro-monoplane No. 2 single-seater	Borwick & Sons	Bowness-on-Windermere, Westmorland	1911	1	1	
Avro Curtiss-type *Lakes Water Bird* **Hydro-biplane** two-seater	A.V. Roe & Co.	Brownsfield Mill, Ancoats, Manchester; Brooklands, Surrey	1911	1	1	Built for Capt. E.W. Wakefield of the Lakes Flying Company, Windermere. Float made by Borwick & Sons.
Gnosspelius Curtiss-type *Lakes Water Hen* **Hydro-biplane** two-seater	Lakes Flying Company	Cockshot Point, Bowness-on-Windermere, Westmorland	1912	1	1	Used Avro wings, Borwick floats.
Lakes Sea Bird **Hydro-biplane** two-seater	Lakes Flying Company	Cockshot Point, Bowness-on-Windermere, Westmorland	1912	1	1	Rebuild of Avro Type D/E 'Duigan Biplane'.
Gnosspelius/Trotter Hydro-biplane two-seater	Borwick & Sons	Bowness-on-Windermere, Westmorland	1913	1	1	
Gnosspelius Lakes Hydro-monoplane two-seater	Borwick & Sons	Bowness-on-Windermere, Westmorland	1913	1	1	
Avro Type D two-seat biplane	A.V. Roe & Co.	Brownsfield Mill, Ancoats, Manchester; Brooklands, Surrey; Shoreham, Sussex	1911–1912	7	7	
Avro Type E two-seat military biplane	A.V. Roe & Co.	Brownsfield Mill, Ancoats, Manchester; Brooklands, Surrey; Shoreham, Sussex	1912	1	1	

1 Aircraft Type	2 Producer	3 Location(s)	4 Production Dates (at Locations in Col. 3)	5 Production Numbers		6 Notes
				5A North West Locations (Col. 3)	5B Grand Total (all UK and Worldwide)	
Avro Type F cabin monoplane	A.V. Roe & Co.	Brownsfield Mill, Ancoats, Manchester; Brooklands, Surrey	1912	1	1	
Avro Type G cabin biplane	A.V. Roe & Co.	Brownsfield Mill, Ancoats, Manchester; Brooklands, Surrey	1912	1	1	
Burga Monoplane two-seater	A.V. Roe & Co.	Brownsfield Mill, Ancoats, Manchester; Shoreham, Sussex	1912	1	1	Built for Lt. Burga of the Peruvian Navy.
Avro 500 (Type E) two-seat biplane military trainer	A.V. Roe & Co.	Brownsfield Mill, Ancoats, Manchester; Shoreham, Sussex	1912-1913	12	12	
Avro 501 two-seat biplane, military landplane and seaplane	A.V. Roe & Co. Ltd.	Brownsfield Mill Ancoats, Clifton Street Miles Platting, Manchester; Shoreham, Sussex	1912-1913	1	1	Float designed by O. Gnosspelius.
Avro 502 (Type Es) single-seat military biplane	A.V. Roe & Co. Ltd.	Brownsfield Mill Ancoats, Clifton Street Miles Platting, Manchester; Shoreham, Sussex	1913	5	5	
Avro 503 (Type H) two-seat biplane, military landplane and seaplane	A.V. Roe & Co. Ltd.	Brownsfield Mill Ancoats, Clifton Street Miles Platting, Manchester; Shoreham, Sussex	1913	4	4	
Avro 504 (A-R) two-seat biplane, military trainer and reconnaissance landplane and seaplane	A.V. Roe & Co. Ltd.	Clifton Street Miles Platting, Park Works Newton Heath, Manchester; Hamble, Hants.	1913-1932	4,500	10,800	Also built by some 15 UK subcontractors and another ten worldwide.

1 Aircraft Type	2 Producer	3 Location(s)	4 Production Dates (at Locations in Col. 3)	5 Production Numbers 5A North West Locations (Col. 3)	5B Grand Total (all UK and Worldwide)	6 Notes
Avro 508 two-seat 'pusher' military reconnaissance biplane	A.V. Roe & Co. Ltd.	Clifton Street, Miles Platting, Manchester; Brooklands, Surrey	1913	1	1	
Avro 510 two-seat racing and military biplane and seaplane	A.V. Roe & Co. Ltd.	Clifton Street, Miles Platting, Manchester	1914	5	5	
Avro 511 'Arrowscout' single-seat scout biplane	A.V. Roe & Co. Ltd.	Clifton Street, Miles Platting, Manchester; Brooklands, Surrey	1914	1	1	Also referred to as 'Arrowplane'.
Avro 519, 522 single and two-seat bomber biplane	A.V. Roe & Co. Ltd.	Park Works, Newton Heath, Manchester; Hamble, Hants.	1916	4	4	
Avro 521 two-seat fighter trainer biplane	A.V. Roe & Co. Ltd.	Park Works, Newton Heath, Manchester; Hamble, Hants.	1916	4	4	Estimated numbers. Fewer than the intended 25 production aircraft were built.
Avro 523, 523A Pike three-seat, twin-engine reconnaissance fighter, day and night bomber biplane	A.V. Roe & Co. Ltd.	Park Works, Newton Heath, Manchester; Hamble, Hants.	1916	2	2	
Avro 527 two-seat, single-engine reconnaissance fighter biplane	A.V. Roe & Co. Ltd.	Park Works, Newton Heath, Manchester; Hamble, Hants.	1916	1	1	
Avro 528 'Silver King' two-seat, single-engine bomber biplane	A.V. Roe & Co. Ltd.	Park Works, Newton Heath, Manchester; Hamble, Hants.	1916	1	1	
Avro 529, 529A three-seat, twin-engine long range bomber biplane	A.V. Roe & Co. Ltd.	Park Works, Newton Heath, Manchester; Hamble, Hants.	1916–1917	2	2	
Avro 530 two-seat, single-engine fighter biplane	A.V. Roe & Co. Ltd.	Park Works, Newton Heath, Manchester; Hamble, Hants.	1917	2	2	

1 Aircraft Type	2 Producer	3 Location(s)	4 Production Dates (at Locations in Col. 3)	5 Production Numbers		6 Notes
				5A North West Locations (Col. 3)	5B Grand Total (all UK and Worldwide)	
Avro 531, 538 Spider single-seat, single-engine biplane fighter and civil racer	A.V. Roe & Co. Ltd.	Park Works, Newton Heath, Manchester; Hamble, Hants.	1918-1919	2	2	
Avro 533 Manchester Mk.I, II three-seat, twin-engine bomber and reconnaissance fighter biplane	A.V. Roe & Co. Ltd.	Hamble, Hants.	1918	-	3	Two complete aircraft and one airframe constructed at Hamble.
HMA No. 9 rigid airship	Vickers Ltd.	Barrow-in-Furness	1914-1916	1	1	
HMA Nos. 5, 6, 7 Parseval-type non-rigid patrol and training airships	Vickers Ltd.	Barrow-in-Furness	1915-1916	3	30	27 built in Germany by Parseval Luftshiffe of Leipzig.
HMA Nos. 17, 18, 20, 21, 23, 24, 25, 32, 33, 34 'SS' Sea Scout non-rigid airships	Vickers Ltd.	Barrow-in-Furness	1915-1916	10	50	Others built at Kingsnorth and Folkestone (Kent), Wormwood Scrubs and elsewhere.
HMA Nos. 23, 26 (R.26) '23' Class rigid airships	Vickers Ltd.	Barrow-in-Furness	1915-1918	2	6	Others built by Beardmore at Inchinnan near Glasgow (2) and Armstrong Whitworth at Barlow, near Selby, Yorks. (2).
R.80 rigid airship	Vickers Ltd.	Barrow-in-Furness	1917-1918	1	1	Designed by Barnes Wallis.
Parseval-type non-rigid airship	Vickers Ltd.	Barrow-in-Furness	1920-1921	1	1	Built for Japanese Imperial Navy.
Royal Aircraft Factory B.E.2d, 2e two-seat, single-engine general purpose biplane	Vulcan Motor & Engineering Co. Ltd.	Crossens, Southport	1915	300	3,535	Vulcan built 100 'd's and 200 'e's. Majority built by Royal Aircraft Factory, Farnborough and some 20 subcontractors elsewhere.

1 Aircraft Type	2 Producer	3 Location(s)	4 Production Dates (at Locations in Col. 3)	5 Production Numbers		6 Notes
				5A North West Locations (Col. 3)	5B Grand Total (all UK and Worldwide)	
Aircraft Manufacturing Co. (Airco from 1918) D.H.4 two-seat, single-engine day bomber biplane	Vulcan Motor & Engineering Co. Ltd.	Crossens, Southport	1916-1918	100	6,310	Also built by AMC Ltd. at Hendon, London and 11 other UK subcontractors; 4,846 in the USA by five companies; and 15 in Belgium.
Aircraft Manufacturing Co. (Airco) D.H.9 two-seat, single-engine long range day bomber biplane	Vulcan Motor & Engineering Co. Ltd.	Crossens, Southport	1917-1918	100	4,650	Majority built elsewhere by AMC Ltd. at Hendon, London and 14 other UK subcontractors; also in Belgium and Spain. Not all 4,650 were completed. See also under N.A.F. No. 2, Heaton Chapel, Stockport.
Aircraft Manufacturing Co. (Airco) D.H.9A two-seat, single-engine strategic day bomber biplane	Vulcan Motor & Engineering Co. Ltd.	Crossens, Southport	1918	350	2,650	Not all were necessarily completed and delivered. Built elsewhere by AMC Ltd. at Hendon, London, ten other UK subcontractors and a small number in the USA.
Aircraft Manufacturing Co. (Airco) D.H.9 two-seat, single-engine long range day bomber biplane	National Aircraft Factory No. 2 (N.A.F. No. 2)	Heaton Chapel, Stockport	1917-1918	444	4,650	See also under Vulcan Motor & Engineering, Crossens, Southport.
Aircraft Manufacturing Co. (Airco) D.H.10 'Amiens' three-seat, twin-engine heavy bomber biplane	National Aircraft Factory No. 2 (N.A.F. No. 2)	Heaton Chapel, Stockport	1918	7	1,295	Only some 220 of the total ordered are likely to have been delivered. Built elsewhere by AMC Ltd. at Hendon, London and five other UK subcontractors.
Bristol and Colonial Aeroplane Co. Type 22 F.2B Bristol Fighter two-seat, single-engine biplane	National Aircraft Factory No. 3 (N.A.F. No. 3)	Aintree, Liverpool	1918-1919	126	5,308	Majority built by BCAC at Filton and Brislington, Bristol and some ten other subcontractors in the UK and USA.

1 Aircraft Type	2 Producer	3 Location(s)	4 Production Dates (at Locations in Col. 3)	5A North West Locations (Col. 3)	5B Grand Total (all UK and Worldwide)	6 Notes
Handley Page 0/400 three-seat, twin-engine heavy bomber biplane	Waring & Gillow/ Alliance Aeroplane Co.	Oldham Aircraft Factory, Hollinwood and Shaw	1918	10	554	The ten believed to have been completed at Oldham were supplied as kits by the Standard Aircraft Corporation of the USA, but subsequently dis-assembled and returned. Rest of production by Handley Page at Cricklewood and various UK subcontractors.
Felixstowe F.3 four-seat, twin-engine patrol flying boat biplane	Dick, Kerr & Co. Ltd.	Strand Road, Preston; and Lytham	1917-1919	61	200+	The total of 200+ includes Felixstowes of all types. See F.5 below.
Felixstowe F.5 four-seat, twin-engine patrol flying boat biplane	Dick, Kerr & Co. Ltd.	Strand Road, Preston; and Lytham	1918-1919	2	200+	The total of 200+ includes Felixstowes of all types. Others produced by contractors including S.E. Saunders of the Isle of Wight, Aircraft Manufacturing Co. of Hendon, London. See F.3 above.
Fairey N.4 *Atalanta* five-seat, four-engine long range flying boat biplane	Dick, Kerr & Co. Ltd. (from Dec. 1918 the English Electric Co. Ltd.)	Strand Road, Preston; and Lytham	1918-1921	1	3	*Atalanta II* built by Phoenix Dynamo at Bradford. *Titania* built by Fairey Aviation Co. at Hayes.
English Electric S.1 Wren single-seat, single-engine, ultra-light trainer monoplane	English Electric Co. Ltd.	Strand Road, Preston; and Lytham	1923	4	4	
English Electric M.3 Ayr four-seat, single-engine fleet gunnery and reconnaissance flying boat	English Electric Co. Ltd.	Strand Road, Preston; and Lytham	1923-1925	1	1	

1 Aircraft Type	2 Producer	3 Location(s)	4 Production Dates (at Locations in Col. 3)	5 Production Numbers — 5A North West Locations (Col. 3)	5B Grand Total (all UK and Worldwide)	6 Notes
English Electric P.5 Kingston Mks. I, II, III four-seat, twin-engine coastal patrol and anti-submarine flying boat biplane	English Electric Co. Ltd.	Strand Road, Preston; and Lytham	1923-1926	7	7	Production: MkI(5), MkII(1), MkIII(1).
Avro 534, 543, 554 Baby single-seat, single-engine light sporting biplane, landplane and floatplane	A.V. Roe & Co. Ltd.	Hamble, Hants.	1919-1922	-	12	
Avro 536 five-seat, single-engine passenger biplane	A.V. Roe & Co. Ltd.	Newton Heath, Manchester; Hamble, Hants.	1919	12	26	Built at Manchester (12), Hamble (10) and by Surrey Flying Services Ltd., Croydon (4).
Avro 539 single-seat, single-engine racing biplane, floatplane and landplane	A.V. Roe & Co. Ltd.	Hamble, Hants.	1919	-	1	
Avro 547, 547A five-seat, single-engine commercial cabin triplane	A.V. Roe & Co. Ltd.	Newton Heath, Manchester; Hamble, Hants.	1920	-	2	
Avro 548 three-seat, single-engine passenger biplane	A.V. Roe & Co. Ltd.	Newton Heath, Manchester; Hamble, Hants.	1919-1924	-	7	Principally Hamble-built. Another 30 converted from Avro 504s by five other companies in UK, Canada and Australia, two by Berkshire Aviation Co. Ltd. at Barton Aerodrome, Manchester during 1931-32.
Avro 549 Aldershot I, II, III, IV four-seat, single-engine long range heavy bomber biplane	A.V. Roe & Co. Ltd.	Newton Heath, Manchester; Hamble, Hants.	1920-1923	-	17	Principally Hamble-built.

1 Aircraft Type	2 Producer	3 Location(s)	4 Production Dates (at Locations in Col. 3)	5 Production Numbers		6 Notes
				5A North West Locations (Col. 3)	5B Grand Total (all UK and Worldwide)	
Avro 552, 552A two-seat, single-engine touring and training biplane, landplane and seaplane	A.V. Roe & Co. Ltd.	Newton Heath, Manchester; Hamble, Hants.	1920-1932	-	23	Principally Hamble-built (16), also by C.B. Field, Surrey (3) and in Canada (4).
Avro 555 Bison I, II three/four-seat, single-engine deck-landing maritime reconnaissance and fleet gunnery spotting biplane	A.V. Roe & Co. Ltd.	Hamble, Hants; Newton Heath, Manchester; Woodford, Cheshire	1921-1927	53	56	Three prototypes built at Hamble, all subsequent production (53) at Manchester/Woodford.
Avro 557 Ava five-seat, twin-engine long range coastal defence bomber biplane	A.V. Roe & Co. Ltd.	Hamble, Hants.	1924-1927	-	2	
Avro 558 single-seat, single-engine sporting and trials light biplane	A.V. Roe & Co. Ltd.	Hamble, Hants.	1923	-	2	
Avro 560 single-seat, single-engine ultra-light trials monoplane	A.V. Roe & Co. Ltd.	Hamble, Hants.	1923	-	1	
Avro 561 Andover two-crew, 12-passenger single-engine large passenger biplane	A.V. Roe & Co. Ltd.	Hamble, Hants.	1924-1925	-	4	
Avro 562 Avis two-seat, single-engine light biplane	A.V. Roe & Co. Ltd.	Hamble, Hants.	1924	-	1	
Avro 566, 567 Avenger single-seat, single-engine fighter biplane	A.V. Roe & Co. Ltd.	Hamble, Hants.	1926	-	1	
Avro 571, 572 Buffalo two-seat, single-engine deck-landing torpedo bomber biplane	A.V. Roe & Co. Ltd.	Hamble, Hants.	1926-1927	-	1	

1 Aircraft Type	2 Producer	3 Location(s)	4 Production Dates (at Locations in Col. 3)	5A North West Locations (Col. 3)	5B Grand Total (all UK and Worldwide)	6 Notes
Avro 574, 586, 587, 576 (Cierva C.6C, C.8V, C.6D, C.8R, C.9) single and two-seat Autogiros	A.V. Roe & Co. Ltd.	Hamble, Hants.	1926-1927	-	5	One C.6A and one C.6B also built by Cierva in Spain. Fuselages based on Avro 504K, but the Avro 576 (Cierva C.9) used a new-design fuselage subsequently adopted for the Avro Avian.
Avro 575, 611, 617 (Cierva C.8L) two-seat Autogiros	A.V. Roe & Co. Ltd.	Hamble, Hants.	1927-1928	-	4	Fuselages based on Avro 504N.
Avro 612, 620 (Cierva C.17, C.19) two-seat Autogiros	A.V. Roe & Co. Ltd.	Hamble, Hants.	1928-1929	-	32	Shared Avro Avian fuselages.
Avro 581, 594, 605, 616 Avian I, II, III, IV, IVM single/two-seat, single-engine touring biplane, landplane and seaplane	A.V. Roe & Co. Ltd.	Hamble, Hants; Newton Heath, Manchester; Woodford, Cheshire	1926-1933	345	390	Two built as Avro 625 monoplanes. Some Avians assembled in USA. Rest built at Hamble.
Avro 584 Avocet single-seat, single-engine carrier-borne biplane and floatplane fighter	A.V. Roe & Co. Ltd.	Hamble, Hants.	1927	-	2	
Avro 604 Antelope two-seat, single-engine day bomber biplane	A.V. Roe & Co. Ltd.	Hamble, Hants.	1928	-	1	
Avro 618 Ten two-crew, eight-passenger tri-motor monoplane	A.V. Roe & Co. Ltd.	Newton Heath, Manchester; Woodford, Cheshire	1928-1936	14	14	
Avro 619 Five one-crew, four-passenger tri-motor monoplane	A.V. Roe & Co. Ltd.	Newton Heath, Manchester; Woodford, Cheshire	1929-1930	4	4	

1 Aircraft Type	2 Producer	3 Location(s)	4 Production Dates (at Locations in Col. 3)	5 Production Numbers 5A North West Locations (Col. 3)	5B Grand Total (all UK and Worldwide)	6 Notes
Avro 624 Six two-crew, four-passenger tri-motor monoplane	A.V. Roe & Co. Ltd.	Newton Heath, Manchester; Woodford, Cheshire	1930–1933	3	3	
Avro 642/2m Eighteen two-crew, 16-passenger twin-engine monoplane	A.V. Roe & Co. Ltd.	Newton Heath, Manchester; Woodford, Cheshire	1933	1	1	
Avro 642/4m Star of India two-crew, seven-passenger four-engine monoplane	A.V. Roe & Co. Ltd.	Newton Heath, Manchester; Woodford, Cheshire	1934	1	1	
Avro 621 Trainer (Tutor) two-seat, single-engine biplane trainer	A.V. Roe & Co. Ltd.	Newton Heath, Manchester; Woodford, Cheshire	1930–1936	795	855	Also built under licence in South Africa (57 aircraft) and Denmark (3).
Avro 626, 637 (Prefect) two/three-seat, single-engine multi-purpose fighter trainer, bomber, landplane and seaplane biplane	A.V. Roe & Co. Ltd.	Newton Heath, Manchester; Woodford, Cheshire	1930–1940	206	206+	Additional aircraft built under licence in Portugal.
Avro 627 Mailplane single-seat, single-engine biplane	A.V. Roe & Co. Ltd.	Newton Heath, Manchester; Woodford, Cheshire	1930–1931	1	1	
Avro 631, 643 Cadet, 638 Club Cadet two-seat, single-engine light trainer biplanes	A.V. Roe & Co. Ltd.	Newton Heath, Manchester; Woodford, Cheshire	1931–1939	131	131	
Avro 639 Cabin Cadet, 640 Cadet three-seat biplanes						
Avro 636, 667 two-seat, single-engine biplane fighter trainer	A.V. Roe & Co. Ltd.	Newton Heath, Manchester; Woodford, Cheshire	1935	4	4	

1 Aircraft Type	2 Producer	3 Location(s)	4 Production Dates (at Locations in Col. 3)	5A North West Locations (Col. 3)	5B Grand Total (all UK and Worldwide)	6 Notes
Avro 641 Commodore five-seat, single-engine biplane cabin tourer	A.V. Roe & Co. Ltd.	Failsworth Works, Manchester; Woodford, Cheshire	1934	6	6	
Avro 652, 652A Anson Mks. I-22 three/five seat, twin-engine coastal reconnaissance and crew-trainer monoplane	A.V. Roe & Co. Ltd.	Newton Heath and Chadderton, Manchester; Woodford, Cheshire; Yeadon, Yorks.	1934-1952	4,161	11,020	4,161 built by Avro at Newton Heath/Chadderton/Woodford and 3,957 at Yeadon, Yorks. 2,902 built by seven companies in Canada during WW2. Overall total of 11,020 recently put at 10,996 due to possible miscount. NB: First two aircraft built in 1934 as Avro 652 four-passenger aircraft for Imperial Airways.
Avro 671 Rota I (Cierva C.30A) two-seat Autogiro	A.V. Roe & Co. Ltd.	Newton Heath, Manchester; Woodford, Cheshire	1934-1938	81	146	Versions also produced by companies in Germany and France.
Hawker Audax two-seat, single-engine army co-operation biplane trainer	A.V. Roe & Co. Ltd.	Newton Heath, Manchester; Woodford, Cheshire	1935-1937	287	624+	Produced also by Hawker, Bristol and Westland.
Avro 674 two-seat, single-engine army co-operation biplane	A.V. Roe & Co. Ltd.	Newton Heath, Manchester; Woodford, Cheshire	1937-1938	24	24	Avro's final biplane design – a development of the Hawker Audax.
Mignet Pou-de-Ciel 'Flying Flea' single-seat, single-engine tandem monoplane or super-staggered tailless biplane	F. Hills & Sons Ltd.	Trafford Park, Manchester	1935	1	400+	Single example assembled by Hills' employees. Large numbers produced by amateur constructors in Europe and USA. Over 120 were on the British register, including 14 in the North West.
Hillson Praga two-seat, single-engine sport and training monoplane	F. Hills & Sons Ltd.	Trafford Park, Manchester	1936-1938	35	102	Balance built by Praga in Czechoslovakia.
Hillson Pennine two-seat, single-engine cabin monoplane	F. Hills & Sons Ltd.	Trafford Park, Manchester	1937-1938	1	1	

1 Aircraft Type	2 Producer	3 Location(s)	4 Production Dates (at Locations in Col. 3)	5 Production Numbers 5A North West Locations (Col. 3)	5B Grand Total (all UK and Worldwide)	6 Notes
Hillson Helvellyn two-seat, single-engine monoplane trainer	F. Hills & Sons Ltd.	Trafford Park, Manchester	1939	1	1	
Percival P.28 Proctor **Mk.I, II, III, IV** three/four-seat, single-engine communications aircraft and radio trainer	F. Hills & Sons Ltd.	Trafford Park, Ringway and Barton, Manchester	1940-1945	812	1,269	Hills' production comprised Mk.I (25), Mk.II (100), Mk.III (437), Mk.IV (250).
Hillson Bi-mono single-seat, single-engine slip-wing biplane/monoplane research aircraft	F. Hills & Sons Ltd.	Trafford Park, Manchester	1941	1	1	
Hillson FH40 single-seat, single-engine slip-wing biplane/monoplane research fighter	F. Hills & Sons Ltd.	Trafford Park and Barton, Manchester	1942-1943	1	1	Modified Hawker Hurricane Mk.I.
Fairey Hendon Mk.II five-seat, twin-engine heavy bomber monoplane	Fairey Aviation Co. Ltd.	Heaton Chapel, Stockport; Barton, Manchester	1935-1937	14	15	Single prototype built by Fairey at Hayes and Great West Aerodrome, Heathrow, London.
Comper C.L.A.7 Swift single-seat, single-engine ultra-light sport and touring monoplane	Comper Aircraft Ltd.	Hooton Park, near Ellesmere Port	1929-1933	30+	41	Comper also built the Swift at Heston, near Hounslow, London.
Ford 4-AT-E Tri-Motor two-crew transport monoplane	Comper Aircraft Ltd.	Hooton Park, near Ellesmere Port	1930	2	203	Majority built by Ford in the USA. Possibility exists that three were assembled at Hooton Park.
Cierva C.25 Autogiro	Comper Aircraft Ltd.	Hooton Park, near Ellesmere Port	1931	1	1	

1 Aircraft Type	2 Producer	3 Location(s)	4 Production Dates (at Locations in Col. 3)	5 Production Numbers		6 Notes
				5A North West Locations (Col. 3)	5B Grand Total (all UK and Worldwide)	
Slingsby Sailplanes Type 8 Kirby Tutor, Cadet TX Mk.2; Type 21 Sedbergh, T.21B, TX Mk.1; Type 24 Falcon 4; Kites, Kadets and Motor Tutors	Martin Hearn & Co. Ltd.	Hooton Park, near Ellesmere Port	1945-1957	72+	320+	Grand total relates to known production and could be significantly higher.
Mosscraft M.A.1, M.A.2 two-seat, single-engine sporting/racing monoplane	Moss Brothers Aircraft Ltd.	Moor Road, Chorley	1937-1939	2	2	
Fairey Battle three-seat, single-engine day bomber and reconnaissance monoplane	Fairey Aviation Co. Ltd.	Heaton Chapel, Stockport; Barton and Ringway, Manchester	1936-1940	1,171	2,200+	Produced also by Austin Motors at Longbridge (1,029) and factories in Australia and Belgium.
Fairey Fulmar Mk.I, II two-seat, single-engine carrier-borne fighter bomber	Fairey Aviation Co. Ltd.	Heaton Chapel, Stockport and Ringway, Manchester	1939-1942	600	600	Comprised Mk.I (250), Mk.II (350).
Bristol Beaufighter Mk.IF, IC, VIC two-seat, twin-engine night and maritime patrol fighter	Fairey Aviation Co. Ltd.	Errwood Park, Stockport and Ringway, Manchester	1940-1943	498	5,928	Rest produced by Bristol Aeroplane Co. at Filton and Weston-super-Mare (5,066) and in Australia (364).
Handley Page H.P.57 Halifax B.Mk.III, V, VII; A.Mk.VII six/seven-seat, four-engine, long range heavy bomber and airborne forces glider tug	Fairey Aviation Co. Ltd.	Errwood Park, Stockport and Ringway, Manchester	1942-1945	661	6,178	Production comprised B.Mk.III (325), Mk.V (246), Mk.VII (21) and A.Mk.VII (69). See also under English Electric at Preston and Samlesbury; Rootes Securities at Speke.
Fairey Barracuda Mk.I, II, III, V three-seat, single-engine carrier-borne torpedo dive bomber	Fairey Aviation Co. Ltd.	Heaton Chapel, Stockport and Ringway, Manchester	1942-1947	1,160	2,572	Rest produced by Fairey, Westland, Blackburn and Boulton Paul.

1 Aircraft Type	2 Producer	3 Location(s)	4 Production Dates (at Locations in Col. 3)	5 Production Numbers		6 Notes
				5A North West Locations (Col. 3)	5B Grand Total (all UK and Worldwide)	
Bristol Blenheim Mk.I, IV three-seat, twin-engine light bomber	A.V. Roe & Co. Ltd.	Newton Heath and Chadderton, Manchester; Woodford, Cheshire	1938-1941	1,005	6,000+	Avro production comprised approximately Mk.I (255), Mk.IV (750). 676 built in Canada as the Bolingbroke. Also built under licence in Finland and Turkey pre-war. See also under Rootes Securities at Speke.
Avro 679 Manchester Mk.I, IA seven-seat, twin-engine medium bomber	A.V. Roe & Co. Ltd.	Newton Heath and Ringway, Manchester; Woodford, Cheshire	1939-1941	159	)	
	Metropolitan-Vickers Ltd.	Trafford Park, Manchester	1939-1942	43	) 202)	
Hawker Tornado single-seat, single-engine fighter	A.V. Roe & Co. Ltd.	Yeadon, Yorks.	1940-1941	-	5	One aircraft flown at Woodford in 1941.
Avro 683 Lancaster B.Mk.I, III seven-seat, four-engine heavy bomber	A.V. Roe & Co. Ltd.	Newton Heath, Chadderton and Ringway, Manchester; Woodford, Cheshire	1940-1945	3,050	)	Comprised Mk.I (900) and Mk.III (2,150). An additional 623 made by Avro at Yeadon, Yorks. comprised Mk.I (53) and Mk.III (570).
Avro 683 Lancaster B.Mk.I, III	Metropolitan-Vickers Ltd.	Trafford Park, Manchester	1941-1945	1,080	)	Comprised Mk.I (948) and Mk.III (132). Assembled by Avro at Woodford.

1 Aircraft Type	2 Producer	3 Location(s)	4 Production Dates (at Locations in Col. 3)	5 Production Numbers		6 Notes
				5A North West Locations (Col. 3)	5B Grand Total (all UK and Worldwide)	
Avro 683 Lancaster B.Mk.I	Vickers-Armstrongs Ltd.	Broughton/Hawarden, near Chester	1944-1945	235	7,377	Of the 235, 23 were assembled by V-A Ltd. at Chester from sub-assemblies supplied by M-V Ltd. of Trafford Park. Another 300 built by Vickers-Armstrongs at Castle Bromwich (all Mk.I). 1,329 built by Armstrong Whitworth at Baginton and Bitteswell comprised Mk.I (911), Mk.II Bristol Hercules (300), Mk.III (118). 330 built by Austin Motors at Longbridge comprised Mk.I (150), Mk.VII (180). 430 built by Victory Aircraft, Ontario, Canada (all Mk.X).
Avro 691 Lancastrian C.Mk.I, II, III, IV three/four-crew, 9-13 passenger; four-engine transport	A.V. Roe & Co. Ltd.	Chadderton and Ringway, Manchester; Woodford, Cheshire	1944-1946	82	82	Nine Lancasters also converted to Lancastrians in Canada.
Avro 685 York C.Mk.I three/four-crew, nine/54passenger; four-engine long range passenger and cargo aircraft	A.V. Roe & Co. Ltd.	Chadderton and Ringway, Manchester; Woodford, Cheshire; Yeadon, Yorks.	1942-1948	180	258	Production: Chadderton/ Ringway (153), Woodford (27), Yeadon (77), Canada (1).
Avro 694 Lincoln B.Mk.I, II seven-seat, four-engine long range heavy bomber	A.V. Roe & Co. Ltd.	Chadderton and Ringway, Manchester; Woodford, Cheshire; Yeadon, Yorks.	1944-1946	165		Avro built an additional six Lincolns at Yeadon comprising two B. Mk.Is and four B.Mk.IIs, their total production being 171.

1 Aircraft Type	2 Producer	3 Location(s)	4 Production Dates (at Locations in Col. 3)	5 Production Numbers		6 Notes
				5A North West Locations (Col. 3)	5B Grand Total (all UK and Worldwide)	
Avro 694 Lincoln B.Mk.I, II seven-seat four-engine long range heavy bomber	Metropolitan-Vickers Ltd.	Trafford Park, Manchester	1944-1945	80	605	Comprised B.Mk.I (28), B.Mk.II (52). Of the 80 M-V Ltd. Lincolns, 11 were finally assembled by Vickers-Armstrongs at Chester, June–August 1945. 299 (B.Mk.II) built by Armstrong Whitworth at Coventry. 54 (24 Mk.30B, 30 Mk.30A/B) built by Australian Government Aircraft Factory. One built by Victory Aircraft, Ontario, Canada.
Handley Page H.P.52 Hampden Mk.I four-seat, twin-engine medium bomber	English Electric Co. Ltd.	Preston and Samlesbury	1939-1942	770	1,432	Handley Page built 502 and a further 160 were built in Canada.
Handley Page H.P.57 Halifax B.Mk.II, III, VI, VII; A.Mk.VII six/seven-seat, four-engine, long range heavy bomber and airborne forces glider tug	English Electric Co. Ltd.	Preston and Samlesbury	1940-1945	2,145	6,178	Production comprised B.Mk.II (900), Mk.III (900), Mk.VI (325), Mk.VII (12), A.Mk.VII (8). See also under Fairey Aviation at Erwood Park and Ringway; Rootes Securities at Speke.
Vickers Wellington B. Mk.I, IA, IC, III, IV, X, XII, XIV six-seat, twin-engine medium bomber	Vickers-Armstrongs Ltd.	Broughton/Hawarden, near Chester; Cranage, near Holmes Chapel, Cheshire	1939-1945	5,540	11,461	Vickers built 2,515 at Weybridge. See also under V-A Ltd. at Blackpool, below.
Vickers Wellington B.Mk.IC, III, X, XI, XIII, XIV, XVIII six-seat, twin-engine medium bomber	Vickers-Armstrongs Ltd.	Squires Gate and Stanley Park, Blackpool	1940-1945	3,406	11,461	Vickers built 2,515 at Weybridge. See also under V-A Ltd. at Chester, above.

1 Aircraft Type	2 Producer	3 Location(s)	4 Production Dates (at Locations in Col. 3)	5 Production Numbers		6 Notes
				5A North West Locations (Col. 3)	5B Grand Total (all UK and Worldwide)	
Bristol Blenheim Mk.I, IV, V three-seat, twin-engine light bomber	Rootes Securities	Speke, Liverpool	1938-1942	2,555	6,000+	Production comprised Mk.I (250), Mk.IV (2,230), Mk.V (75). Rest built by Bristol Aeroplane Co., Rootes at Blythe Bridge, also Mk.IV in Canada as the Bolingbroke (676); and under licence in Finland and Turkey pre-war. See also under Avro at Manchester. Mk.V originally known as the Bisley.
Handley Page H.P.57 Halifax B.Mk.II, III, V; A.Mk.III, A.Mk.VII six/seven-seat, four-engine, long range heavy bomber, and airborne forces glider tug	Rootes Securities	Speke, Liverpool	1942-1945	1,070	6,178	Production comprised B.Mk.II (12), Mk.III (280), Mk.V (658), A.Mk.VII (120). See also under Fairey Aviation at Errwood Park and Ringway; English Electric at Preston and Samlesbury. Rest built by Handley Page (1,592) and the London Aircraft Production Group (710).
Short S.25 Sunderland Mk.III ten-seat, four-engine maritime reconnaissance flying boat bomber	Short Brothers Ltd. (from 1943 Short Bros. & Harland Ltd.)	White Cross Bay, Troutbeck, Windermere	1942-1944	35	749	Rest built by Shorts at Rochester and Belfast, and by Blackburn at Dumbarton.
Fairey Spearfish two-seat, single-engine dive and torpedo bomber	Fairey Aviation Ltd.	Heaton Chapel, Stockport; Ringway, Manchester	1945	2	5	Five prototypes built, two at Heaton Chapel, three at Hayes, Middlesex.
Fairey FD1 single-seat, single-turbojet delta wing research aircraft	Fairey Aviation Ltd.	Heaton Chapel, Stockport; Ringway, Manchester	1948-1950	1	1	
De Havilland D.H.100 Vampire FB. Mk.9 single-seat, single-turbojet twin-boom fighter bomber	Fairey Aviation Ltd.	Ringway, Manchester	1952-1953	67	4,342	See also under English Electric at Preston and Samlesbury, and de Havilland at Broughton/Chester. Total includes Vampires of all types.

1 Aircraft Type	2 Producer	3 Location(s)	4 Production Dates (at Locations in Col. 3)	5A North West Locations (Col. 3)	5B Grand Total (all UK and Worldwide)	6 Notes
De Havilland D.H.115 Vampire Trainer two-seat, single-turbojet twin-boom trainer	Fairey Aviation Ltd.	Ringway, Manchester	1954-1955	30	963	See also under de Havilland at Broughton/Chester. Total applies to all Vampire two-seat trainers built in UK, Australia and India.
De Havilland D.H.112 Venom FB. Mk.1, NF.Mk.51 (J.33) single-seat, single turbojet twin-boom fighter bomber and two-seat night fighter	Fairey Aviation Ltd.	Ringway, Manchester	1953-1956	37	1,143	See also under de Havilland at Broughton/Chester.
Fairey Firefly T.Mk.7, U.Mk.8, 9 two-seat, single-engine anti-submarine trainer and radio-controlled target drone	Fairey Aviation Ltd.	Heaton Chapel, Stockport; Ringway, Manchester	1952-1956	75	1,702	Total represents all Fireflies produced by Fairey at Heaton Chapel, Hayes and White Waltham and by General Aircraft at Hanworth. Fairey also overhauled and converted many at Heaton Chapel and Ringway 1945-59.
Fairey Gannet AS. Mk.1, 4 three-seat, double-engine carrier-borne anti-submarine aircraft	Fairey Aviation Ltd.	Heaton Chapel, Stockport; Ringway, Manchester	1954-1958	102	356	Balance built by Fairey at Hayes.
Australian Government Aircraft Factory 'Jindivik' Mk.102B single-turbojet autopiloted target drone	Fairey Engineering	Ringway, Manchester	1961	29	34	

1 Aircraft Type	2 Producer	3 Location(s)	4 Production Dates (at Locations in Col. 3)	5 Production Numbers		6 Notes
				5A North West Locations (Col. 3)	5B Grand Total (all UK and Worldwide)	
Hawker Hunter F. Mk.1, 4, Mk.50 single-seat, single-turbojet swept wing interceptor fighter	Hawker Aircraft (Blackpool) Ltd.	Squires Gate, Blackpool	1953-1958	299	1,975	Production comprised F.Mk.1 (26), F.Mk.4 (177), Mk.50 (96). Rest produced by Hawker at Kingston-upon-Thames, Sir W.G. Armstrong Whitworth Aircraft at Coventry and under licence in Belgium and The Netherlands. Other sources indicating a total of 374 Hunters having been built at Blackpool may be overstatements due to: 1) curtailment of F.6 production and reallocation to Kingston and Coventry; 2) reallocation of a T.7 (two-seater trainer) contract to Kingston.
De Havilland D.H.98 Mosquito NF.Mk.38; Sea Mosquito TR. Mk.37 two-seat, twin-engine night fighter and torpedo reconnaissance aircraft	De Havilland Aircraft Company Ltd.	Broughton/Hawarden, near Chester	1948-1950	65	7,781	Production comprised NF.Mk.38 (51), TR.Mk.37 (14). Rest produced by D.H. at Hatfield and Leavesden, D.H. Canada at Toronto, D.H. at Sydney, Australia; Airspeed Ltd. at Bournemouth; Standard Motor Co. Ltd. and Percival Aircraft at Luton.

1 Aircraft Type	2 Producer	3 Location(s)	4 Production Dates (at Locations in Col. 3)	5 Production Numbers		6 Notes
				5A North West Locations (Col. 3)	5B Grand Total (all UK and Worldwide)	
De Havilland D.H.103 Hornet F.Mk.3, FR.Mk.4; Sea Hornet F.Mk.20, NF.Mk.21, PR.Mk.22 single and two-seat twin-engine fighter, naval fighter, night fighter and photographic reconnaissance aircraft	De Havilland Aircraft Company Ltd.	Broughton/Hawarden, near Chester	1948-1952	149	409	Rest produced by de Havilland at Hatfield 1944-48. Some cancelled orders may have reduced total production to below 400 and Chester output closer to 120.
De Havilland Canada D.H.C.1 Chipmunk T. Mk.10, 20, Mk.21 two-seat, single-engine military and civil trainer	De Havilland Aircraft Company Ltd.	Broughton/Hawarden, near Chester	1950-1956	889	1,278	Rest of production comprised D.H. Canada at Toronto (218), D.H. at Hatfield (111) and OGMA in Spain (60).
De Havilland D.H.100 Vampire FB.Mk.5, 9, 50 (J.28B), 52; D.H.113 Vampire NF.Mk.10, 54; D.H.115 Vampire Trainer T.11, T.55 single and two-seat single turbojet twin-boom fighter bomber, night fighter and trainer	De Havilland Aircraft Company Ltd. (from Jan. 1960 Hawker Siddeley de Havilland Division)	Broughton/Hawarden, near Chester	1949-1963	1,244	4,342	Production comprised FB.Mk.5 (87), Mk.9 (255), Mk.50/J.28B (297), Mk.52 (114), NF.Mk.10 (55), Mk.54 (12), T.11 (260), T.55 (164). See also under English Electric at Preston and Samlesbury, and Fairey Aviation at Ringway, Manchester. Rest of production by D.H. at Hatfield and Bournemouth; D.H. in Sydney, Australia; and under licence in India, France, Italy and Switzerland.

311

1 Aircraft Type	2 Producer	3 Location(s)	4 Production Dates (at Locations in Col. 3)	5 Production Numbers 5A North West Locations (Col. 3)	5 Production Numbers 5B Grand Total (all UK and Worldwide)	6 Notes
De Havilland D.H.112 Venom FB.Mk.1, 4; NF.Mk.2,3, 51 (J.33); Sea Venom FAW. Mk.20, 21, 22 single and two-seat, single turbojet twin-boom fighter bomber, night and all weather naval fighter	De Havilland Aircraft Company Ltd.	Broughton/Hawarden, near Chester	1952-1958	834	1,143	Production comprised FB.Mk.1 (302), Mk.4 (73), NF.Mk.2 (139), Mk.3 (83), Mk.51/J.33 (62), FAW. Mk.20 (38), Mk.21 (99), Mk.22 (38). See also under Fairey Aviation at Ringway, Manchester. Rest of production by D.H. at Hatfield, Christchurch/Bournemouth; and under licence in France, Italy and Switzerland.
De Havilland D.H.104 Dove, Devon and Sea Devon two-crew, 8/11 passenger twin-engine light transport, executive, civil and military aircraft	De Havilland Aircraft Company Ltd. (from 1960 Hawker Siddeley Group – de Havilland Division, from 1963 Hawker Siddeley Aviation, from 1965 HSA Hatfield – Chester Division)	Broughton/Hawarden, near Chester	1951-1967	244	542	First 298 aircraft produced by de Havilland at Hatfield 1945-51.
De Havilland D.H.114 Heron, Sea Heron two-crew, 14-17 passenger four-engine light civil and military transport	De Havilland Aircraft Company Ltd. (from 1960 Hawker Siddeley Group – de Havilland Division, from 1963 Hawker Siddeley Aviation, from 1965 HSA Hatfield – Chester Division)	Broughton/Hawarden, near Chester	1953-1967	143	150	First seven aircraft built by de Havilland at Hatfield 1950-53.

1 Aircraft Type	2 Producer	3 Location(s)	4 Production Dates (at Locations in Col. 3)	5 Production Numbers 5A North West Locations (Col. 3)	5B Grand Total (all UK and Worldwide)	6 Notes
De Havilland D.H.106 Comet Mk.2, 4, 4B, 4C three-four crew, 36-101 passenger four-turbojet civil passenger airliner and military transport	De Havilland Aircraft Company Ltd. (from 1960 Hawker Siddeley Group – de Havilland Division, from 1963 Hawker Siddeley Aviation)	Broughton/Hawarden, near Chester	1957-1964	40	120	Approximately 80 Comets built by de Havilland at Hatfield. Numbers rounded to account for prototypes, unfinished aircraft, Nimrod diversions.
De Havilland Canada D.H.C.2 Beaver A.L.Mk.1 one-crew six-seven passenger single-engine light utility transport	Hawker Siddeley Group – de Havilland Division (from 1963 Hawker Siddeley Aviation, from 1965 HSA Hatfield – Chester Division)	Broughton/Hawarden, near Chester	1960-1967	46	1,692	Bulk of production by D.H.C. at Downsview, Toronto, Canada.
De Havilland D.H.110 Sea Vixen FAW. Mk.1, 2 two-seat, twin-turbojet twin-boom carrier-borne attack fighter	Hawker Siddeley Group – de Havilland Division (from 1963 Hawker Siddeley Aviation, from 1965 HSA Hatfield – Chester Division)	Broughton/Hawarden, near Chester	1962-1966	30	151	Main production by de Havilland at Christchurch near Bournemouth.

1 Aircraft Type	2 Producer	3 Location(s)	4 Production Dates (at Locations in Col. 3)	5 Production Numbers 5A North West Locations (Col. 3)	5 Production Numbers 5B Grand Total (all UK and Worldwide)	6 Notes
De Havilland D.H.125, Hawker Siddeley HS.125 Series 1-700, British Aerospace BAe 125 Series 1-700, 800, 1000 two-crew, twin-turbojet medium to long range executive, corporate and VIP business jet and military navigation trainer	Hawker Siddeley Group – de Havilland Division (from 1963 Hawker Siddeley Aviation, from 1965 HSA Hatfield – Chester Division, from 1977 British Aerospace (BAe), from 1978 BAe Aircraft Group Hatfield – Chester Division, from 1981 BAe PLC, from 1989 BAe Corporate Aircraft Division/BAe Commercial Aircraft Ltd., Airbus Division, from 1992 British Aerospace Airbus Ltd., British Aerospace Corporate Jets Ltd., from 1993 Raytheon Aircraft Company, Raytheon Corporate Jets Inc.)	Broughton/Hawarden, near Chester	1962-1996	871	873	Two prototypes built at Hatfield, all ensuing production at Broughton. Dates refer to manufacture and assembly of complete aircraft. Since 1996 well over 300 kits have been made by BAe, BAE Systems (from 1999), and Airbus UK for assembly by Raytheon in the USA as the Raytheon Hawker 800 XP (Extra Performance).
Andreasson BA-4B single-seat, single engine aerobatic light biplane	Crosby Aviation Ltd.	Knutsford, Cheshire	1960s	Not known	Not known	Small number believed to have been produced at Knutsford.
Avro 688 Tudor 1, 3, 4, 4B, 8 three/four-crew, 12-44 passenger and cargo four-engined commercial transport	A.V. Roe & Co. Ltd.	Chadderton and Ringway, Manchester; Woodford, Cheshire				
Avro 689 Tudor 2, 5, 7 44-60+ passenger transport		Chadderton, Manchester; Woodford, Cheshire	1945-1948	33	33	The Tudor 6, proposed for use over the South Atlantic by an Argentinian airline, was never built.

1 Aircraft Type	2 Producer	3 Location(s)	4 Production Dates (at Locations in Col. 3)	5 Production Numbers		6 Notes
				5A North West Locations (Col. 3)	5B Grand Total (all UK and Worldwide)	
Avro 706 Ashton Mk.1, 2, 3, 4 five-crew, four-turbojet research aircraft	A.V. Roe & Co. Ltd.	Chadderton, Manchester; Woodford, Cheshire	1950-1952	6	6	
Avro 701 Athena T.Mk.1, 2 two/three-seat single-engine trainer	A.V. Roe & Co. Ltd.	Chadderton, Manchester; Woodford, Cheshire	1948-1950	22	22	
Avro 696 Shackleton MR.1, 1A, 2, 3; AEW. 2 ten-crew, four-engine maritime reconnaissance, anti-submarine and airborne early warning aircraft	A.V. Roe & Co. Ltd.	Chadderton, Manchester; Woodford, Cheshire	1948-1958	191	191	AEW.2 aircraft were conversions of existing MR.2s. 12 were undertaken during 1970-73, one at Woodford, eleven at Bitteswell, Leics.
Avro 707 A, B, C single (A, B) and two-seat (C) single turbojet delta wing research aircraft	A.V. Roe & Co. Ltd.	Chadderton, Manchester; Woodford, Cheshire; Bracebridge Heath, Lincs	1948-1953	5	5	Comprised single 707 prototype, two 707A high speed research, one 707B low speed research, one 707C two-seat familiarisation aircraft.
Avro 698 Vulcan B.Mk.1, 1A, 2, 2A; B.Mk.2MRR; K.Mk.2 five-crew, four turbojet long range delta wing heavy bomber; later converted for maritime reconnaissance and as aerial tankers	A.V. Roe & Co. Ltd. (from 1963 Avro-Whitworth Division of Hawker Siddeley Aviation)	Chadderton, Manchester; Woodford, Cheshire	1951-1965	136	136	Six B.2s converted to K.Mk.2 tankers at Woodford, 1982.

1 Aircraft Type	2 Producer	3 Location(s)	4 Production Dates (at Locations in Col. 3)	5 Production Numbers		6 Notes
				5A North West Locations (Col. 3)	5B Grand Total (all UK and Worldwide)	
Avro 720 Single-seat, mixed powerplant (rocket and turbojet) high altitude missile-carrying interceptor fighter.	A.V. Roe & Co. Ltd.	Chadderton, Manchester	1954-1956	1	1	Single aircraft built almost to point of completion before being scrapped in defence cuts.
English Electric Canberra B.2 two-crew, twin turbojet light bomber	A.V. Roe & Co. Ltd.	Chadderton, Manchester; Woodford, Cheshire	1952-1955	75	1,376	See also under English Electric at Preston, Accrington and Samlesbury.
Avro 748, Hawker Siddeley HS. 748, British Aerospace BAe 748 Series 1, 2, 2A, 2B, F 44-62 passenger/cargo, twin turboprop feeder liner; **Avro/Hawker Siddeley 748 Andover C.Mk.1 MF, C.C.Mk.II** military freighters and transports	A.V. Roe & Co. Ltd. (from 1963 Avro-Whitworth Division of Hawker Siddeley Aviation, from 1965 HSA Manchester Division, from 1977 British Aerospace Civil Aircraft Division Manchester Unit)	Chadderton, Manchester; Woodford, Cheshire	1959-1988	380	380	Total comprises prototypes (4), Series I (18), Series 2 (101), Series 2A (102), Series 2B (35), RAF Andover C.Mk.1 military freighters (31), aircraft assembled by Hindustan Aeronautics Ltd. in India from components made by Avro (89) comprising four Series I and 85 Series 2. HSA Chester completed two 748s and converted another to an HS.748 Coastguarder during 1974-76.
British Aerospace ATP (Advanced TurboProp) 68-72 passenger twin-turboprop regional airliner	British Aerospace Civil Aircraft Division Manchester Unit, BAe Commercial Aircraft	Chadderton, Manchester; Woodford, Cheshire	1984-1994	62	62	Latterly assembly briefly transferred to BAe Prestwick as the Jetstream J61.

1 Aircraft Type	2 Producer	3 Location(s)	4 Production Dates (at Locations in Col. 3)	5A North West Locations (Col. 3)	5B Grand Total (all UK and Worldwide)	6 Notes
Hawker Siddeley HS. 146, British Aerospace BAe 146 Series 100, 200, 300, RJ 70, 85, 100, 115, Avro International RJ Avroliner, BAE Systems Avro RJX 92-128 seat, four-turbofan regional airliner	Hawker Siddeley Aviation (from 1977 British Aerospace Civil Aircraft Division Manchester Unit, BAe Commercial Aircraft; from 1993 Avro International Aerospace Division of British Aerospace Regional Aircraft/ Commercial Aircraft, from 1999 BAE Systems)	Chadderton, Manchester; Woodford, Cheshire	1988-2001	229	394	Woodford build comprised BAe 146 (56), Avro RJ (170), Avro RJX (3). Remaining 165 aircraft produced at Hatfield 1980-93.
Hawker Siddeley HS. 801 Nimrod MR.Mk.1, R.Mk.1, MR.Mk.2, British Aerospace Nimrod MR.Mk.2, AEW.Mk.3 12-crew, four turbofan land-based maritime reconnaissance patrol, anti-submarine/surface vessel aircraft	Hawker Siddeley Aviation Hatfield – Chester Division; Hawker Siddeley Aviation Manchester Division (from 1977 British Aerospace Aircraft Group Manchester Division)	Broughton/ Hawarden, near Chester; Woodford, Cheshire	1966-1986	46	46	One prototype conversion (from a Comet 4C) undertaken at Chester, another at Woodford. 41 airframe structures made at Chester 1966-70 for assembly at Woodford where total production was 46. 35 MR.1s upgraded to MR.2s at Woodford 1975-84. Seven MR.1 airframes involved in the AEW.Mk.3 project, cancelled 1986.
British Aerospace/ BAE Systems Nimrod MRA4 four turbofan maritime reconnaissance and attack aircraft	British Aerospace (from 1999 BAE Systems plc)	Woodford, Cheshire	1996-			Re-manufacture of existing Nimrod MR.Mk.2s. First three aircraft all expected to have flown by late 2005. 'Controlled production stop' on Aircraft 4-18 (see text). Programme includes BAE Systems' sites at Warton, Chadderton, Farnborough, Filton, Brough and Prestwick.

1 Aircraft Type	2 Producer	3 Location(s)	4 Production Dates (at Locations in Col. 3)	5 Production Numbers		6 Notes
				5A North West Locations (Col. 3)	5B Grand Total (all UK and Worldwide)	
De Havilland D.H.100 Vampire F.Mk.1, 2, 3, FB.Mk.5, 9; Sea Vampire F.Mk.20 single and two-seat, single turbojet twin-boom fighter, fighter bomber and naval equivalents	English Electric Co. Ltd.	Preston and Samlesbury	1944-1952	1,369	4,342	See also under de Havilland at Broughton/Chester and Fairey Aviation at Ringway, Manchester.
English Electric Canberra B.Mk.1, 2, PR.3, B.5, T.4, B.6, P.R.7, B(I)6, B(I)8 and other variants, two-three crew, twin turbojet light bomber, photo-reconnaissance, trainer and interdictor	English Electric Co. Ltd.	Preston, Accrington, Warton and Samlesbury	1949-1959 -1964	631	1,376	See also under A.V. Roe at Chadderton and Woodford who built 75. Other producers: Handley Page at Cricklewood (75), Shorts at Belfast (144), Glenn Martin as the Martin B-57 in the USA (403) and the Government Aircraft Factory in Australia (48). See text for end dates.
English Electric P.1, 1A, 1B, P.2/T.4, Lightning F.1, 1A, 2, 2A, 3, 3A, 6, 52, 53, 53K, T.5, 54, 55, 55K (BAC Lightning) single and two-seat, twin turbojet supersonic interceptor fighter, trainer and strike fighter	English Electric Co. Ltd. (from 1959 English Electric Aviation Ltd., from 1960 British Aircraft Corporation (BAC) Ltd., from 1964 BAC Ltd. Preston Division)	Preston, Accrington, Warton and Samlesbury	1953-1972	341	341	
Lancashire Prospector E.P.9 one-crew, one to five-passenger; single-engine light utility transport	Lancashire Aircraft Co. Ltd. (established by Samlesbury Engineering Ltd.)	Squires Gate, Blackpool; Samlesbury	1958-1961	28	28	Edgar Percival Aircraft Ltd. built 20 earlier versions as the E.P.9 light utility transport and crop sprayer at Stapleford, Essex, 1954-58.

1 Aircraft Type	2 Producer	3 Location(s)	4 Production Dates (at Locations in Col. 3)	5 Production Numbers		6 Notes
				5A North West Locations (Col. 3)	5B Grand Total (all UK and Worldwide)	
British Aircraft Corporation (BAC Ltd.) TSR.2 two-seat, twin turbojet nuclear and conventional tactical strike and reconnaissance aircraft	BAC Ltd. (English Electric Aviation Ltd.) (from 1964 BAC Ltd. Preston Division)	Preston, Accrington, Samlesbury and Warton	1960-1965	5	5	Joint production with BAC Ltd. (Vickers-Armstrongs (Aircraft) Ltd.) Weybridge Division. Additional airframes were at various stages of construction when project cancelled.
British Aircraft Corporation (Hunting [Percival] Aircraft) 145 Jet Provost T.Mk.5, 55 two-seat, single-turbojet trainer and strike aircraft	BAC Ltd. Preston Division (from 1971 Military Aircraft Division)	Warton	1966-1972	115	115	More than 400 P.84 Jet Provost T.Mk.1, 2, 3, 4 were produced by Hunting (Percival) Aircraft Ltd. at Luton 1954-66 before production was transferred to Warton by BAC. Total production of all marks of JP for the RAF was 509, with another 79 made for export. BAC updated 175 T.Mk.3/5 to T.Mk.3A/5A with avionics 1973-76, 93 of which as T.5As.
British Aircraft Corporation BAC 167 Strikemaster; British Aerospace BAe Strikemaster two-seat, single-turbojet strike aircraft and trainer	BAC Ltd. Preston Division (from 1971 BAC Military Aircraft Division, from 1977 British Aerospace (BAe) Warton Division)	Warton	1967-1984	156	156	Strikemaster production transferred from Warton to Hurn in 1984.
SEPECAT Jaguar GR.Mk.1, T.Mk.2; Jaguar International single and two-seat twin turbofan tactical strike aircraft and trainer	BAC Ltd. Preston Division (from 1971 BAC Military Aircraft Division, from 1977 British Aerospace (BAe) Warton Division)	Warton	1969-1984	300	628+	Total includes production by Dassault-Breguet in France (205) and HAL in India (123+). Ongoing Jaguar upgrade work at Warton.

1 Aircraft Type	2 Producer	3 Location(s)	4 Production Dates (at Locations in Col. 3)	5 Production Numbers		6 Notes
				5A North West Locations (Col. 3)	5B Grand Total (all UK and Worldwide)	
PANAVIA Tornado IDS GR. 1, 1A, 1B, 4; Tornado ADV F.Mk.2, 3 two-seat, twin turbofan multi-role swing-wing interdictor strike, reconnaissance, maritime attack, air defence fighter and operational trainer	BAC Ltd. Military Aircraft Division (from 1977 British Aerospace (BAe) Warton Division, from 1986 BAe Military Aircraft Division, from 1992 British Aerospace Defence Ltd., subsequently Military Aircraft and Aerostructures)	Warton	1973-1998	527	992	The 527 assembled at Warton comprised nine prototype and development aircraft, 398 for the RAF (228 IDS and 170 ADV) and 120 for Saudi Arabia (96 IDS and 24 ADV). The balance of 465 was assembled by MBB in Germany and Aeritalia in Italy. GR.4 versions are upgrades of 142 existing GR.1s undertaken by BAe (from 1999 BAE Systems) at Warton between 1998-2003.
British Aerospace (BAe) EAP single-seat, twin turbofan air superiority Experimental Aircraft Programme (EAP) technology demonstrator aircraft	British Aerospace (BAe) Warton Division (from 1986 BAe Military Aircraft Division)	Warton, Samlesbury	1983-1986	1	1	
British Aerospace (BAe)/ BAE Systems Hawk 100, 200 Series single and two-seat, single turbofan advanced trainer and light combat aircraft	British Aerospace Military Aircraft Division, (from 1992 British Aerospace Defence Ltd., subsequently Military Aircraft and Aerostructures, from 1999 BAE Systems)	Warton, Samlesbury	1991-	190+	736+	Totals represent all Hawk production at Kingston, Dunsfold, Brough and Warton 1972 to end of September 2003. Hawk remains in production with over 900 now delivered, ordered or selected. Manufactured post-1999 at Brough, thence transported to Warton for wing attachment and flight test.

1 Aircraft Type	2 Producer	3 Location(s)	4 Production Dates (at Locations in Col. 3)	5 Production Numbers		6 Notes
				5A North West Locations (Col. 3)	5B Grand Total (all UK and Worldwide)	
British Aerospace (BAe)/ McDonnell Douglas Harrier T.Mk.10 two-seat, single vectored-thrust turbofan, combat-capable V/STOL trainer	British Aerospace Defence Ltd., subsequently Military Aircraft and Aerostructures	Warton	1994-1995	13	831	Aircraft (13) assembled at Warton from components received from Dunsfold, Brough, Samlesbury and McDonnell Douglas in the USA. Majority of Harriers of all types built at Kingston, Dunsfold and by McDonnell Douglas. Ongoing Harrier upgrade work at Warton.
						Currently in production to meet requirements for 232 for the RAF and major sub-assemblies for 180 for Germany, 121 for Italy and 87 for Spain.
Eurofighter Typhoon single and two-seat, twin turbofan, swing-role air combat and attack fighter	British Aerospace Defence Ltd. Military Aircraft and Aerostructures (from 1999 BAE Systems)	Warton	1992-	See notes	See notes	19 aircraft completed at Warton by September 2005. Also a total of 135 were in production at different stages of completion in the four countries. The first UK Eurofighter Development Aircraft DA2 made its maiden flight in April 1994.

NB: Production dates (Col. 4) refer to years of significant production. 'Lead-in' and 'winding down' operations could well extend many of the periods shown. Production numbers (Col. 5) include prototypes and development aircraft where known. For details of ongoing production (2005) see notes and main text.

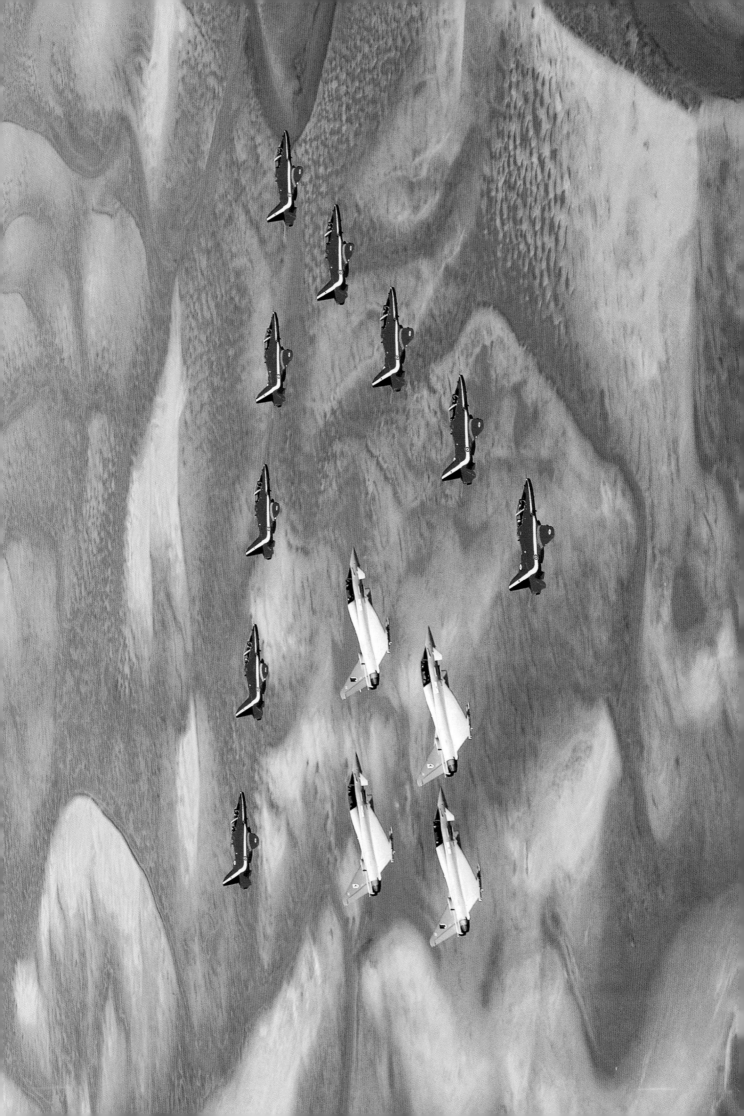

Appendix 3
What became of...?

Brief histories of the twenty-seven airframe manufacturers and eight aero-engine companies that comprised the British aircraft industry in 1945, the majority of which being referred to in the main text.

AIRSPEED LTD.

Formed in 1931, re-established as Airspeed (1934) Ltd. at Portsmouth. Taken over by de Havilland in 1940, becoming the Airspeed Division of de Havilland in 1951.

SIR W.G. ARMSTRONG WHITWORTH AIRCRAFT LTD.

Originated as the Aircraft Department of the heavy engineering and armaments firm Sir W.G. Armstrong Whitworth & Co. Ltd. in 1914, to be established under the above name at Coventry in 1919. Together with Armstrong Siddeley Motors it came to be controlled by John Siddeley under the Armstrong Siddeley Development Company. A founder member of the Hawker Siddeley Aircraft Company Ltd. (a holding company) from 1935 which from 1948 became the Hawker Siddeley Group of companies. From 1961 it was the Whitworth Gloster Division, combined in 1963 as the Avro Whitworth Division, of Hawker Siddeley (Hawker Siddeley Aviation).

AUSTER AIRCRAFT LTD.

The Taylorcraft Aircraft Corporation of the USA established Taylorcraft Aeroplanes (England) Ltd. in Leicester in 1939. This became Auster in 1946. Acquired in 1961 by British Executive & General Aircraft Ltd. (BEAGLE – est. 1960) becoming Beagle-Auster Aircraft Ltd., from 1962 known as Beagle Aircraft Ltd. Closed 1970.

A.V. ROE & CO. LTD.

See main text. Briefly, established in Manchester in 1910. Acquired by John Siddeley of the Armstrong Siddeley Development Company in 1928. A founder member of Hawker Siddeley in 1935. Part of the Avro Whitworth Division of Hawker Siddeley Aviation (HSA) from 1963, fully absorbed into HSA in 1965. The Avro name was revived briefly by the Avro International Aerospace Division of British Aerospace (BAe) in 1993. [BAe was created in 1977 by the nationalisation of the British aircraft industry then comprising Hawker Siddeley Aviation, Hawker Siddeley Dynamics, British Aircraft Corporation and Scottish Aviation].

BLACKBURN AIRCRAFT LIMITED

Founded in 1911 at Leeds by Robert Blackburn. From WWI was also located at Brough. Merged in 1949 with General Aircraft Ltd. of Croydon (est. 1931), forming Blackburn & General Aircraft Ltd. Taken over by the Hawker Siddeley Group in 1960, becoming the Hawker Blackburn Division of Hawker Siddeley Aviation from 1963, fully absorbed into HSA in 1965.

BOULTON PAUL AIRCRAFT LTD.

Established in 1915 as the Aircraft Department of Boulton & Paul Ltd. of Norwich. Renamed Boulton Paul Aircraft Ltd. in 1934. Ceased aircraft production in 1954. Part of the Dowty Group from 1961.

BRISTOL AEROPLANE CO. LTD.

Established in 1910 as the British & Colonial Aeroplane Co. Ltd., becoming the Bristol Aeroplane Co. Ltd. in 1920. Aero-engine and armaments divisions became progressively more independent in the 1940s and 1950s. The Bristol Aeroplane Co. became part of the British Aircraft Corporation (BAC) from 1960 when Bristol's helicopter activities were acquired by Westland. Bristol became the BAC Filton Division in 1963.

CIERVA AUTOGIRO CO. LTD.

Founded in 1926. Taken over by Saunders-Roe Ltd. in 1951 to become part of their Helicopter Division.

CUNLIFFE-OWEN AIRCRAFT LTD.

Established in 1938 in Southampton. The company abandoned the aircraft business in 1948.

DE HAVILLAND AIRCRAFT CO. LTD.

Origins lay in the Aircraft Manufacturing Co. Ltd. (AIRCO) established at Hendon in 1912, where Geoffrey de Havilland was Chief Designer from 1914. AIRCO was liquidated in 1920 and the same year G. de H. established the de Havilland Aircraft Co. at Stag Lane, Edgware. Absorbed into the Hawker Siddeley Group in 1960.

ENGLISH ELECTRIC CO. LTD.

See main text. Briefly, established in 1918 by Dick, Kerr of Preston, Phoenix Dynamo of Bradford and Coventry Ordnance Works. English Electric Aviation Ltd., formed in 1959, became part of the British Aircraft Corporation (BAC) Ltd. in 1960. Fully absorbed into BAC by 1964.

FAIREY AVIATION CO. LTD.

Established in 1915 at Hayes, Middlesex. Taken over by Westland Aircraft Ltd. in 1960.

FOLLAND AIRCRAFT LTD.

Established in 1935 as British Marine Aircraft Ltd. at Hamble, Southampton. Renamed Folland Aircraft Ltd. in 1937. Taken over by the Hawker Siddeley Group in 1960, becoming the Hamble Division of Hawker Siddeley Aviation in 1963.

GENERAL AIRCRAFT LTD.

See under Blackburn Aircraft Ltd.

GLOSTER AIRCRAFT CO. LTD.

Established in 1917 at Cheltenham as the Gloucestershire Aircraft Co. Ltd., renamed Gloster in 1926. Acquired by Hawker in 1934, becoming part of Hawker Siddeley in 1935. Whitworth Gloster Division of the Hawker Siddeley Group from 1961, part of Hawker Siddeley Aviation from 1963, fully absorbed within HSA in 1965.

HANDLEY PAGE LTD.

Established in 1909 at Cricklewood. Remained independent, liquidated in 1970.

HAWKER AIRCRAFT LTD.

Originated as the Sopwith Aviation Co. established at Kingston-upon-Thames in 1912. Renamed Sopwith Aviation & Engineering Co. Ltd. in 1919, liquidated in 1920. Succeeded by H.G. Hawker Engineering Co. Ltd. in 1921, becoming Hawker Aircraft Ltd. in 1933. Hawker acquired Gloster Aircraft Ltd. in 1934. A holding company, the Hawker Siddeley

Aircraft Company Ltd. was formed in 1935, amalgamating Hawker with the Armstrong Siddeley Development Company which itself controlled Sir W.G. Armstrong Whitworth Aircraft, Armstrong Siddeley Motors, Air Service Training and A.V. Roe. The Hawker Siddeley Aircraft Company Ltd. became the Hawker Siddeley Group in 1948. Reorganised in 1963 as Hawker Siddeley Aviation Ltd. and Hawker Siddeley Dynamics Holdings Ltd. Hawker Siddeley Aviation Ltd. comprised the Avro Whitworth (incorporating the former Whitworth Gloster), Hawker Blackburn, Hamble and de Havilland Aircraft Divisions.

MARTIN-BAKER AIRCRAFT CO. LTD.

Established in 1934, moved to Heston. Ceased aircraft production after WW2 to concentrate on the manufacture of aircraft ejector seats.

MILES AIRCRAFT LTD.

Established in 1943 at Reading. Liquidated in 1947 with its aircraft interests taken over by Handley Page (Reading) Ltd. F.G. Miles Ltd. formed at Redhill in 1951, acquired in 1961 by British Executive and General Aviation Ltd. (BEAGLE – est. 1960), becoming Beagle-Miles Aircraft Ltd. Beagle Aircraft Ltd. from 1962. Closed 1970.

PERCIVAL AIRCRAFT LTD.

Established in 1932 in Kent, renamed as above at Luton in 1936. Part of the Hunting Group from 1944, renamed Hunting Percival Aircraft Ltd. in 1946 and Hunting Aircraft Ltd. in 1957. Part of BAC from 1960.

PORTSMOUTH AVIATION LTD.

Established in 1932 operating air services to the Isle of Wight, overhauling and building aircraft until closure in 1949.

SAUNDERS-ROE LTD.

See main text. Established in 1928 at Cowes, Isle of Wight. Acquired the Cierva Autogiro Co. Ltd. in 1951. Became part of Westland Aircraft Ltd. in 1960.

SCOTTISH AVIATION LTD.

Established in 1935 at Prestwick. Nationalised and became part of British Aerospace (BAe) in 1977.

SHORT BROTHERS LTD.

Established at Battersea in 1908. Later became Short Brothers (Rochester and Bedford) Ltd. A new factory established at Belfast in 1936, linked with the Harland & Wolff shipyard, resulted in the formation of Short & Harland Ltd. In 1943 the British Government took control, merging Short Brothers (Rochester and Bedford) Ltd. with Short & Harland Ltd., the result in 1947 being Short Brothers & Harland Limited. The name reverted to Short Brothers Ltd. in 1977, becoming Short Brothers Plc in 1984 and subsequently Shorts. The firm was sold by the British Government to Bombardier Inc. of Canada in 1989.

VICKERS-ARMSTRONGS (WEYBRIDGE)

See main text. Originated with the Vickers family of steel makers in Sheffield in the early part of the nineteenth century, later including armaments and shipbuilding activities elsewhere. Vickers & Co. became Vickers Sons & Co. in 1867 and, in 1897, as a new company Vickers Sons & Maxim Ltd. formed by amalgamation with the Maxim Nordenfeldt Guns & Ammunition Co. Ltd. of Erith, Kent, took over the Barrow-in-Furness Shipyard of the Naval Construction & Armaments Co. Ltd. In 1911 the company became Vickers Ltd. and established an Aviation Department at Erith and, in 1912, facilities at Brooklands. In 1928 Vickers' heavy engineering activities merged with those of Sir W.G. Armstrong Whitworth & Co. of Newcastle to form

Vickers-Armstrongs Ltd. However, Sir. W.G. Armstrong Whitworth Aircraft Ltd. remained outside the merger to become, via the Armstrong Siddeley Development Company, a founding member of Hawker Siddeley. Also in 1928 Vickers took over the Supermarine Aviation Works at Southampton [see under Vickers - Armstrongs (Supermarine)], which became Vickers (Aviation) Ltd. Supermarine Works. In 1938 Vickers-Armstrongs Ltd. assumed full responsibility for both Vickers (Aviation) Ltd. at Weybridge and the then Supermarine Aviation Works (Vickers) Ltd., the latter becoming Vickers-Armstrongs Ltd. (Supermarine Division). Vickers-Armstrongs (Aircraft) Ltd. was formed in 1954, uniting all Weybridge and Supermarine aircraft work. This was merged with Bristol Aircraft Ltd., English Electric Aviation Ltd. and Hunting Aircraft Ltd. in 1960 to form the British Aircraft Corporation (BAC).

VICKERS-ARMSTRONGS (SUPERMARINE)

Supermarine originated as Pemberton-Billing Ltd. at Southampton in 1913, renamed the Supermarine Aviation Works Ltd. in 1916. See Vickers-Armstrongs (Weybridge) above.

WESTLAND AIRCRAFT LTD.

Established by engineers Petters Ltd. as the Westland Aircraft Works at Yeovil in 1915, becoming Westland Aircraft Ltd. in 1935. Acquired the helicopter interests of Saunders-Roe, Bristol and Fairey in 1959-60. Became Westland Helicopters Ltd. from 1966, later GKN Westland Ltd. and now AgustaWestland.

1960 AND SUBSEQUENT RATIONALISATION

BRITISH AIRCRAFT CORPORATION (BAC) LTD.

Created in 1960 by the merging of English Electric Aviation Ltd., Bristol Aircraft Ltd., Vickers-Armstrongs (Aircraft) Ltd. and Hunting Aircraft Ltd. BAC was nationalised in 1977 to become British Aerospace (BAe).

HAWKER SIDDELEY

The Hawker Siddeley Group dated from 1935 as the Hawker Siddeley Aircraft Company Ltd., a holding company and loose association of Hawker Aircraft, Gloster Aircraft, Sir W.G. Armstrong Whitworth Aircraft, Armstrong Siddeley Motors, Air Service Training and A.V. Roe. Joined in 1959-60 by Blackburn, de Havilland and Folland, the HS Group reorganised into Hawker Siddeley Aviation Ltd. and Hawker Siddeley Dynamics Holdings Ltd. In 1977 both were merged with the nationalised British Aircraft Corporation and Scottish Aviation to become British Aerospace (BAe). See also under Hawker Aircraft Ltd.

BRITISH AEROSPACE (BAe)

Created in 1977 by the nationalisation of the UK aircraft industry by the enforced merging of the British Aircraft Corporation, Hawker Siddeley Aviation, Hawker Siddeley Dynamics Holdings and Scottish Aviation. Individual company identities were retained initially but later became operating divisions and business units of BAe. This became British Aerospace plc in 1981, with H.M. Government retaining a 48.4 per cent share. BAe was fully privatised in 1985. BAe amalgamated with Marconi Electronic Systems in November 1999 to form BAe Systems.

BAE SYSTEMS

Formed in November 1999 by the amalgamation of British Aerospace (BAe) with Marconi Electronic Systems. See also under British Aerospace (BAe).

POST-WAR AERO-ENGINE MANUFACTURERS

ALVIS LTD.

Ceased to be involved with aero-engines in the late 1950s.

ARMSTRONG SIDDELEY MOTORS LTD.

Acquired Metropolitan-Vickers in 1949, merged with Bristol Aero-Engines in 1958 to form Bristol Siddeley Engines Ltd., taken over by Rolls-Royce Ltd. in 1966.

BLACKBURN AIRCRAFT LTD. (CIRRUS)

In 1940 Blackburn took over the Cirrus Hermes Engineering Co. Ltd. who had moved from Croydon to Brough in 1934, forming Blackburn Engines. Absorbed by Bristol Siddeley in 1961.

BRISTOL AEROPLANE CO. LTD.

Bristol Aero-Engines Ltd., formed in 1955 from the long-established Bristol Engine Department which itself resulted from the acquisition of the Cosmos Engineering Co. in 1920, merged with Armstrong Siddeley Motors in 1958 to form Bristol Siddeley Engines Ltd. This was taken over by Rolls-Royce Ltd. in 1966.

DE HAVILLAND ENGINE CO. LTD.

Became part of Bristol Siddeley Engines in 1961.

METROPOLITAN-VICKERS ELECTRICAL CO. LTD.

Acquired by Armstrong Siddeley Motors in 1949.

D. NAPIER & SON LTD.

Joined Rolls-Royce in 1961.

ROLLS-ROYCE LTD.

Acquired Bristol Siddeley Engines in 1966 to become the sole British aero-engine manufacturer. Liquidated in 1971 in the aftermath of development costs of the RB.211, later to become an outstanding success. Re-formed as Rolls-Royce (1971) Ltd., later reverting to the name Rolls-Royce Ltd.

Appendix 4
Overview of the restructuring of the British Aircraft Industry

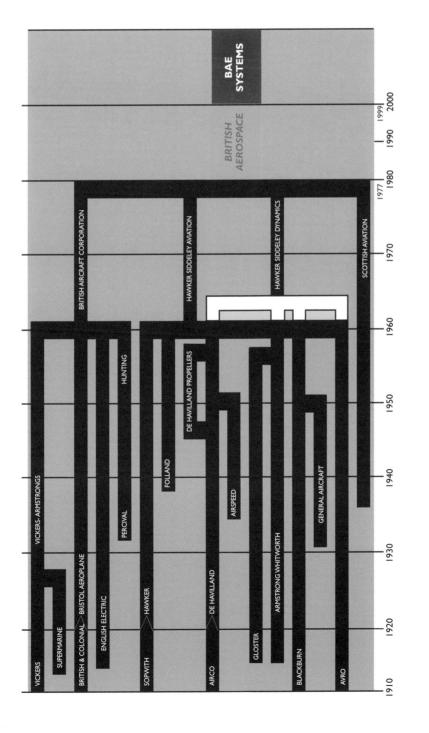

Source: British Aerospace (BAe)(1977), updated to show BAE Systems following amalgamation of BAe and Marconi Electronic Systems in 1999

331

Appendix 5
Abbreviations

I. AIRCRAFT TYPES, AIR SYSTEMS AND TECHNOLOGY

AAM	Air-to-Air Missile
ACA	Agile Combat Aircraft
ACT	Active Control Technology
ADF	Automatic Direction Finding
ADV	Air Defence Variant
AEW	Airborne Early Warning
AFVG	Anglo-French Variable Geometry
AI	Airborne Interception
AJT	Advanced Jet Trainer
ALARM	Air Launched Anti-Radiation (Radar) Missile
AMRAAM	Advanced Medium Range Air- to-Air Missile
AO	Auxiliary Oiler
ARA	Atmospheric Research Aircraft
AS	Anti-Submarine
ASR	Air-Sea Rescue
ASRAAM	Advanced Short Range Air-to-Air Missile
AST	Air Staff Target
ASUW	Anti-Surface Unit Warfare
ASV	Air to Surface Vessel
ASW	Anti-Submarine Warfare
ATP	Advanced TurboProp
AWACS	Airborne Warning and Control System
B	Bomber
C	Cargo/passenger freighter
CAD	Computer Aided Design
CAM	Computer Aided Manufacturing
CATIA	Computer Aided Three Dimensional Interactive Application
CFC	Carbon Fibre Composite
CTOL	Conventional Take-Off and Landing
DLF	Direct Line Feed
DVI	Direct Voice Input
E	Experimental
EAP	Experimental Aircraft Programme
ECA	European Combat Aircraft
ECAT	École de Combat et d'Appui Tactique
ECF	European Combat Fighter
ECM	Electronic Counter Measures
EFA	European Fighter Aircraft
F	Fighter
F(AW)	Fighter (All Weather)
FADEC	Full Authority Digital Engine Control
FB	Fighter Bomber
FBW	Fly-by-Wire
FOAS	Future Offensive Air System
GIG	Global Information Grid
GOR	General Operational Requirement
GR	General Reconnaissance/Ground Attack
HE	High Explosive
HMA	His Majesty's Airship
HMSS	Helmet Mounted Symbology System
HP	Horsepower
HUD	Head-Up Display
ICBM	Intercontinental Ballistic Missile
ICY	Interchangeability
IDS	Interdictor Strike
ILFPS	Integrated Lift-Fan Propulsion System
IPA	Instrumented Production Aircraft
IRAN	Inspect, Repair As Necessary
JCA	Joint Combat Aircraft
JIT	Just In Time
JSF	Joint Strike Fighter
LIF	Lead-In Fighter
LPD(A)	Landing Platform Dock (Auxiliary)
LRU	Line Replacement Unit
LVER	Low Voltage Electromagnetic Riveting
MAD	Magnetic Anomaly Detector
MF	Military Freighter
MR	Maritime Reconnaissance
MRA	Maritime Reconnaissance and Attack
MRCA	Multi-Role Combat Aircraft
MRR	Maritime Radar Reconnaissance
NAVWASS	Navigation and Weapons Aiming Sub-System
NCW	Network Centric Warfare
NEC	Network-Enabled Capability
NF	Night Fighter
ORP	Operational Readiness Platform
P	Prototype/Project
PR	Photographic Reconnaissance
PTFE	Polytetrafluoroethylene
QRA	Quick Reaction Alert
R	Radar
R&D	Research and Development
RJ	Regional Jet
RPM	Revolutions per minute
S	Strike
SAM	Surface-to-Air Missile
SAR	Search and Rescue
SDD	System Development and Demonstration
SS	Sea Scout/Submarine/Sea Searcher
SST	Supersonic Transport
ST	Static Thrust
STA	Small Tactical Aircraft
STOL	Short Take-Off and Landing
STOVL	Short Take-Off Vertical Landing
T	Trainer
TIALD	Thermal Imaging Airborne Laser Designator
TSR	Torpedo, Spotter and Reconnaissance
TSR	Tactical Strike and Reconnaissance
UAV	Unmanned Air Vehicle
UCAV	Unmanned Combat Air Vehicle
UFO	Unidentified Flying Object
VG	Variable Geometry
VIFF	Vectoring In Forward Flight
V/STOL	Vertical/Short Take-Off and Landing
VTOL	Vertical Take-Off and Landing
WT	Wireless/Radio Telegraphy/Telephony

2. ORGANISATIONS AND INFRASTRUCTURE

A&AEE	Aircraft and Armament Experimental Establishment
AAP	Aircraft Acceptance Park
AAU	Aircraft Assembly Unit
AEI	Associated Electrical Industries
A&E(M)	Aero & Engineering (Merseyside) Ltd.
AFEE	Airborne Forces Experimental Establishment
AIA	Avro International Aerospace
AIC	Aerospace Innovation Centre
AIC	Airbus Integrated Company
AI(R)	Aero International (Regional)
AIRCO	Aircraft Manufacturing Co. Ltd.
AIRDISCO	Aircraft Disposal Company
ATA	Air Transport Auxiliary
AV-MF	Aviatsiya Voenno-morskovo Flota (USSR Naval Air Service)
BAC	British Aircraft Corporation
BAD	Base Air Depot
BADA	Base Air Depot Area
BAe	British Aerospace
BAE NWHG	BAE Systems North West Heritage Group
BEA	British European Airways
BEAGLE	British Executive & General Aircraft Ltd.
BOAC	British Overseas Airways Corporation
BSAA	British South American Airways
CENTO	Central Treaty Organisation
DHC	De Havilland Canada
DTI	Department of Trade and Industry
EADS	European Aeronautics Defence and Space Company
EE Co.	English Electric Company
EMI	Electrical and Musical Industries
FAA	Fleet Air Arm
FAM	Facility for Airborne Measurements
FTS	Flying Training School
GEC	General Electric Co.
HCU	Heavy Conversion Unit
HSA	Hawker Siddeley Aviation
HSD	Hawker Siddeley Dynamics
IAF	Indian Air Force
ISTAR	Intelligence, Surveillance, Target Acquisition and Reconnaissance
LCC	Lancashire County Council
LCDL	Lancashire County Developments Ltd.
MAEE	Marine Aircraft Experimental Establishment
MAP	Ministry of Aircraft Production
MBB	Messerschmitt-Bolköw-Blohm
MoD	Ministry of Defence
MoS	Ministry of Supply
MSIM	Museum of Science and Industry in Manchester
NAF	National Aircraft Factory
NAMMO/A	NATO MRCA Management Organisation/Agency
NATO	North Atlantic Treaty Organisation
NERC	National Environmental Research Council
NETMA	NATO Eurofighter and Tornado Management Agency
NFTC	NATO Flying Training School in Canada
NWAA	Northwest Aerospace Alliance
NWDA	Northwest Development Agency
OCU	Operational Conversion Unit
OEM	Original Equipment Manufacturer
OEU	Operational Evaluation Unit
OTU	Operational Training Unit
PFF	Pathfinder Force
PRU	Photographic Reconnaissance Unit
QUANTAS	Queensland and Northern Territory Aerial Services
RAE	Royal Aircraft Establishment
RAeS	Royal Aeronautical Society
RAAF	Royal Australian Air Force
R Aux. AF	Royal Auxiliary Air Force
RAF	Royal Air Force
RAF MU	Royal Air Force Maintenance Unit
RAFVR	Royal Air Force Volunteer Reserve
RCAF	Royal Canadian Air Force
RFC	Royal Flying Corps
RNAS	Royal Naval Air Service/Station
RNVR	Royal Navy Volunteer Reserve
R-R	Rolls-Royce
R-RHT	Rolls-Royce Heritage Trust
RSAF	Royal Saudi Air Force
SAAF	South African Air Force
SACEUR	Supreme Allied Command Europe
SACLANT	Supreme Allied Command Atlantic
SBAC	Society of British Aerospace Companies – formerly Society of British Aircraft Constructors
SEPECAT	Societé Européanne Production de L'Avion ECAT
TCA	Trans-Canada Air Lines
TTTE	Tri-National Tornado Training Establishment
USAAF	United States Army Air Force
USAF	United States Air Force
USMC	United States Marine Corps
VSEL	Vickers Shipbuilding and Engineering Ltd.

Bibliography

The following is but a selection from a large number of aviation publications that have come to the author's attention. It is by no means exhaustive and is offered merely as a guide for those seeking further information or wishing to view more photographs.

The World of Wings and Things — Sir Alliott Verdon-Roe
Hurst & Blackett 1939

War Diary of The English Electric Company Ltd.
March 1938-August 1945

The Aircraft of the World — William Green & Gerald Pollinger
Macdonald 1955

The Air Forces of the World — William Green & John Fricker
Macdonald 1958

Famous Fighters of the Second World War — William Green-Macdonald 1957

Famous Bombers of the Second World War — William Green-Macdonald 1959

British Naval Aircraft Since 1912 — Owen Thetford-Putnam 1958 et seq.

Aviation - An Historical Survey from its origins to the end of World War II — Charles H. Gibbs-Smith
Science Museum – HMSO 1970

Guinness Book of Aircraft Facts and Feats — Michael Taylor & David Mondey
Guinness 1970 et seq.

Civil Aircraft of the World — John W.R. Taylor & Gordon Swanborough
Ian Allan 1974

Military Aircraft of the World — John W.R. Taylor & Gordon Swanborough
Ian Allan 1975

Fairey Aircraft Since 1915 — H.A. Taylor
Putnam 1974 et seq.

Handley Page Aircraft Since 1907 — C.H. Barnes
Putnam 1976 et seq.

Sunderland at War — Chaz Bowyer
Ian Allan 1976

Aviation in Manchester –
A Short History — Brian R. Robinson
Royal Aeronautical Society (Manchester Branch) 1977

British Aircraft Corporation –
A History — Charles Gardner
Batsford 1981

Pioneering Years 1918-1961 — C.E. Fielding
British Aerospace Plc (Manchester Division) 1982

In the Shadow of the Eagle's Wing –
A History of Aviation in the Cumbria,
Dumfries and Galloway Region
Part 1 1825-1914
Part 2 1915-1930 — Peter Connon
St. Patrick's Press 1982-84

All our Working Lives — Peter Pagnamenta & Richard Overy
BBC 1984

V-Bombers — Robert Jackson
Ian Allan 1981

Avro Vulcan — Andrew Brookes
Ian Allan 1985

Dizzy Heights – The Story of
Lancashire's First Flying Men — Chris Aspin
Helmshore Local History Society 1988

English Electric Aircraft and
their Predecessors — Stephen Ransom & Robert Fairclough
Putnam 1987 et seq.

De Havilland Aircraft Since 1909 — A.J. Jackson
Putnam 1987 et seq.

Avro Aircraft Since 1908 — A.J. Jackson
Putnam 1965-90 et seq.

British Aerospace – A Proud Heritage — Geoff Green 1988

Royal Air Force Burtonwood – Fifty Years in Photographs — Aldon P. Ferguson, Airfield Publications 1989

An Illustrated History of the RAF — Roy Conyers Nesbit, Colour Library Books 1991

TSR.2: Phoenix, or Folly? — Frank Barnett-Jones, GMS Enterprises

Avro – The Story of Manchester's Aircraft Company — Harry Holmes, Neil Richardson 1993

Avro – The History of an Aircraft Company — Harry Holmes, Airlife 1994

The Last Flying Boat – Sunderland ML814 Islander — Peter Smith, Ensign Publications 1993

The Vulcan Story — Tim Laming, Cassell 1993 et seq.

The Lancaster Story — Peter Jacobs, Cassell 1996 et seq.

The Shackleton – Avro's Maritime Heavyweight — Chris Ashworth, Aston Publications 1990

Avro Manchester – The Legend behind the Lancaster — Robert Kirby, Midland Publishing 1995

British Aircraft Manufacturers Since 1908 — Gunter Endres, Ian Allan 1995

Battlebags – British Airships of the First World War — Ces Mowthorpe, Wrens Park/Alan Sutton Publishing 1995

Classic World War II Aircraft Cutaways — Bill Gunston, Osprey (with Aeroplane Monthly/Flight International) 1995-97

Flying to the Limit — Roland P. Beamont, Patrick Stephens 1996

Avro Test Pilots since 1907 — Peter V. Clegg, GMS Enterprises 1997

Berlin Airlift — Arthur Pearcy, Airlife 1997

Proud Heritage – A Pictoral History of British Aerospace Aircraft — Phil Coulson, Royal Air Force Benevolent Fund Enterprises 1995

The World's Greatest Air Depot – The US 8th Air Force at Warton 1942-1945 — Harry Holmes, Airlife 1998

Tales of the Cheshire Planes — John McDaniel, GMS Enterprises 1998

Hawker Hunter — Barry Jones, Crowood Press 1998

English Electric Canberra and Martin B-57 — Barry Jones, Crowood Press 1999

Panavia Tornado — Andy Evans, Crowood Press 1999

Milestones of Flight — Michael J.H. Taylor, Chancellor Press 1999

Fairey Aircraft — Ray Sturtivant, Alan Sutton Publishing 1995

Avro Aircraft — Roger Jackson, Alan Sutton Publishing 1995

Shorts Aircraft — Mike Hooks, Chalford Publishing 1995

Hawker Aircraft — Derek N. James, Chalford Publishing 1996

Bristol Aeroplane Company — Derek N. James, Chalford Publishing 1996

Avro	Harry Holmes	Chalford Publishing 1996
Supermarine	Norman Barfield	Chalford Publishing 1996
De Havilland Aircraft Company	Maurice F. Allward & John W.R. Taylor	Tempus Publishing 1996
Vickers Aircraft	Norman Barfield	Chalford Publishing 1997
English Electric	Derek N. James	Tempus Publishing 1999
The English Electric Lightning	Martin W. Bowman	Tempus Publishing 1999
Handley Page	Alan Dowsett	Tempus Publishing 1999
Avro Anson	Harry Holmes	Tempus Publishing 2000
Britten Norman	George Marsh	Tempus Publishing 2000
Warton in Wartime	Harry Holmes	Tempus Publishing 2001
Broughton – From Wellington to Airbus	Norman Barfield	Tempus Publishing 2001
Manchester Airport – Ringway Remembered	Barry Abraham & Les Jones	Tempus Publishing 2001
BAe/McDonnell Douglas Harrier	Stewart Wilson	Airlife 2000
The Magic of a Name – The Rolls-Royce Story	Peter Pugh	Icon Books 2000-4
The Bluebird Years – Donald Campbell and The Pursuit of Speed	Arthur Knowles with Graham Beech	Sigma 2001
Airlife's World Aircraft	Rod Simpson	Airlife 2001
The Years Flew Past	Roland P. Beamont	Airlife 2001
The Encyclopedia of World Aircraft	Paul Eden & Soph Moeng	Silverdale 2002
Lancashire Airfields in the Second World War	Aldon P. Ferguson	Countryside Books 2004
British Aerospace plc/BAE Systems plc – Annual Reports The Facts	BAe/BAE Systems 1998-2004	
Rolls-Royce Heritage Trust Archive Journals and Newsletters	RRHT	
BAE Systems North West Heritage Group	BAE NWHG	
Aerospace Heritage magazines		
Aeroplane Monthly	www.aeroplanemonthly.com	
Flight International		
Rapide	The Magazine for the North West Vintage Aviation Enthusiast (Editor/Publisher: Michael Lewis)	
RAF Souvenir Yearbooks 1967 et seq.		

Index

Photographs are shown in *italics*

A.V. Roe & Company Ltd. 325
 Manchester and Brooklands 9-11, 14-17
 Manchester and Hamble 28-32
 Manchester, Hamble and Woodford 50-65
 Newton Heath, Chadderton, Woodford,
  Ringway and Yeadon 78-93
 part of Hawker Siddeley Group,
  Chadderton and Woodford 150,
  169, 173-185
Accrington 72, 206, 209, 223
Adams, H. Stanley 21, 22
Agile Combat Aircraft (ACA) 263
Aintree, Liverpool
 National Aircraft Factory (NAF) No.3 35-6,
  43
Airbus 140-50
 A300/310 142, 144
 A300B 141
 A300-600 ST Super Transporter 'Beluga'
  144, *145*
 A318/319 142, 144
 A320/321 141-2, 144
 A330 142, *142-3*, 144
 A340-500/600 142, 144
 A380 Superjumbo 144-150, *147-9*
 sites in Europe 147-8
Airbus UK Ltd.
 Broughton (Hawarden), near Chester 140-
  50
airships 13, *17, 25, 27,* 18-28, 33, 37, 41, 44,
  103, 291-2, 295
Airspeed Ltd. 325
Alcock, John William (later Sir) 10
Alexandra Park 37, 50, 53, 54
 Aerodrome 37, *50*
Alliance Aeroplane Company Ltd. 36
Alvis Ltd., aero-engine manufacturers 329
Andover C.Mk.I *182*, 183
Anson see Avro Anson Mk.I, Avro Anson
  T.Mk18
Armstrong Siddeley Development Co. 57, 328
Armstrong Siddeley Motors Ltd., aero-engine
  manufacturers 329
ATP (British Aerospace Advanced TurboProp)
  185-6, *185*, 316
Auster Aircraft Ltd. 325
Australia 52, 56, 59, 89
Australian Government Aircraft Factory, Jindivik
  Mk.102B 124, 232, 309
Avro '12' car 51-2
Avro aircraft
 Avro 500 16, 17, 293
 Avro 501/502/503 17, 293
 Avro 504 17, 28-31, *30,* 50-51, *50, 51,* 293
 Avro 504K *30, 50, 51, 168-9*
 Avro 504N (Avro Lynx) 54-5
 Avro 504R 'Gosport' 55
 Avro 508/510/511 17, 294
 Avro 519/521/522 294
 Avro 523 Pike 32, 294
 Avro 528 Silver King 294
 Avro 529 32, 294
 Avro 530 294
 Avro 531 295
 Avro 533 Manchester 32, 80, 295
 Avro 534 Baby *52, 52,* 298
 Avro 536 52-3, 298
 Avro 538 Spider 295
 Avro 539 racing floatplane 53, 298
 Avro 545 54

Avro 547 commercial triplane 53, 298
Avro 548 passenger biplane 53, 54, 298
Avro 549 Aldershot 53, 298
Avro 552 54, 299
Avro 555 Bison 53, 53-4, 299
Avro 557 Ava 55, 299
Avro 561 Andover 55, 299
Avro 566 Avenger 55, 299
Avro 581 Avian 56-7, *56-7,* 300
Avro 584 Avocet 57, 300
Avro 586 Autogiro 55, 300
Avro 604 Antelope 57, 300
Avro 618 Tens *58-9, 59,* 300
Avro 619/624s 59, 300, *301*
Avro 621 Tutor 61-2, 301
Avro 624 Six *60,* 301
Avro 626 *61,* 62, 301
Avro 627 mail plane 62, 301
Avro 631/643 Cadet 62, 301
Avro 637 Prefect 62, 301
Avro 638/639/640 Club Cadet/
  Cabin Cadet/Cadet three seater 62,
  301
Avro 641 Commodore 62, 302
Avro 642/2m and 4m 59, *59, 61,* 301
Avro 671 Rota I Autogiro 56, 63, *64,* 78, 302
Avro 674 64, 302
Avro 685 York 90-2, *91,* 306
Avro 691 Lancastrian 89-90, *89,* 306
Avro 696 Shackleton 160-2, *160, 161, 169,*
  315
Avro 698 Vulcan 163, 164, *165, 166, 166,*
  167-9, 169, *170-2,* 173-9, *174, 175-8,*
  180, 181, 315
Avro 706 Ashton 157-9, *157-8,* 315
Avro 707 163-5, *164-5,* 315
Avro 720 179-81, *180,* 316
Avro 730 181
Avro 748/BAe 748 181, *182-4,* 183-5, 316
Avro Anson Mk.I 63, 78-9, *79,* 302
Avro Anson T.Mk18/20/21 150, *151-2,* 156
Avro Atlantic 181
Avro Avian IVM 58, 61, 300
Avro C.6A/B Autogiro 55-6, 300
Avro Curtiss-type 21, 292
Avro K2 tanker 179, *180, 181*
Avro Lancaster 82, *83-5,* 84-9, 92, 105,
  305, 306
Avro Lincoln 92-3, *92,* 105, *203,* 306, 307
Avro Manchester 80-2, *81,* 305
Avro RJ *186-8,* 188-90, 317
Avro T.Mk.I Athena 159, *159,* 315
Avro Tudor 152-7, *153-5,* 157, 314
Avro Type 652 62, 302
Avro Type 688 152
Avro Type D 14, 292
Avro Type E 14-16, *15-16,* 292,
Avro Type F 16, 293
Avro Type G 16, 293
Avro-Curtiss 21, 292
Avro International Aerospace, British Aerospace
  Regional Aircraft Ltd 188
Avro Transport Company 50-1, 61
Avro-Whitworth Division of Hawker Siddeley
  Aviation 173

B.E.2 32, 295
BAC 145 Jet Provost 230, 232, *244,* 319
BAC 167 Strikemaster *231-233,* 233, *244, 246,*
  319
BAe 146 186, 188, 189, *189,* 317
 see also HS. 146
BAe 748 (Avro 748) 181, *182-4,* 183-5, 316
BAE Systems North West Heritage Group
  18, 286
BAE Systems 329, 331
 BAE Systems, Airbus UK, Broughton
  (Hawarden), near Chester 140-50
 BAE Systems Hawk 249, 253-6, *254-261,*
  266, 320
 BAE Systems, Chadderton and Woodford
  150, 199
 BAE Systems, Preston, Samlesbury and
  Warton
  Eurofighter Typhoon 271, *270-8,* 279-80,
   280-3, 290, 321, *322*
  JSF 280, *283,* 284
balloonists 1-2
Barlow, Major Thomas 66
Barnoldswick 72, 88, 99
Barnwell, Frank 35
Barrow-in-Furness 14, 17-20, *19,* 23-28, *25, 27,*
  44, 86, *260,* 285
Barton Aerodrome 65-6, 67, 107-8
 F. Hills & Sons Ltd. 65-6, 107-8
Barton Moss 54
BBC announcer Frank Phillips 87
Beamont, Wg./Cdr. Roland P. 201, 202, 204,
  206, 211
 English Electric test pilot 212, 213, *216,* 217,
  223, 224, 226
Beaufighter 76-7, *76,* 94, 304
Beaver see D.H.C.2 Beaver
Berlin Airlift 156-7
Bermuda Triangle, loss of Star Tiger and Star
  Ariel 153
Blackburn Aircraft Ltd 39, 325, 329
Blackburn, Harold 33
Blackpool 5-9, 11-13, 50, 69-70, *70*
 Vickers-Armstrongs Ltd. 102-7
 Hawker Aircraft (Blackpool) Ltd. 127-130
 Air Pageant 1928 55, 70
 'Flying Carnival' 1910 11-13, *11-12*
 'Flying Week' 1909 5-9, *5, 6, 7, 8*
 photographs of aircraft over Blackpool
  EAP, Hawk, Sea Harrier, Harrier, Tornado
   266
  Jaguar International *237*
  MRCA prototype over Blackpool Tower
   243
  Lightning (1965) *218*
 see also Squires Gate, Stanley Park
Blackpool and West Coast Air Services 70
Blenheim 79-80, *109,* 305, 308
Blériot, Louis 3, 5, 7
Blue Steel 173, *174-5,* 177
Boorer, N.W. 240
Bootle/Liverpool, photograph of Vulcan over
  167
Borwick & Sons 20-22, 40, 292
Boulton Paul Aircraft Ltd. 326
Bowen, Donald 224
Bowland Fells/Ribble Valley, photograph of
  Strikemaster over *233*
Brabazon Committee 135, 152
Brackley, Maj. H.G. 45, 46
Brancker, Sir Sefton 55
Bristol Aeroplane Co. Ltd. 35-6, 73, 326, 329
Bristol Beaufighter 76-7, *76,* 94, 304
Bristol Blenheim 79-80, *109,* 305, 308
Bristol F.2B Fighter 35, 296
British Aerospace (BAe) 244, 328
 BAe (Commercial Aircraft) Ltd., Chadderton
  and Woodford 150

BAe Advanced TurboProp (ATP) 185-6, *185*, 316
BAe Airbus, Broughton (Hawarden), near Chester 140-50
BAe Regional Aircraft Ltd, Avro International Aerospace 188
BAe Regional Aircraft, Chadderton and Woodford 150
BAe, Preston, Samlesbury and Warton 244-269
BAe/McDonnell Douglas Harrier 256, 260-2, *262-3, 266, 283*, 321,
British Aircraft Corporation (BAC) Ltd., Preston, Samlesbury and Warton 209, 223, 230, 233, 244, 328
British Amphibious Airline Ltd. 69-70, *70*
British Association for the Advancement of Science, Manchester meeting 1861 2
Broadsmith, Harry 58
Brooklands 9-10, 11, 14-16, 17, 20, 31, 100, 102
Roe 1 Biplane 4-5, *4*
Brooklands Museum 9, 10, 107
Brough 39, 249, 253, 254, 262
Broughton/Hawarden
British Aerospace (BAe)/BAE Systems, Airbus UK, Airbus wing production 140-50
de Havilland Aircraft Co. Ltd. at Hawarden Aerodrome, Broughton, near Chester 130-140
Vickers-Armstrongs Ltd. 100-05
Brown, Arthur Whitten 10
Brown, Capt. H.A. 'Sam' 50, 61, 80, 82, 85, 87, 89-90, 91-2
Budden, Wg./Cdr H. *151*
Burga Monoplane 16, 293
Burtonwood 77, 80, 93, 110, 111-3, 120, 121, 204, 206
Butler-Stoney, Major C.K. 35

C.30A 63, 302
C.L.A.7 Swift 67-8, 303
Camm, Sydney (later Sir) 63, 128, 129, 230, 256
Canada 61-2, 79, 89, 91-2, 111, 132-3, 258
de Havilland Aircraft of Canada Ltd. 133, 138
Canadian Government Trans Atlantic Air Service 89
Canberra *see* English Electric Canberra
Chadderton
A.V. Roe & Company Ltd. 74, 78-80, 82, 85, 89, 90
employment 85
Hawker Siddeley Aviation 150, 160-2, 164, 181, 183, 186, 194, 262
Chadwick, Roy 14, 17, 31, 51-2, *52*, 56, 57-8, 80, 82, 84, 87, 90, 150, 152, 154, 156, 163
Chester
British Aerospace (BAe)/BAE Systems, Airbus UK, Airbus wing production 140-50
de Havilland Aircraft Co. Ltd. at Hawarden Aerodrome, Broughton, near Chester 130-140
employment Chester 1940-43 104
Vickers-Armstrongs Ltd. 100-05
Chorley 69, 86
Chown, W.R. 66, 108
Chipmunk *see* D.H.C.1 Chipmunk
Churchill, Winston (later Sir) 90, 122
Cierva Autogiro *55, 56*, 63, 302
Cierva Autogiro Co. Ltd. 56, 326
Cierva C.25 68, 303
Class 23 airship 26-7, 295
Class 33 airship 26-7
'Classic and Modern Aero-Engines associated with Lancashire and the North West of England' 72
Clayton-le-Moors, Accrington 72, 206, Canberra at 209

Clitheroe 72, 88, 99
Cobham, Sir Alan 65, 68, 69
Cody, Samuel Franklin 3, 35
Comet *see* D.H.106 Comet
Comper Aircraft Ltd., Hooton Park Aerodrome 67-8
Comper, Flt.Lt. Nicholas 67
Concorde SST 230, 233
Cordes, Major James 111
Cranage 102, 104, 108
Creasey, Ray F. 202, 221, 240
Crewe, Rolls-Royce Shadow Factory 72
Cripps, Sir Stafford 77, 117
Crossley Motors 34, 52, 55, 66, 122
Crowe, F.D. 93
Cuban Missile Crisis 1962 176
Cunliffe-Owen Aircraft Ltd. 326
Cunningham, John 'Cats Eyes' 136
Curtiss, Glen H. 21, 38

D. Napier & Son Ltd 72, 97, 329
D.H. Hornet 130, *132*, 132-3, 311
D.H. Mosquito 130-2, *131*, 310
D.H.4 32-3, *33*, 296
D.H.9 32-4, *34*, 36, 296
D.H.10 Amiens 32, 34, *34*, 296
D.H.100 Vampire 99, 100, *101*, 123, 130, 133-4, 308, 309, 311, 318
D.H.100 Vampire F.1/F.2/F.3 200-1, *200*
D.H.104 Dove 135, *135*, 312
D.H.106 Comet 130, 135-8, *137*, 313
D.H.110 Sea Vixen 138-9, 313
D.H.112 Venom 123, 134, *134*, 309, 312
D.H.114 Heron 135, 312
D.H.125 139-40, *139*, 314
D.H.C.1 Chipmunk 133, *133*, 311
D.H.C.2 Beaver 138, 313
Daily Mail Light Aeroplane Competition 1923 45
Daily Mail Transatlantic Air Race 1969 261
Davies, Stuart 82, 154, 159, 163
Dawson, George 6
de Havilland Aircraft Company Ltd., Hawarden Aerodrome, Chester 130, 326
de Havilland Aircraft of Canada Ltd. 133, 138
de Havilland Engine Co. Ltd 329
de Havilland Heritage Centre, display of Mosquito prototype 132
de Havilland Jnr, Geoffrey 100, 131, 133, 138
de Havilland, Geoffrey 32
de la Cierva, Juan 55
de Villiers, Desmond, English Electric test pilot 213, *216*, 217
Defence White Paper 1957 130, 181, 212, 221, 284
Dell, Jimmy, 213, *216*, 217, 225, 235
Derry, John 138-9
Dick, Kerr & Company Ltd., English Electric Company Ltd., Preston and Lytham
Ayr/Kingston/Wren 44-5, *49*
employment 44
Felixstowe F.3 37-8, 39-41, 43
Ding, Rowland 39
Dobson, Jack 89
Dobson, Roy (later Sir) 17, 31, 52, 58, 82, 90-1, 150, *151*, 154, 156, 165, 166, 169, 173 221, 285
Dowty, George 62
Duigan, John R. 21

EADS, the European Aeronautic Defence and Space Company 142, 266, 269, 280, 284
Eagles, Dave 243, 248, 264
Edwards, Maurice 9
Edwards, Sir George 221, 230
Edwards, William 9
Elliott-Lynn, Sophie 57, *57*
employment
Airbus wing work, jobs in Wales 150
Avro, around 1943 85
BAE Systems in North West 286

Blackpool, loss of jobs 1958 130
Burtonwood 1940 112
Chester 1940-43 104
Dick, Kerr, during WWI 44
English Electric 1940 93, 94
English Electric 1943 97
Fairey post-war 123
Fairey wartime 77
Fairey, 1930's workforce 66
Heaton Chapel 66
NAF No.2, Heaton Chapel 34
NAF No.3, Aintree 35
Strand Road Preston, around 1938 93
Troubeck Bridge, Windermere 116
TSR2, loss of jobs 229
Typhoon 279, 280
Woodford 2004 199
Empress Biplane 10, 291
Empress Monoplane 10, 291
engines 71-3, 88, 99, 230
'Classic and Modern Aero-Engines associated with Lancashire and the North West of England' 72
engine manufacturers 329
Alvis Ltd 329
Armstrong Siddeley Motors Ltd 329
Blackburn Aircraft Ltd (Cirrus) 329
Bristol Aeroplane Co. Ltd 72, 73, 326, 329
D. Napier & Son Ltd 72, 97, 329
de Havilland Engine Co. Ltd 329
Lucas 72, 88, 99, 173, 263
Metropolitan-Vickers Electrical Co. Ltd 88, 329
Rolls-Royce Ltd 72, 88, 99, 286, 329
Rover 72, 88, 99
see also jet engine, development
English Electric Aviation Ltd., Preston, Samlesbury, Warton 199, 222, 223
English Electric
A1 201-2
Canberra 202-10, *202-5, 207, 208, 209, 228, 244, 246*, 316, 318
M.3 Ayr 44, 48, *49-50*, 297
P.5 Kingston 44, *45-8, 45-9*, 49, 298
S.1 Wren 44-5, *45*, 211, 297
English Electric Company Ltd. 326
employment in 1940/1943 93, 94, 97
test pilots 213, *216*, 217
Errwood Park 73, 74-7, *76*, 77
Esler, Eric 'Red' 163
Eurofighter 2000 267, *267, 268*, 271
prototypes 267, 269
Eurofighter Typhoon 271, *270-8*, 279-80, *280-3, 290*, 321, *322*
European Combat Aircraft (ECA) 263
European Combat Fighter (ECF) 263
European Fighter Aircraft (EFA) 264, 266-7
Euxton, Chorley 86
Evans R.H. (later Sir Richard) 238
Ewans, J.R. 169, 181
Experimental Aircraft Programme (EAP) 263-4, *265-6*, 320

F. Hills & Sons Ltd., Ringway and Barton 65, 107-8
F-35 Joint Strike Fighter (JSF) 280, *283*, 284
Fairey Aviation Co. Ltd. 326
Heaton Chapel and Ringway 122-7
Heaton Chapel, Barton and Ringway 66-7
Heaton Chapel, Errwood Park and Ringway 74-8
employment 66, 77, 123
Fairey
Barracuda 77-8, *77*, 304
Battle 74-5, *75*, 304
Delta FD1 122-3, *125*, 308
Delta FD2 123, *125*, 211
Firefly Mk.7 123-4, 309
Fulmar 76, 304
Gannet 124, *126*, 309
Hendon 66-7, 303
Spearfish 122, 308
Specification N.4 Atalanta 41, *42*, 297

Fairey, C. Richard (later Sir) 66, 77, 127
Falk, Wg. Cdr. R.J. 'Roly' 163, 165-6, 169
Falklands War 179, 209, 262
Farman, Henry (Henri) 3, 7
Farman-type biplane 10, 291
Farnborough, first official flight in Britain 3
Farnborough 1925, C.6A/B Autogiro 56
Farnborough 1952,
Farnborough Air Show
    1950
        Ashton Mk.I 159
        Avro 707B in static park 163
        Lincoln/RAF 93
    1952
        Avro 698 (later named Vulcan) 165
        D.H.110 prototype broke up 139
    1953
        Shackleton 160
        Vulcan prototype 165, 166
    1982 ACA 263
    1986 EAP 264
Farren, Bill (later Sir William) 163
Felixstowe F.3 39-40, 39-40, 297
Fenwick, Robert 33
Ferguson, Tim, English Electric test pilot 213,
    237, 243
Fern, Sgt. 77
Fielding C. E. (Teddy) 53, 84
films, aircraft appearance in
    inspired by Roe IV 14
    Sunderlands, in 1942 film 114
    restored Avro 504K, in 1956 film 168
first official flight, in Britain 3
first powered flight in Lancashire 7
Fletcher, Charles 10
Flookburgh 26-7
flying boats
    Felixstowe 39-41, 39-40, 43, 44, 49, 297
    Short Sunderland 114-120, 115-6, 118-20,
        308
'Flying Flea' 65, 302
Fokker F.VII 58
Folland Aircraft Ltd. 97, 99, 210, 326
Ford 4-AT-E tri-motor 68, 303
Fournier, at Blackpool 'Flying Week' 7
Friedrichshafen raid 29
Fylde Coast, photographs of aircraft flying over
    1987, EAP 265
    Eurofighter/Typhoon 270-2
    See also Blackpool

Garland, F/O D.E. 75
Gatward, Flt. Lt. 77
Gaunt, John 17, 33
General Aircraft Ltd. 326
General Operational Requirement (GOR) 339
    221-2
Gibson, Wing Commander Guy 86-87, 132
Glaisher, James 2
Gloster Aircraft Ltd. 326
Gnoss-pelius
    Gnosspelius/Trotter Hydro-biplane 21, 22,
        292
    Hydro-monoplane No. I 20, 292
    Hydro-monoplane No. 2 20-1, 292
    Lakes Hydro-monoplane 22, 292
Gnosspelius, Oscar Theodore 20-1, 22
Godfrey, Dougie 87
Goshawk 253, 254, 269
Gouge, Arthur 22
Grahame-White, Claude 11, 13-14, 285
Gray, Sgt. T. 75
Green, Charles 1-2
Green, Charles George 1
Groves, James Grimble 16

Hall, English Electric test pilot 213
Hamble 50, 55, 56, 57, 58 61
Handley Page
    0/400 36-7, 297
    Halifax 77, 77, 93-4, 96-7, 96-8, 99-100,
        109-110, 304, 307, 308
    Hampden 93-4, 95, 307
    Victor HP 80 Victor B.2/K.2 163, 165, 175,
        177, 178, 178, 179
Handley Page Ltd. 93, 178, 326
Handley Page, Sir Frederick 93, 179, 221
Hare, Maurice 105
Harrier see British Aerospace/McDonnell
    Douglas Harrier
Harrison, Jimmy 181
Hawarden see Broughton/Hawarden
Hawk see BAE Systems Hawk
Hawker Aircraft Ltd, 63, 326-7
Hawker Aircraft (Blackpool) Ltd., Squires Gate
    127-30
Hawker Audax 63, 64, 78, 302
Hawker Hunter 127-130, 129, 280, 310
Hawker Siddeley Aviation, Broughton
    (Hawarden), near Chester 140, 141,
    185, 186, 190, 328
Hawker Siddeley Group 137, 139, 150, 169,
    183, 222
Hawker Tornado 84, 305
Healey, Denis (later Lord) Minister of Defence
    227, 233, 240
Hearn, Martin 68, 110-11
Heath, B. Oliver 221, 241
Heaton Chapel
    National Aircraft Factory (NAF) No.2 33-4,
        34, 44, 66
    Fairey Aviation Company Ltd. 66-7, 74-8,
        75, 76, 77, 122-7
Helvellyn, aircraft lands on summit 55
Hendon Air Display 1927 55
Hesketh Park 33, 41, 68, 111
Hillson Bi-mono 108, 108, 303
Hillson FH.40 108, 108, 303
Hillson Helvellyn 66, 303
Hillson Praga E114 'Air Baby' 66, 302
Hillwood, Peter, English Electric test pilot 213,
    216, 217
Hinkler, H.J. 'Bert' 52, 55, 56, 56
HMA No. I Hermione 'Mayfly' 13, 18-20, 19, 23,
    291
HMA No. 4 24
HMA Nos. 5, 6 and 7 24, 295
HMA No. 9 24, 295
HMA No. 23 26, 27, 295
HMA No. 26 26, 27, 295
Hollinwood, 'Government Factory for
    Assembling American Aircraft' 36-7
Holmes Chapel 100, 102
Hooker, Dr. Stanley (later Sir), Rolls-Royce Chief
    Engineer 121, 256
Hoon, Geoff, Secretary of State for Defence
    271
Hooton Park
    Comper Aircraft 67-8
    Martin Hearn Ltd. 110-11
Hornet see D.H. Hornet
HS 801 Nimrod 138, 190, 190-1, 191, 317
HS.146 186, 188, 317
Hubble, John 52
Hunter 127-30, 129, 310

Imperial War Museum, Duxford 108, 227
Ingham, Harold 66, 165-6, 179
Isherwood, English Electric test pilot 213

Jaguar see SEPECAT Jaguar, SEPECAT Jaguar
    International
Jakimiuk, W.J. 133
JAP Avroplane Company 5
JAS 39 Gripen 269
jet engine, development 72, 88, 89-90, 93, 99
    Canberra 202-10
    Vampire 100, 121-3, 133-4
    Comet 135, 136
    Regional Jetliner (RJ) 188-90
Jindivik Mk.102B 124, 309
Johnson, Amy 68
JSF (F-35 Joint Strike Fighter) 280, 283, 284

K2 tankers (Victor, Vulcan) 175, 177-81, 178-9,
    180-1
Kemp, Ronald C. 21, 22
Kermit Weekes' 'Fantasy of Flight' museum,
    Florida USA 120
Kingston see English Electric P5 Kingston
Knight, Don, English Electric test pilot 213, 216,
    217

Lake Hoklingen, Norway, loss of Halifax 96-7
Laker, Freddie 157
Lakes Flying Company, Windermere 20-1, 22
Lakes Water Bird 14, 21, 292
Lakes Water Hen 14, 21, 21, 292
Lambie, Jack 69
Lancashire Aero Club 1909 5, 6, 13
Lancashire Aero Club 1922 54, 55
Lancashire Aero Club 1946 65
Lancashire Coast, Typhoon, Hawk, Red Arrows
    over 289, 290, 322
Lancashire County Council 'Classic and Modern
    Aero-Engines associated with Lancashire
    and the North West of England' 72
Lancashire Prospector E.P.9 218, 220, 318
Lancashire School of Aviation 69
Lancaster Bomber see Avro Lancaster
Lancastrian (Avro 691) 89-90, 89, 306
Langfelder, Helmut 241
Latham, Hubert, at Blackpool 'Flying Week' 7
Leblanc, Alfred, at Blackpool 'Flying Week' 7
Leeming, John F. 54, 55
Lightning 213-8, 214-6, 218-9, 220, 228, 244,
    246, 318
Liverpool, photograph of aircraft over
    Avro Ashton 158
    Vulcan 167
Lloyd, John, Armstrong Whitworth's Chief
    Designer 62
Lockheed Martin, JSF 280, 284
Lockheed Overseas Corporation - British
    Reassembly Division, No. I AAU Speke
    110-111
Lord, John 17, 51, 58
Lostock, Bolton 71, 284
Lucas 72, 88, 99, 173, 263
Lunardi, Vincenzo 1
Lygo, Sir Raymond 1986 BAe's Chief Executive
    264
Lytham 37-8, 41, 42, 43, 44-50, 45-7, 49, 50
Lytham Yacht Club
    1984 photograph of Tornado, Lightning,
    Strikemaster, Canberra over 246

M55 1975, Jaguar takes off from *236*, 237
Manchester 1, 9-11, 14-16, *15, 16,*
    A.V. Roe & Company Ltd. WWI 28-32
    Interwar years 50-65
    Metropolitan-Vickers Ltd., Trafford Park 72,
       78, 81, 85, 99
    Photograph of
       Avro Lancaster over Manchester *84*
       BAe 745 over Central Manchester 1981
         184
Manchester Bomber 80-2, *81*, 305
Manning, Lt. William Oke 38, 39, 44
Manser, Flt. Lt. Leslie 81-2
Manton, Marcus D. 38, 46
Martin Hearn Ltd.
    Hesketh Park 111
    Hooton Park 110
Martin-Baker Aircraft Co. Ltd. 327
MBDA plant, Lostock 284
McDonnell F-4 Phantom 218, 230, 233, 263
Melly, Henry 33
Menzies, Duncan 67, 75, 76
Merrill, Dick 69
Metropolitan-Vickers Electrical Co. Ltd 329
Metropolitan-Vickers Ltd. (Metrovicks), Trafford
    Park 72, 78, 81, 85, 99
Mignet, Henri 65
Miles Aircraft Ltd. 327
Miles Platting 16, 28
Millett, Paul 243
Monk, Flt. Lt. R.H.C. 70
Monocar 51
Moore-Brabazon, J.T.C. (later Lord Brabazon)
    3, 5, 7, 38
Morecambe Bay/Grange-over-Sands, Hawk
    over (2003), *261*
Mosquito *see* D.H. Mosquito
Moss Brothers Aircraft Ltd. (Mosscraft),
    Chorley 69
Moss, William Henry 69, 110
Mosscraft M.A.1, M.A.2 69, 304
Mountbatten, Admiral Lord, Chief of the
    Defence Staff 226
MRCA programme (multi-role combat aircraft)
    240-4, *242-4*
Museum of Science & Industry, Manchester 7,
    66, 162, 163, 212, 286

National Aircraft Factory (NAF) No.2, Heaton
    Chapel 31, 33-4, *34*, 35, 44, 66, 74
National Aircraft Factory (NAF) No.3, Aintree
    35-6, 43
Nelson, H. George (later Lord) 93, 97, 99, 100,
    221
Nettleton, VC, John Sqn. Ldr. 86
Newton Heath, Manchester 29, 51, *59*, 61, 64,
    65 74, 78-80, 82, 85, 89
nicknames
    Advanced Turbo Prop (ATP) 185
    Avro Anson 79
    Fairey Hendon 66
    Hampden 94
    Mosquito 131
    Shackleton 162
    Sunderland 117
    Wellington 104
Nimrod *see also* HS.801 Nimrod
    AEW.Mk.3 194
    MR1/MR2 191, *192-3*, 194,
    MRA4 190, 194-9, *195-9*, 287-8
Northcliffe, Lord 4, 6
Northern Aircraft Company 22, 39
Northwest Aerospace Alliance (NWAA) 286
Northwest Development Agency (NWDA)
    256, 286, 287

Oldham 36-7
Oldham Aircraft Factory 36-7, 43, 67
Orrell, Jimmy 85, 89, *151*, 152, 154, 159, 160,
    165, *169*

P(Project).1, P.1A/P.1B 210-13, *211, 212-3*, 318
P.110 263
P.5 Cork 39, 44
Page, F.W. 'Freddie' (later Sir Frederick) 210,
    221, 233, 237-8, 244
Panavia Tornado 243-4, *245-7*, 248-9, *250-2,
    253*, 262-3, *266*, *283*, 320
Parker, John Lankester 22, 39, 114
Parrott, Reginald J. 14, 31, *56*
Paulhan, Louis, at Blackpool 'Flying Week' 7
Percival Aircraft Ltd. 107, 220, 327
Percival Proctor 107-8, *107*, 303
Petter, W.E.W. 'Teddy' 99, 201, *201*, 210
Phillips, Frank, BBC announcer 87
Phoenix Works, Bradford 38-9, 41, 44
Piel Castle/Morecambe Bay, photograph of
    Canberra over *207*
Pixton, Howard 14, 51
Plowden Committee of Enquiry into the
    Aircraft Industry 233
Pobjoy, Capt. Douglas 68
Porte, Squadron Commander John 39
Portsmouth Aviation Ltd. 327
Poulton-le-Fylde/Thornton, photograph of
    Strikemaster over *232*
Praga 66, 302
Pratt, Hartley B. 18, 24, 25, 26
prefab manufacture, Blackpool and Chester
    127
Preston 37-41, 44-50, 99,
    Canberra 209, 223
    photograph of
       Eurofighter 2000 over Preston *268*
       P.1B over Ribble estuary *213*
       Preston Guild 1822, balloon flight 1
    see also Strand Road, Preston
Prestwich, J.A. 5

Queensland Museum, Brisbane 56

R.80 27, 27-8, 295
R.100 28
RAF Fairford *152*
RAF Museum, Cosford 227, 238
RAF Museum, Hendon 88, 97, 107, 133, 179,
    201, 206, 232
Raynham, Fred 14
Red Arrows 253 *254, 290*, 322
Regional Jetliner (RJ) Series 188-9
Ribble Estuary/Fylde Coast
    photograph of Strikemaster over *231*
    photograph of P.1B over *212-3*
Ribble Valley
    Bowland Fells, photograph of Strikemaster
       over *233*
    Longridge, photograph of Hawk over *258*
Richman, Harry 69
Ringway 65, 66-7, 74-8, 80, 81, 82, 85, 90, 92,
    107-8, 122-7, 150, 152
Roe I Biplane 3-5, *4*, 291
Roe I Triplane 5, 6-9, *6-7*, 8
Roe I Triplane, at the Science Museum, London
    7
Roe II Triplane 9, 10, 11, 291
Roe III Triplane 10, 11, *11-12*, 13-14, 291
Roe IV 14, 291
Roe, Alliott Verdon 3-7, *4*, *6-7*, *8*, *11*, 9-11,
    13-14, 31, 32, 51, 52, 57, 58
Roe, Dr Spencer Verdon 4
Roe, Everard Verdon 32
Roe, Humphrey Verdon 5, 9, 16, 17, 32
Rolls-Royce Ltd 71, 72, 80, 81, 82, 88, 99, 329
Rootes Group 44, 73, 79, 80
    Rootes Securities Ltd., Speke 108-110
Rose, J.D. 100

Rothermere, Lord 79
Rougier, Henri, at Blackpool 'Flying Week' 7
Rover 72, 88, 99, 112
Royal Air Force (RAF), formed 1918 32
Royal Aircraft Factory, Farnborough 32
Royal Ordnance Factory, Euxton, Chorley 86
Ruhr Dams 86-7

Sadler, James 1
Sadler, William Wyndham 1
Salford, balloon flight 2
Samlesbury 74, 93, 94, *95, 96, 96*, 97-100, 142
    BAC 209, 222, 223, 224-244
    Canberra 206, *207, 208*, 209,
    Eurofighter/Typhoon 269, 274,
    JSF 280
    Lancashire Prospector E.P.9 218-220, 318
    Lightning 214, *215*
    photographs of aircraft flying over
       Samlesbury
       rebuilt Spitfire *208*
       Hawk (2000) *257*
       TSR2 *227*,
       Vampire *101*,
Samlesbury Engineering Ltd. 220
Sandys, Duncan, Defence Secretary 130, 181,
    212, 221
Saudi-Arabia, defence contracts 217, 218, 230,
    233, 248, 249
Saunders-Roe Ltd 327
Schwann, Oliver 14, 18, 20, 29
Science Museum, London 7, 10
Scottish Aviation Ltd. 140, 194, 327
Sea Vixen *see* D.H.110 Sea Vixen
SEPECAT 234
SEPECAT Jaguar 234-8, *235-6, 238-9*, 244,
    246, 283, 319
SEPECAT Jaguar International 237-8,
    237, 319
Shackleton (Avro 696) 160-2, *160, 161, 169*,
    315
Shadow Factories 65, 71-74, 79, 100, 102,
    109, 120, 206, 285
    see under
    Chester
    Clayton-le-Moors, nr. Accrington
    Crewe
    Errwood Park
    Lostock, nr. Bolton
    Samlesbury, nr. Preston
    Speake
    Squires Gate, Blackpool
    Strand Road, Preston
    Walton, Liverpool
Sharples, G.F. 221
Sherwood, John Sqn. Ldr. 86
Short Bros. Ltd., Windermere 113-20, 327
Short Sunderland 114-120, *115-6, 118*,
    119-20, 308
Shute, Neville 28
Siddeley, Sir John D. (later Lord Kenilworth)
    57, 63
Sippe, Sydney 20, 29, 52
Sir W.G. Armstrong Whitworth Aircraft Ltd.
    325
Slade, Gordon 123
Slingsby Sailplanes 304
'Slip' wing 108
Snowdonia, photograph of Hawk over (1990)
    254
Society of British Aircraft Constructors (SBAC)
    31
Sopwith, Sir Thomas 38, 163
Southport 13, 32-33, 41, 44, 50, 68, 69, 111
Speke 68-9, 73, 108-110
Speke Airport, Liverpool 68-9
Spitfire, rebuilt by apprentices at Samlesbury
    1984-6 208
Spriggs, Sir Frank 90-1, 221
Squier, English Electric test pilot 213
Squires Gate, Blackpool
    Air Pageant 1928 55, 70
    Blackpool 'Flying Carnival' 1910 11-12,
       11-13,

Blackpool 'Flying Week' 1909 5-9, *5, 6, 7*
Hawker Aircraft (Blackpool) Ltd. 127-30,
Lancashire Prospector E.P.9 218, 220, 318
Lancashire School of Aviation, Squires Gate
    Aerodrome 69
photograph of Wellington over Squires Gate
    106
Vickers-Armstrongs Ltd., shadow factory 73,
    102, 105
'SS' Class airship 25-6, 295
    'SS' Sea Scout 25-6, *25*
Stanley Park, Blackpool 69-70, 102-3, 107
Stockport 33-4
Strand Road, Preston
    closure of 249, 270
    Dick, Kerr & Company Ltd. 37-41, 44-50
    English Electric Canberra 202
    English Electric Company Ltd. 74, 93-100,
        326
    Handley Page Hampden, Halifax 95, 97-8
    photograph of English Electric S.1 Wren
        at Strand Road 45
    TSR2 222, 224-8
Strikemaster see BAC 167 Strikemaster
Sueter, Maurice 18, 20, 23, 24
Suffroy, at Blackpool 'Flying Week' 7
Summers, 'Mutt' (Vickers' Chief Test Pilot) 87
Supersonic flight 128, 210-3, 214, 217
Swaby, Sidney 33
Sykes, Norman 66

Talbot, Eddie 154
test pilots
    Avro 14, 52, 61, 63, 154, 163, 165, 181
    Avro, late 1930s 65
    BAC 243
    BAe 264, 267
    BAE Systems 199
    de Havillard 100
    English Electric 100, 201, 213, *216,* 217, 235,
        237
    Fairey *67,* 75, 76, 123
    Lockheed at Speke 110
    No. 1 AAU 110
    No. 7 AAU 110
    Short Brothers 22, 114, 117
    Vickers-Armstrongs 105
Thorn, Bill 63, 82, 152, 154, 156
Tomkins, F.B. 62
Tornado see Panavia Tornado
Trafford Park 72, 81, 85, 99
Trans-Canada Air Lines/Canadian Government
    Trans Atlantic Air Service 89
Trotter, J.F.A. 21-2
TSR.2 220-230, *223-5, 227, 228-9,* 319
Turner, John 199
Twiss, Peter 123
Typhoon 271, *270-8,* 279-80, *280-3,* 290, 321,
    322
Tyson, Geoffrey 63

US aircraft 'kit' assembly Lend-Lease 74,
    110-113
USAAF 77, 110
USAAF Base Air Depot (BAD) 1, RAF
    Burtonwood 110, 111-3
USAAF Base Air Depot (BAD) 2, RAF
    Warton 110, 113

Vampire see D.H.100 Vampire
variable geometry (VG) 'swing wing' technology
    240-1
Vickers 23-8
Vickers Ltd., Barrow-in-Furness 10, 17, 23-8, 44
Vickers Sons & Maxim Ltd., Barrow-in-Furness
    17-20
Vickers-Armstrongs Ltd., 100-7, 327-8
Vickers Wellington 102-7, *103, 104, 106,* 307
VIP York 90
Voisin biplane 3, 7
Vulcan see Avro Vulcan
Vulcan Motor & Engineering Co. Ltd., Crossens,
    Southport 32-3, 44

Wakefield, Edward W., Captain 14, 20-22
Wallis, Barnes Neville 24, 25, 26, 27-8, 86-7,
    103, 240
Walney Island 17, 24, 26-7
Walton, Liverpool, Shadow Factory 72, 97
Ward, Sgt. J.A. 105
Waring & Gillow Ltd. 36, 131
Warton
    EFA 264
    Eurofighter Typhoon 272-8, 279-80, *280-1*
        Final Assembly Hall 271, *274-7*
    Harrier upgrade 262-3, *263*
    Hawk 249, 253-6, *254-261, 266,* 320
    Jaguar 234-8
        production *235*
        upgrade *239,*
    JSF 280, *283,* 284
    Lightning F.6 XS928 preserved for static
        display 218
    photographs of aircraft flying over Warton
        Lightnings (1992) 220
        Hawk (1997) 259
        Canberra 209
        Eurofighter 2000 *267,282*
        P.1B *212-3*
    supersonic flight 210-4,
    Tornado production 243-9, *244,* 245,
    TSR2 226
    USAAF BAD 2 RAF Warton 113,
Warwick, Squadron Leader J.B. 132
Webster, John 154
Weger, Peter 267
Weinstock, Arnold (later Lord) 223
Wellington see Vickers Wellington
Westland Aircraft Ltd. 328
Whittle, Frank 55, 72
Wilson, David 154
Windermere 14, 20-2, *21,* 51, *51*
    Northern Aircraft Company 22, 39
    Short Sunderland 113-20, *115, 116, 118-20*
    White Cross Bay 116, *116,* 118, *119-20*

Windermere Steamboat Museum 117
Woodford
    A.V.Roe & Company Ltd. 50-65, 78-86,
        92-3, 154-99
    Ashton Mk.1 159
    Avro 698 164,
    Blue Steel 173, *174, 175*
    fatal crash 154,
    K2 tankers *177-81,* 178-9, *180-1*
    Nimrod 190-9, *191, 195-9,* 190, 192-3, 199
    Shackleton 160-2, *161, 162*
    Victor B.2/K.2 178-9, *177-8*
    Vulcan 163-81, *165-71*
    Weapons Research Division 173,
    Woodford Assembly Hall 85-86, *85*
Woodford Air Display 1990 180
Woodward, Flt. Lt. G.R. 100
Wren see English Electric S.1 Wren
Wright Flyer No.1 3
Wright, Orville and Wilbur 3

Yeadon 84, 85, 91, 92, 105, 150
Yeo, Chris 267
Younger MP, Rt.Hon. George, Secretary of State
    for Defence 264